D1128513

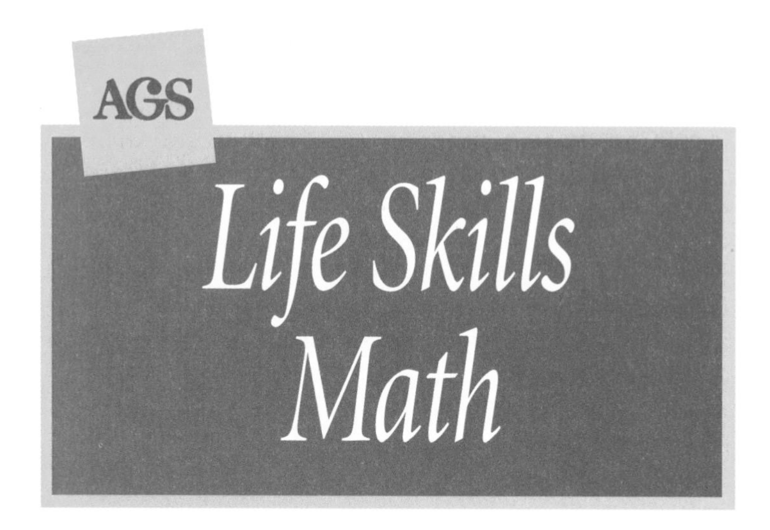

by
Donald H. Jacobs
and
August V. Treff

AGS®
American Guidance Service, Inc.
Circle Pines, Minnesota 55014-1796
800-328-2560

About the Authors

Donald H. Jacobs, M.Ed., teaches high school mathematics for the Baltimore City Public Schools. He has also been the coordinator of computer programming at the Talmudical Academy of Baltimore.

August V. Treff, M.Ed., is Chief of Educational Accountability for the Baltimore City Public Schools. He has been a mathematics teacher and also served as the Director of Research and Evaluation for the school district.

Photo Credits: p. viii—Randy M. Ury/The Stock Market; p. 11—Scott Markewitz/FPG International; pp. 16, 80, 118, 172, 210, 225, 262—Superstock; pp. 28, 244—John Boykin/PhotoEdit; pp. 44, 71, 183, 195, 232, 260—James L. Shaffer; p. 48—Jim and Mary Whitmer; p. 66—T. Tracy/FPG International; p. 94—Cathlyn Melloan/Tony Stone Images; p. 98—Lee Foster/FPG International; p. 103—Cosmo Condina/Tony Stone Images; p. 108—Ken Biggs/Tony Stone Images; p. 115—Chip Henderson/Tony Stone Images; p. 125—Lawrence Migdale/Tony Stone Images; p. 126—Bruce Ayres/Tony Stone Images; p. 132—Charles Thatcher/Tony Stone Images; p. 138—Comstock; p. 141—Ron Rovtar/FPG International; p. 143—David Young-Wolff/Tony Stone Images; p. 151—Ron Chapple/FPG International; p. 153—Mark Lewis/Tony Stone Images; p. 154—Joachim Messerschmidt/FPG International; p. 158—Edward Pieratt/Comstock; p. 176—Frank Cezus/FPG International; p. 180—Jim Cummins/FPG International; pp. 190, 204, 215—Amy Etra/PhotoEdit; p. 220—Barros & Barros/The Image Bank; p. 236—Leverett Bradley/FPG International; p. 239—John Fortunato/Tony Stone Images; p. 253—Mary Kate Denny/PhotoEdit; p. 276—Robert J. Bennett/FPG International

Printed in the United States of America

ISBN 0-7854-0917-3-H (hardcover)

ISBN 0-7854-0439-2-S (softcover)

Product Number 90230 (hardcover)

Product Number 90231 (softcover)

A 0 9 8 7 6 5

Contents

Chapter 1 Counting Calories

Think of the last activity you did. It may have been reading a book, biking to school, or exercising in physical education class. No matter what the activity was, your body was using calories. When you eat food, you take in calories. When you count calories, you add and subtract whole numbers.

In Chapter 1, you will learn how to determine the number of calories you eat and use. You will also learn some of the ways charts and graphs can help you find information.

Goals for Learning

- To compute the total number of calories consumed
- To compute the total number of calories used by activities
- To read and interpret a nutrition label
- To read a graph to find information

Lesson 1 Adding Calories

Calorie

Unit of measure of the energy in food.

This chart shows that different foods have different amounts of **calories**.

Calorie Values of Common Foods

Food	Calories
Hot dog with roll	280
Hamburger with roll	370
Relish, 1 tbsp.	25
Cole slaw	155
Skim milk, 1 cup	110
Cola, 1 cup	50
Frozen yogurt bar	105

You can find how many calories are in several foods by adding the calories in each food.

Consume

To use; to eat or drink up.

EXAMPLE Mike goes to a restaurant for lunch. He has a hamburger with a roll and a cup of skim milk. How many calories does he **consume** in all? Use the chart of calorie values to find the calories in each food.

Solution Add to find the total.

Hamburger with roll	370	Calories
Skim milk, 1 cup	+110	Calories
	480	Total

The total number of calories Mike consumes is 480.

PROBLEM SOLVING

Exercise A Find the total number of calories of other customers' meals ordered at the same restaurant.

1) Misha asks for a hot dog and a cola.

2) Maria orders a hamburger with relish and cole slaw.

3) José wants a hot dog, cole slaw, one cup of skim milk, and a frozen yogurt bar.

Calorie Values of Fruit Servings

Fruit	Calories
Applesauce, 1 cup	230
Banana	120
Blackberries, 1 cup	85
Fruit cocktail, 1 cup	195
Orange	65
Peach	40
Pear	100
Plum, large	33
Raspberries, 1 cup	70

PROBLEM SOLVING

Exercise B Use the chart of calorie values of fruit. Find the answers to these questions by adding the calories.

1) Juan eats a banana, a peach, and an orange. How many calories does he consume?

2) Alan has three plums and a pear. How many calories are in the fruit?

3) Lee fixes himself a cup of applesauce for breakfast and a cup of fruit cocktail for lunch. How many calories does he eat?

4) How many calories are in two cups of applesauce?

5) How many calories are in two oranges and a pear?

6) Sue decides to make her own fruit cocktail for her friends. She uses one orange, one banana, two peaches, and two cups of raspberries. What is the total calorie count for this fruit cocktail?

7) How many calories are in two bananas, a peach, and two plums?

8) Kim mixes one cup of blackberries with one cup of fruit cocktail. What is the total number of calories?

Here are the calorie values of some of the foods served at a local restaurant.

Food	Calories
Chicken, baked	190
Fish, breaded	200
Hamburger steak, 6 oz.	270
Pot roast	320
Spaghetti	245
Beets	65
Black-eyed peas	220
Broccoli	50
Corn, creamed	210
Mixed vegetables	115
Potato, baked	95
Rice	201
Margarine, 1 tbsp.	100
Milk, skim, 1 cup	110
Orange juice, 6 oz.	50
Grape juice, 12 oz.	85
Apple juice, 12 oz.	125

PROBLEM SOLVING

Exercise C Use the calorie chart from the local restaurant. Find the total calorie value of each person's meal by adding the calories.

1) Jimmy chooses chicken, creamed corn, rice, and twelve ounces of grape juice. How many calories are in his dinner?

2) Hashim fills his plate with pot roast, black-eyed peas, a baked potato, and a tablespoon of margarine. Then he drinks a cup of skim milk. What is the total calorie count of his meal?

3) Juanita enjoys breaded fish, broccoli, rice, and twelve ounces of apple juice. How many calories are in her meal?

Some calories have special names such as **fat calories**. These are calories that come from the fat content of the food. Most foods purchased in supermarkets have labels listing calories from fat.

> ***Fat calories***
> *Calories that come from the fat in food.*

Nutrition Facts

Serving Size 1/2 cup (120 mL)
Servings Per Container 5

Amount Per Serving

Calories 130 | Calories from Fat 30

Amount / serving	% Daily value	Amount / serving	% Daily value
Total Fat 3g	**5%**	**Total Carbohydrate** 23g	**8%**
Saturated Fat 0.5g	**3%**	Dietary Fiber 0.5g	**2%**
Cholesterol 0mg	**0%**	Sugars 6g	
Sodium 180mg	**7%**	**Protein** 2g	

This soup label shows 130 calories per serving with 5 servings. The soup also contains 30 calories per serving from fat.

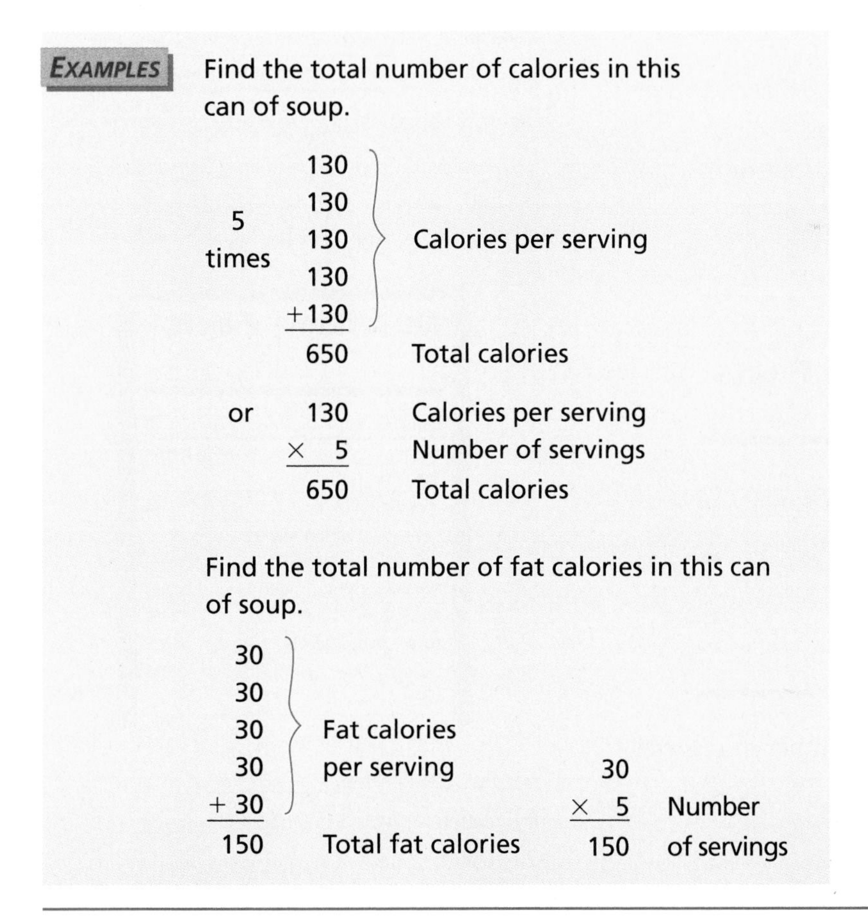

EXAMPLES Find the total number of calories in this can of soup.

```
           130 ⎫
           130 ⎪
 5 times   130 ⎬  Calories per serving
           130 ⎪
         + 130 ⎭
           650    Total calories

 or        130    Calories per serving
         ×   5    Number of servings
           650    Total calories
```

Find the total number of fat calories in this can of soup.

```
  30 ⎫
  30 ⎪
  30 ⎬  Fat calories
  30 ⎪  per serving           30
+ 30 ⎭                     ×   5   Number
 150    Total fat calories   150   of servings
```

Exercise D Use the labels to help you answer the questions.

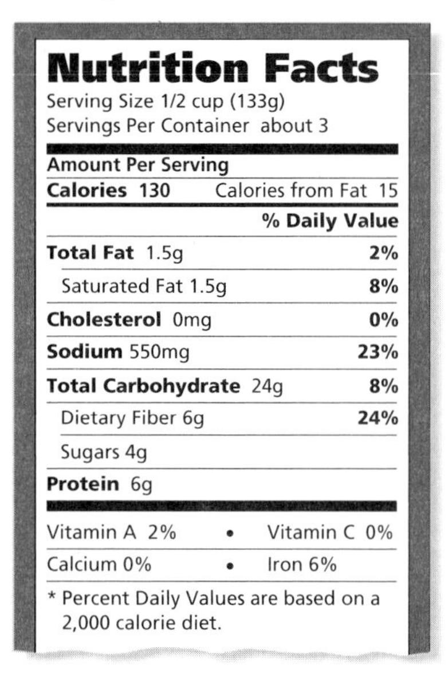
Nutrition Facts
Serving Size 1/2 cup (133g)
Servings Per Container about 3

Amount Per Serving	
Calories 130	Calories from Fat 15
	% Daily Value
Total Fat 1.5g	**2%**
Saturated Fat 1.5g	**8%**
Cholesterol 0mg	**0%**
Sodium 550mg	**23%**
Total Carbohydrate 24g	**8%**
Dietary Fiber 6g	**24%**
Sugars 4g	
Protein 6g	
Vitamin A 2% •	Vitamin C 0%
Calcium 0% •	Iron 6%

* Percent Daily Values are based on a 2,000 calorie diet.

1) Determine the number of calories per serving.
2) How many fat calories per serving?
3) How many servings?
4) Find the total calories from the label.
5) Find the total fat calories from the label.

Nutrition Facts
Serving Size 1/4 cup (60mL)
Servings Per Container about 5

Amount Per Serving	
Calories 30	Calories from Fat 20
	% Daily Value
Total Fat 2g	**3%**
Saturated Fat 1g	**5%**
Cholesterol Less Than 5mg	**1%**
Sodium 300mg	**13%**
Total Carbohydrate 4g	**1%**
Protein 1g	

6) Determine the number of calories per serving.
7) How many fat calories per serving?
8) How many servings?
9) Find the total calories from the label.
10) Find the total fat calories from the label.

Nutrition Facts
Serv. Size 1 cup (252g)
Servings about 2
Calories 260
Fat Cal. 100
* Percent Daily Values (DV) are based on a 2,000 calorie diet.

Amount/Serving	%DV*	Amount/Serving	%DV*
Total Fat 11g	**17%**	**Total Carb.** 31g	**10%**
Sat. Fat 5g	**25%**	Dietary Fiber 5g	**20%**
Cholest. 20mg	**7%**	Sugars 10g	
Sodium 1,150mg	**48%**	**Protein** 11g	

Vitamin A 10% • Vitamin C 2% • Calcium 4% • Iron 15%

11) Serving size equals ___ cups.
12) Calories per serving is ___.

Nutrition Facts
Serv. Size 1/2 cup (130g)
Servings about 2 1/2
Calories 130
Fat Cal. 20
* Percent Daily Values (DV) are based on a 2,000 calorie diet.

Amount/Serving	%DV*	Amount/Serving	%DV*
Total Fat 2g	**3%**	**Total Carb.** 24g	**8%**
Sat. Fat 0.5g	**3%**	Fiber 6g	**24%**
Cholest. 5mg	**2%**	Sugars 8g	
Sodium 420mg	**18%**	**Protein** 5g	

Vitamin A 4% • Vitamin C 0% • Calcium 6% • Iron 8%

13) Fat calories per serving is ___.
14) Calories per serving is ___.

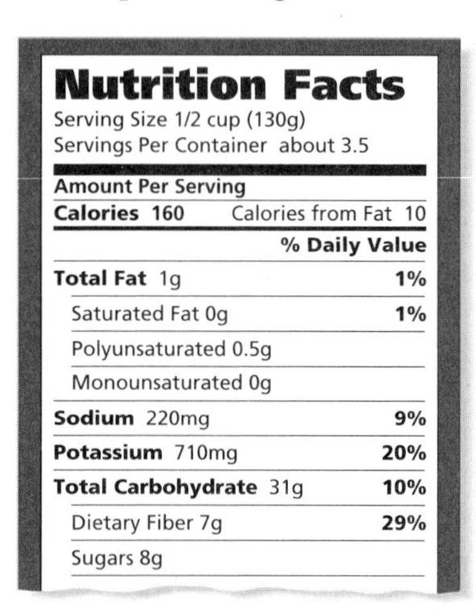
Nutrition Facts
Serving Size 1/2 cup (130g)
Servings Per Container about 3.5

Amount Per Serving	
Calories 160	Calories from Fat 10
	% Daily Value
Total Fat 1g	**1%**
Saturated Fat 0g	**1%**
Polyunsaturated 0.5g	
Monounsaturated 0g	
Sodium 220mg	**9%**
Potassium 710mg	**20%**
Total Carbohydrate 31g	**10%**
Dietary Fiber 7g	**29%**
Sugars 8g	

15) Fat calories is ________.
16) Calories per serving is ________.
17) Serving size is ________.

Lesson 2 Subtracting Calories

You can find the difference between calories consumed and calories used by subtracting.

EXAMPLE Ron consumes 2,900 calories on Monday. Exercising for one hour, his body uses 522 calories. How many calories are not used? To find the answer, subtract the calories used from the calories consumed.

2,900	Calories consumed
− 522	Calories used
2,378	Calories not used (the difference)

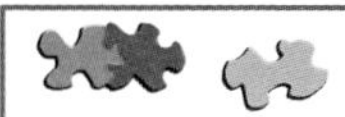

PROBLEM SOLVING

Exercise A Find the answers to these questions by subtracting.

1) Fontana consumes an average of 2,500 calories per day. If her body uses 250 calories in one hour of walking, how many calories remain?

2) Derek's average calorie consumption is 3,100 per day. His main activity is lying on the beach, listening to the waves. If his body burns 95 calories doing this, how many calories are left unused?

Exercise B Find the difference for each example.

1) 3,350 calories consumed
782 calories used

2) 3,641 calories consumed
395 calories used

3) 2,963 calories consumed
463 calories used

4) 2,460 calories consumed
868 calories used

Lesson 3 Adding or Subtracting Calories

Kyle is sixteen years old. He needs 3,600 calories each day to keep active and stay healthy.

The chart shows what Kyle eats for breakfast. It also shows the calorie value for each food.

Food	Calories
2 bowls granola	150 each
3 apricots	25 each
2 slices banana bread	85 each
2 tbsp. margarine	100 each
2 glasses of juice	54 each

EXAMPLE How many calories does Kyle consume at breakfast? Add to find the total.

$$\begin{array}{rl} 150 & \\ 150 & \text{Granola} \\ 25 & \\ 25 & \text{Apricots} \\ 25 & \\ 85 & \\ 85 & \text{Banana bread} \\ 100 & \\ 100 & \text{Margarine} \\ 54 & \\ +\ 54 & \text{Juice} \\ \hline 853 & \text{Total} \end{array}$$

Kyle consumes 853 calories at breakfast.

EXAMPLE How many more calories must Kyle consume during the day to reach the required 3,600 calories? Subtract to find the calories needed.

$$\begin{array}{rl} 3{,}600 & \text{Calories required} \\ -\ 853 & \text{Had at breakfast} \\ \hline 2{,}747 & \end{array}$$

Kyle needs to have 2,747 more calories during the day.

This is what Kyle eats during the rest of the day:

	Food	Calories	Food	Calories
Lunch:	2 slices chicken	160 each	1 slice bread	70
	1 apple	60	1 tbsp. margarine	100
	1 juice drink	145		
Snack:	Pretzels	140	Low-fat milkshake	155
Dinner:	Beef soup	120	Roast beef, 9 oz.	490
	Rice	200	Broccoli, cooked	50
	Carrots, raw	40	2 glasses milk	124 each

Exercise A Answer the following questions by adding or subtracting.

1) How many calories does Kyle have at lunch?

2) How many calories are in his snack?

3) How many calories does Kyle have at dinner?

4) How many total calories does he have during the entire day?

5) Is his total calorie count for the day less than 3,600 or greater than 3,600?

6) What is the difference between his total count and 3,600?

7) For his snack, suppose that Kyle drinks a glass of milk instead of a low-fat milkshake. By how much will he lower his calorie count?

8) If Kyle skips one piece of chicken for lunch, how much lower will his calorie count be?

Lesson 4 Estimating Calories Used

Increase
To make larger.

Graph
A pictorial way to display information.

Vary
To differ in characteristics.

It is sometimes easy for people to **increase** their calories. The more they eat, the more calories they add. However, it can take more time and effort for your body to use calories.

The body gets a certain amount of energy from each calorie. The more active a person is, the faster he or she uses calories.

The **graph** shows the number of calories that are used in one hour of activity. The amounts shown may **vary** from person to person depending on age, weight, and gender.

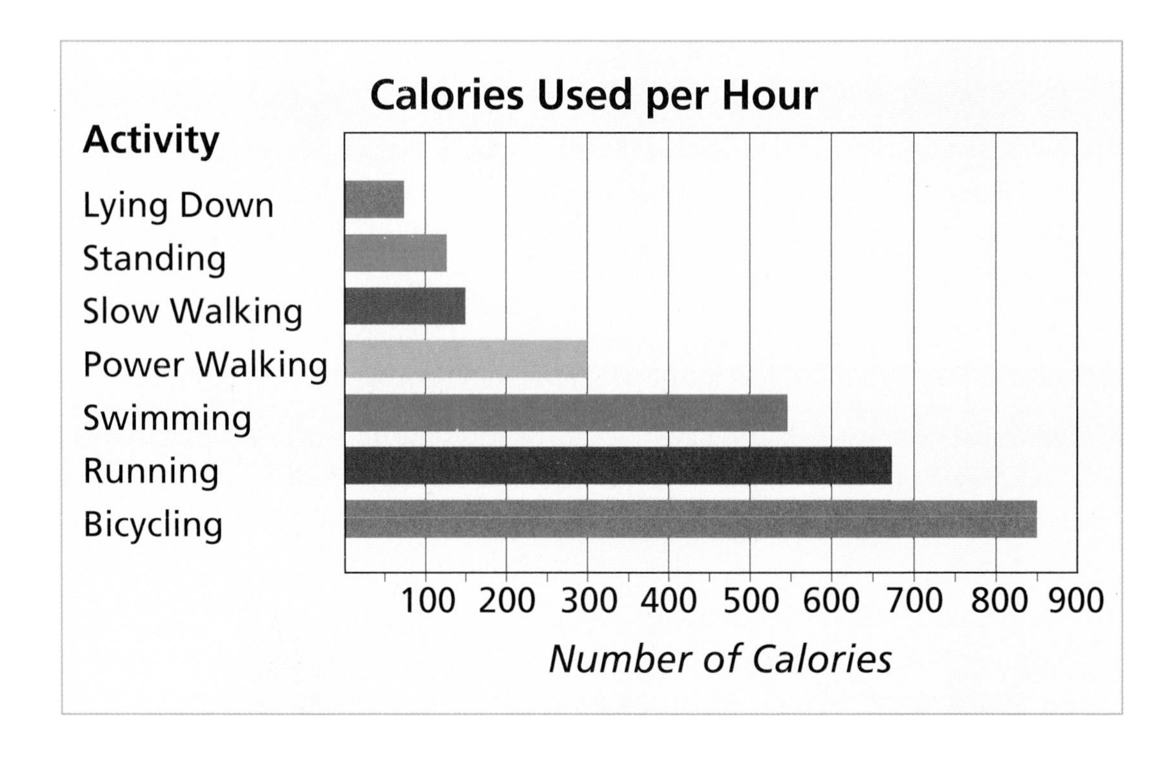

Estimate

To give a reasonable or approximate number.

Use this graph to **estimate**, or guess, needed information. The graph can help you estimate the number of calories used while walking slowly for one hour. The bar for slow walking reaches past the 100 line. Since the end of the bar is about halfway between 100 and 200, the estimate is 150 calories.

Exercise A Use the graph to estimate the number of calories used per hour for each of these activities.

1) Lying down

2) Bicycling

3) Standing

4) Running

5) Swimming

6) Power walking

Besides burning calories, cycling is good for a healthy heart and lungs.

Lesson 5 Adding and Subtracting Calories

The following table shows the number of calories different activities use in one hour.

Calorie Used in One Hour

Activity	Calories
Sitting in class	100
Studying	105
Eating	125
Keyboarding	140
Making beds	175
Washing dishes	180
Playing table tennis	230
Lifting weights	500

EXAMPLE

Tomas consumes 3,295 calories in one day. Then he keyboards for one hour and plays table tennis for one hour. Find the number of calories not used.

First, you add to find the calories used:

140	Keyboarding
+ 230	Playing table tennis
370	Calories used

Then, subtract the calories used from the calories consumed:

3,295	Calories consumed
− 370	Calories used
2,925	Calories not used

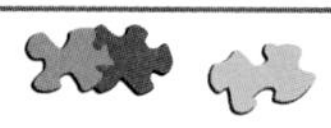

PROBLEM SOLVING

Exercise A Find the number of calories not used.

1) Jim consumes 2,935 calories. He spends one hour studying and one hour keyboarding.

2) Katie's calorie consumption is 3,255. She sits in class for one hour and studies for one hour.

3) Mason consumes 2,892 calories. He makes beds for one hour and washes dishes for one hour.

4) Ann lifts weights for one hour. Then she eats lunch for one hour. Her lunch totals 962 calories.

5) Lamont consumes 1,932 calories. He spends one hour each on making beds, eating, and washing dishes.

Calculator Practice

A calculator can help you add numbers. Key in each number carefully. Then check the number on the calculator display before you go on to the next number.

Calculator Exercise Add each list of calories to find each total.

1)
$$\begin{array}{r} 265 \\ 423 \\ 80 \\ +\ 293 \\ \hline \end{array}$$

2)
$$\begin{array}{r} 120 \\ 460 \\ 290 \\ +\ 310 \\ \hline \end{array}$$

3)
$$\begin{array}{r} 50 \\ 23 \\ 125 \\ +\ 62 \\ \hline \end{array}$$

4)
$$\begin{array}{r} 923 \\ 1{,}063 \\ 103 \\ +\ 40 \\ \hline \end{array}$$

Chapter 1 Review

Food	Calories
Hamburger	270
Lean steak	660
Bean soup	90
French fries	155
Cola	105
Skim milk, 1 cup	110

One-Hour Activity	Calories Used
Baseball	360
Basketball	500
Aerobics	300
Gymnastics	430
Singing	135

Use the information in the charts to find the answer to each problem.

1) Alvaro chooses a hamburger, French fries, and a cola for lunch. How many calories does he consume?

2) Evan has a lean steak, French fries, and two cups of skim milk. How many calories does he consume?

3) Cass needs 2,435 calories each day. She has bean soup, French fries, and a cup of skim milk. How many more calories does she need?

4) Marta has a hamburger and a cola. Sue has a lean steak and a cup of skim milk. Find the difference in how many calories they consume.

5) Joy plays baseball and basketball for one hour each. How many calories does she use?

6) Lance does aerobics for one hour and then does gymnastics for two hours. Find the total calories he uses.

Find the number of calories not used.

7) 2,685 calories consumed. One hour of singing.

8) 3,230 calories consumed. Two hours of baseball.

9) 2,900 calories consumed. Two hours of gymnastics.

10) 3,150 calories consumed. Three hours of basketball.

Use the information in the nutrition label to solve these problems.

11) How many servings are there?

12) Find the total fat calories.

Nutrition Facts

Serving Size 5 crackers = 1 oz. (28.35g)
Servings Per Container 4

Amount Per Serving = 5 crackers	
Calories = 116 Calories from Fat = 20	
	% Daily Value
Total Fat 2.27g	**3%**
Saturated Fat 0.48g	**2%**
Cholesterol 0mg	**0%**
Sodium 213.55mg (0.21355g)	**9%**
Total Carbohydrate 19g	**6%**
Dietary Fiber 3.50g	**14%**
Sugars 2.28g	
Protein 4.61g	
Vitamin A 0% • Vitamin C	0%
Calcium 0% • Iron	6%

Use the graph to estimate the number of calories used per hour for each of these activities.

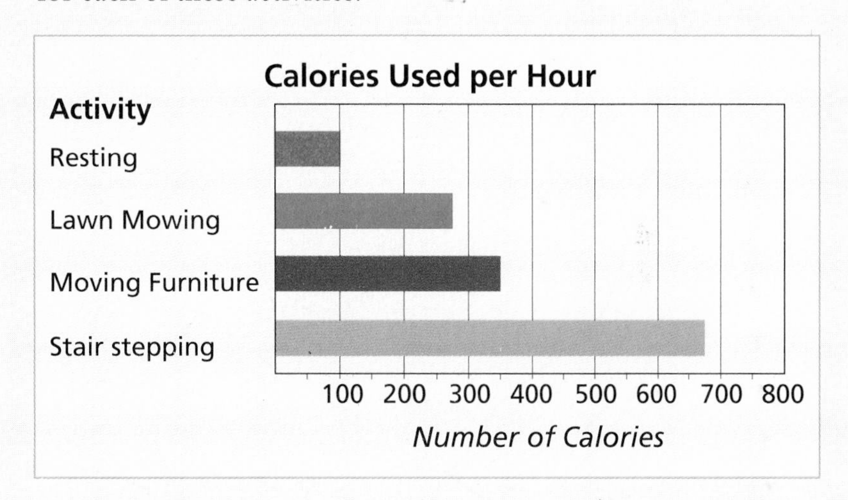

13) Moving furniture

14) Stair stepping

15) Lawn mowing

Test Taking Tip When you read word problems, watch for numbers that are written in word form.

Chapter 2 Home Improvement

Look around your home. Are there changes you would like to make? Maybe a fresh coat of paint would spruce up a drab room. Perhaps carpeting needs to be replaced. Mathematics can help you find out how much wallpaper, paint, or carpeting you will need. You can save money when you know how to find the cost of home improvements.

In Chapter 2, you will learn how to determine the number of double rolls of wallpaper to buy. You will even discover that there is an economical and not-so-economical way to position carpet on the floor.

Goals for Learning

- To compute the surface area of a room
- To find area in square yards when given the dimensions in feet
- To find the cost of tiling a room, given the dimensions of the room and cost of tiles
- To apply a rule for estimating the cost of wallpaper for a room

Lesson 1 Painting Walls

Area

Amount of space inside a shape.

Height

The distance from top to bottom.

Length

The distance from end to end.

Unit

Any fixed amount, quantity, etc., used as a standard.

When starting a project like painting walls, you will need to know the surface area of the walls before you can buy the paint. To find the **area**, multiply the **length** and the **height** of each wall to be painted. Remember to subtract the area of any doors or windows. Area is measured in square **units**.

EXAMPLE

8 ft. × 12 ft. = 96 sq. ft.

7 ft. × 3 ft. = 21 sq. ft.

96 sq. ft. − 21 sq. ft. = 75 sq. ft.

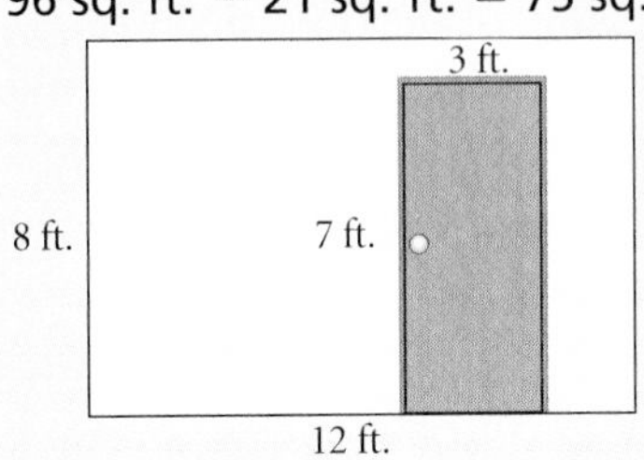

75 square feet to be painted.

Exercise A Find the surface area of each wall.

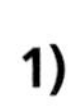

1)

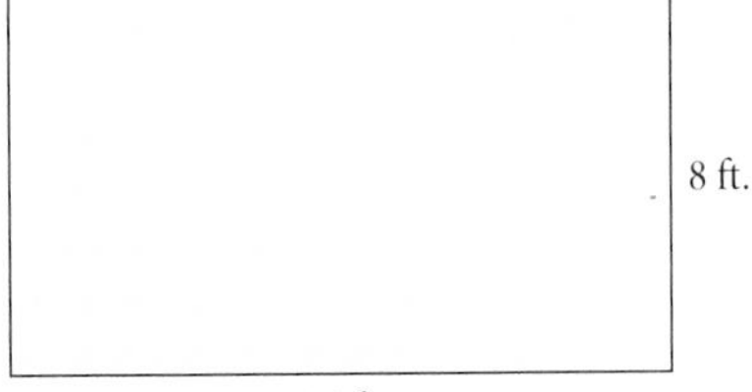

2)

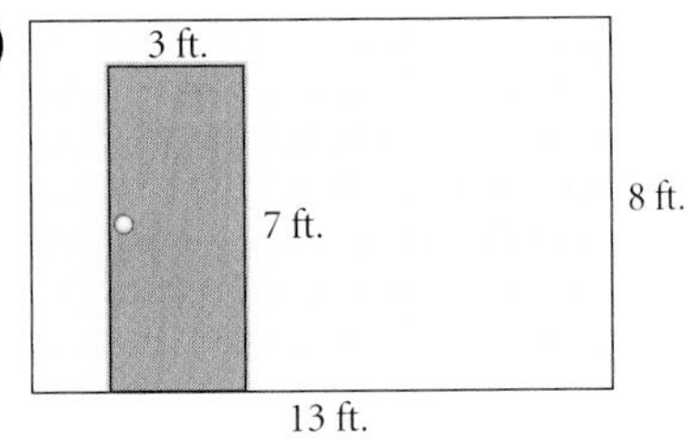

3)

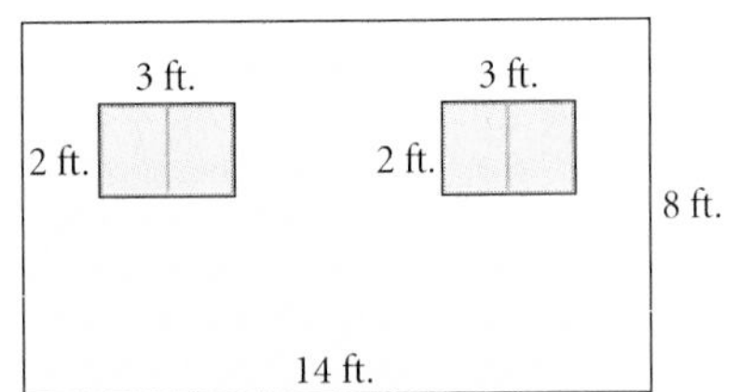

4)

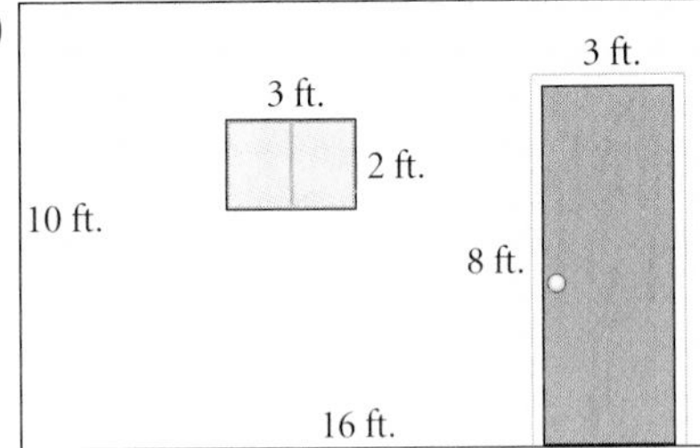

5)

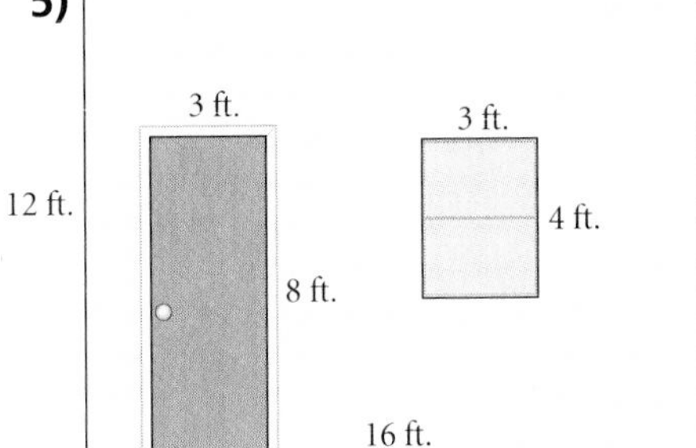

6)

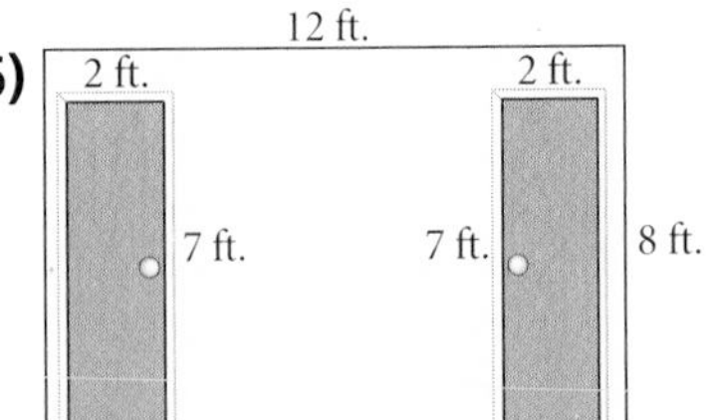

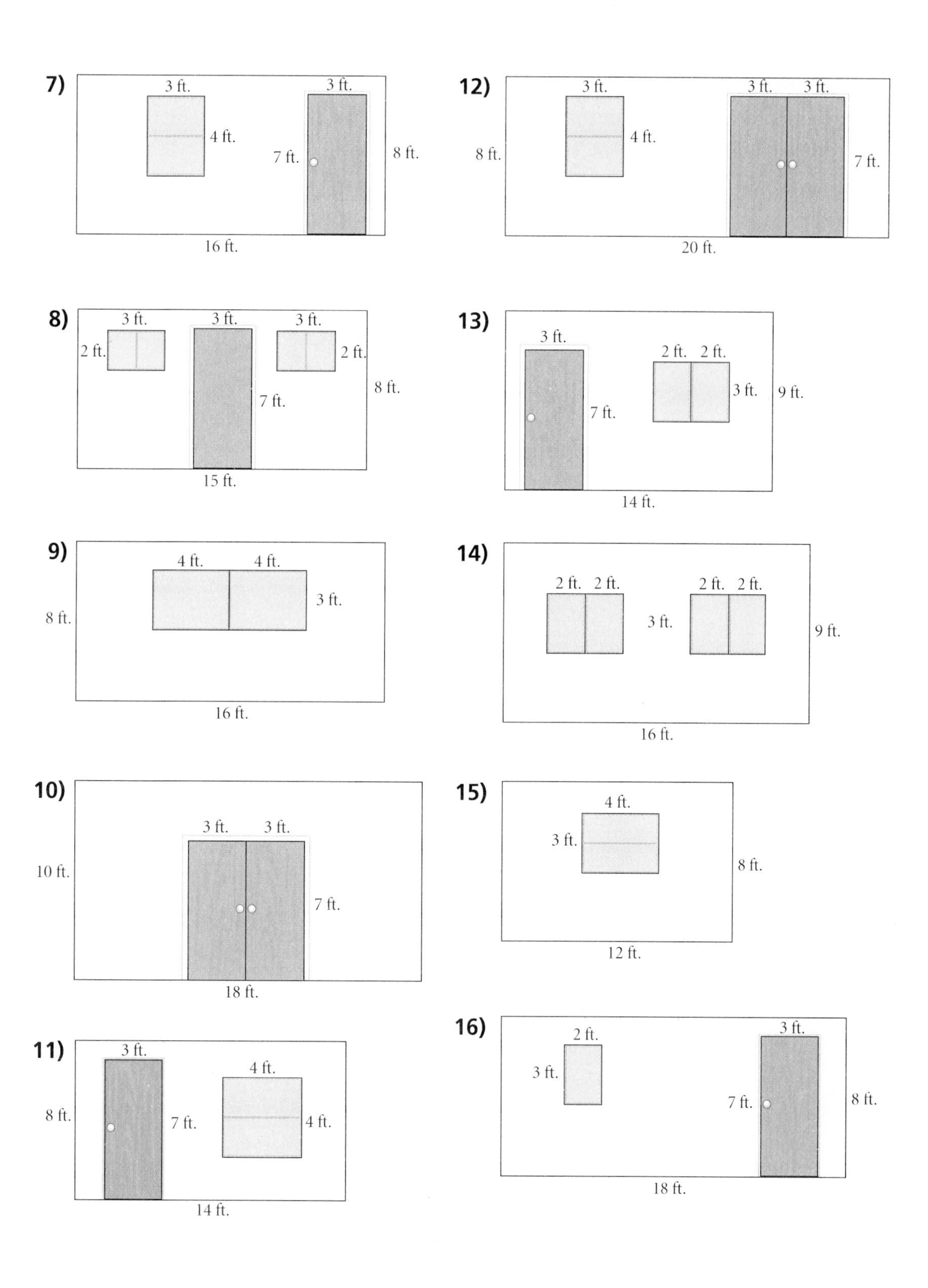
7)
3 ft.
3 ft.
4 ft.
7 ft.
8 ft.
16 ft.
8)
3 ft.
3 ft.
3 ft.
2 ft.
2 ft.
7 ft.
8 ft.
15 ft.
9)
4 ft.
4 ft.
3 ft.
8 ft.
16 ft.
10)
3 ft.
3 ft.
10 ft.
7 ft.
18 ft.
11)
3 ft.
4 ft.
8 ft.
7 ft.
4 ft.
14 ft.
12)
3 ft.
3 ft.
3 ft.
4 ft.
8 ft.
7 ft.
20 ft.
13)
3 ft.
2 ft.
2 ft.
3 ft.
9 ft.
7 ft.
14 ft.
14)
2 ft.
2 ft.
2 ft.
2 ft.
3 ft.
9 ft.
16 ft.
15)
4 ft.
3 ft.
8 ft.
12 ft.
16)
2 ft.
3 ft.
3 ft.
7 ft.
8 ft.
18 ft.

An easy way to find the surface area of a room is to add the lengths of all walls. Then multiply the answer by the height of the room. Finally, subtract the area of any doors and windows.

Example

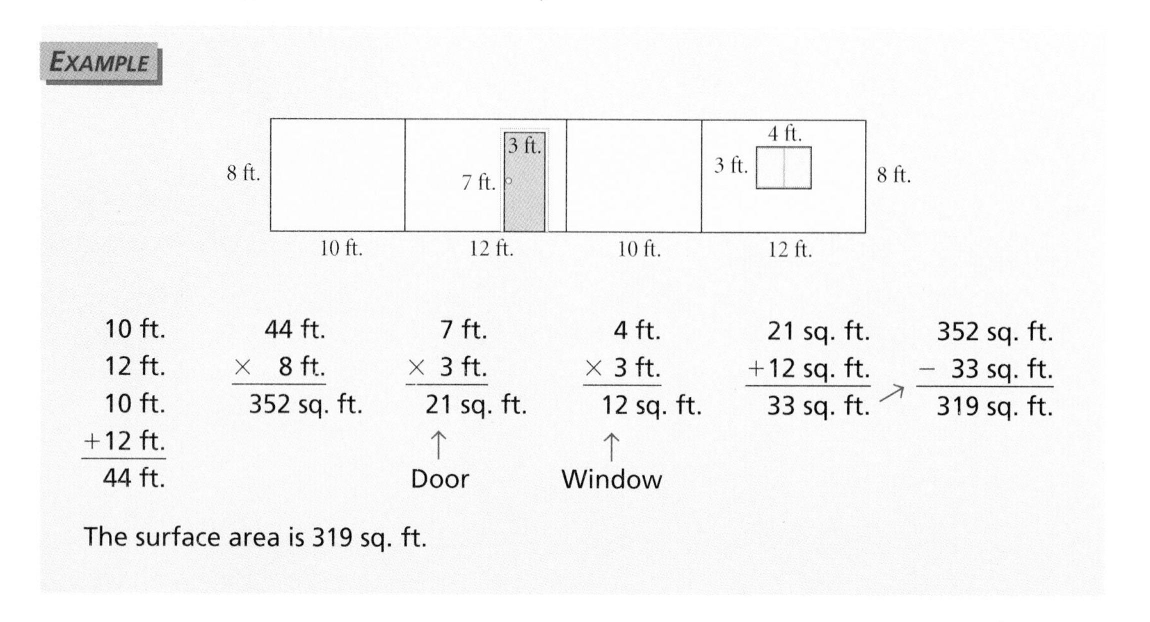

$$\begin{array}{r} 10 \text{ ft.} \\ 12 \text{ ft.} \\ 10 \text{ ft.} \\ +12 \text{ ft.} \\ \hline 44 \text{ ft.} \end{array} \qquad \begin{array}{r} 44 \text{ ft.} \\ \times\ 8 \text{ ft.} \\ \hline 352 \text{ sq. ft.} \end{array} \qquad \begin{array}{r} 7 \text{ ft.} \\ \times\ 3 \text{ ft.} \\ \hline 21 \text{ sq. ft.} \end{array} \qquad \begin{array}{r} 4 \text{ ft.} \\ \times\ 3 \text{ ft.} \\ \hline 12 \text{ sq. ft.} \end{array} \qquad \begin{array}{r} 21 \text{ sq. ft.} \\ +12 \text{ sq. ft.} \\ \hline 33 \text{ sq. ft.} \end{array} \nearrow \begin{array}{r} 352 \text{ sq. ft.} \\ -\ 33 \text{ sq. ft.} \\ \hline 319 \text{ sq. ft.} \end{array}$$

↑ Door (21 sq. ft.) ↑ Window (12 sq. ft.)

The surface area is 319 sq. ft.

Exercise B Find the surface of each of these rooms.

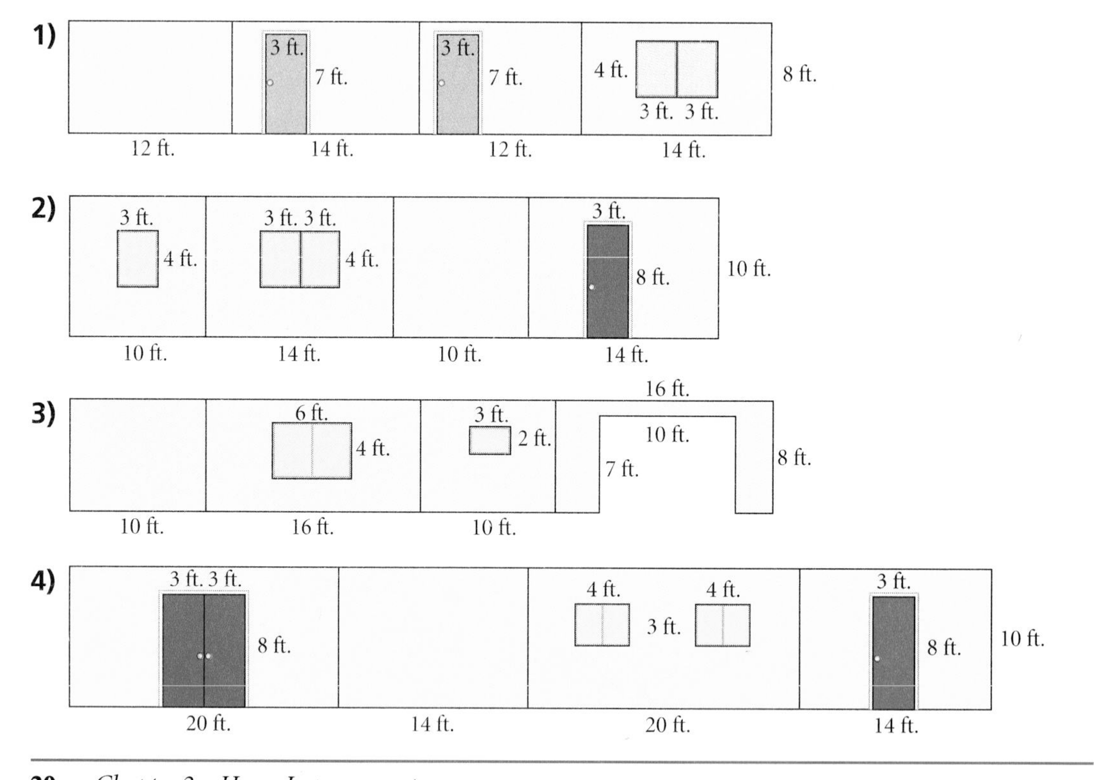

Lesson 2 Determining Carpet Amounts

Carpet is usually sold by the square yard in carpet stores. To find the number of square yards of carpet that you need, find the area of the floor in square feet. Divide this answer by 9. You divide by 9 because there are 9 square feet in one square yard.

EXAMPLE

Step 1 $13 \times 11 = 143$ square feet

Step 2 $143 \div 9 = 15\frac{8}{9}$

There are $15\frac{8}{9}$ square yards.

Exercise A Find the number of square yards of carpet that are needed to carpet each floor.

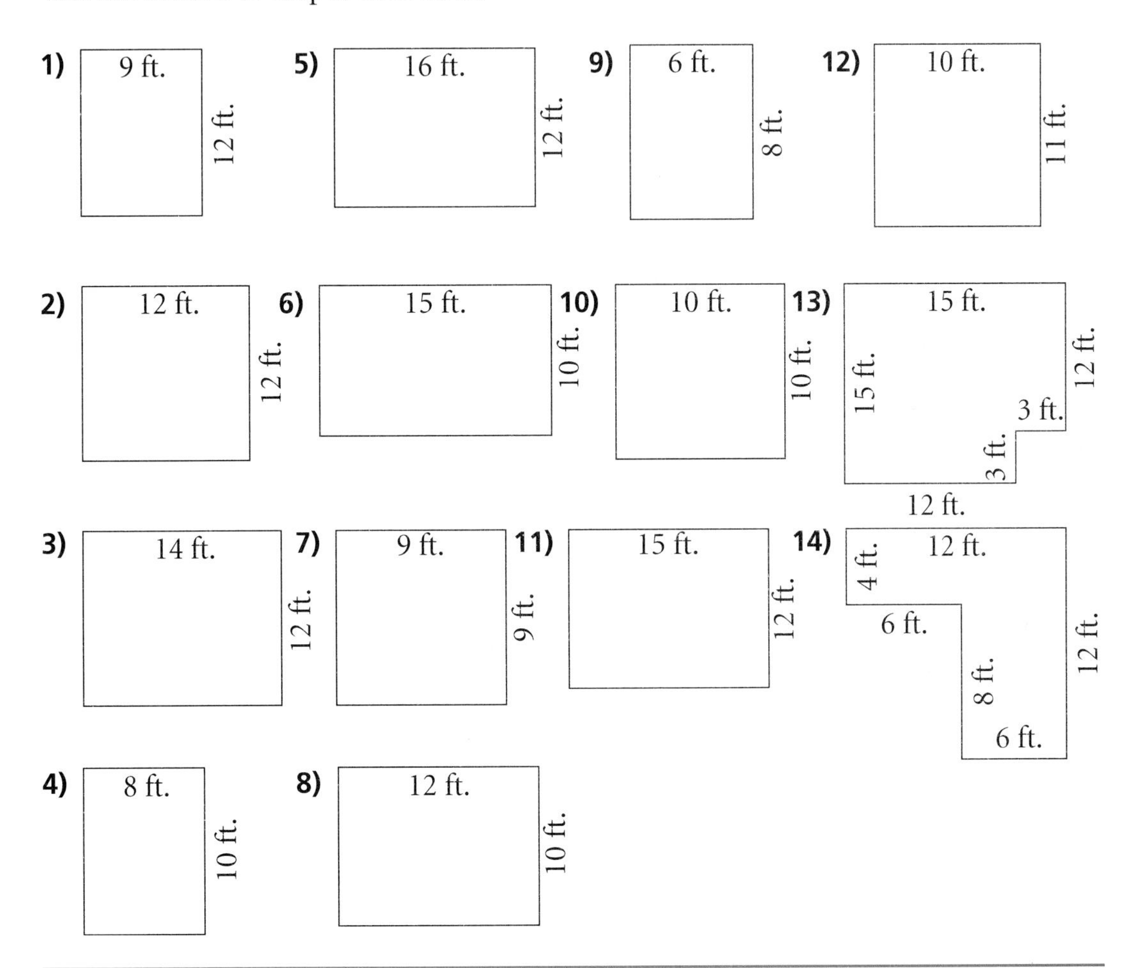

A **standard** width for carpet is twelve feet. You buy the number of feet of carpet you need from a big roll of carpet. It may make a difference in the amount of carpet needed if you use the twelve feet in the wrong direction.

Standard

A rule or model for measuring.

Exercise B Find the lowest price of carpet for each floor. The laid carpet must be one complete piece. Some carpet will need to be trimmed.

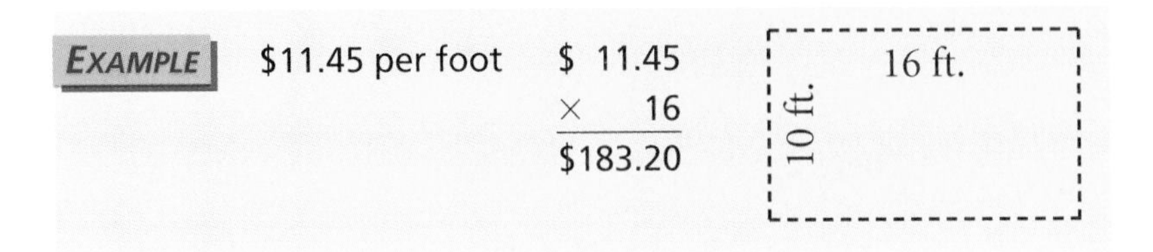

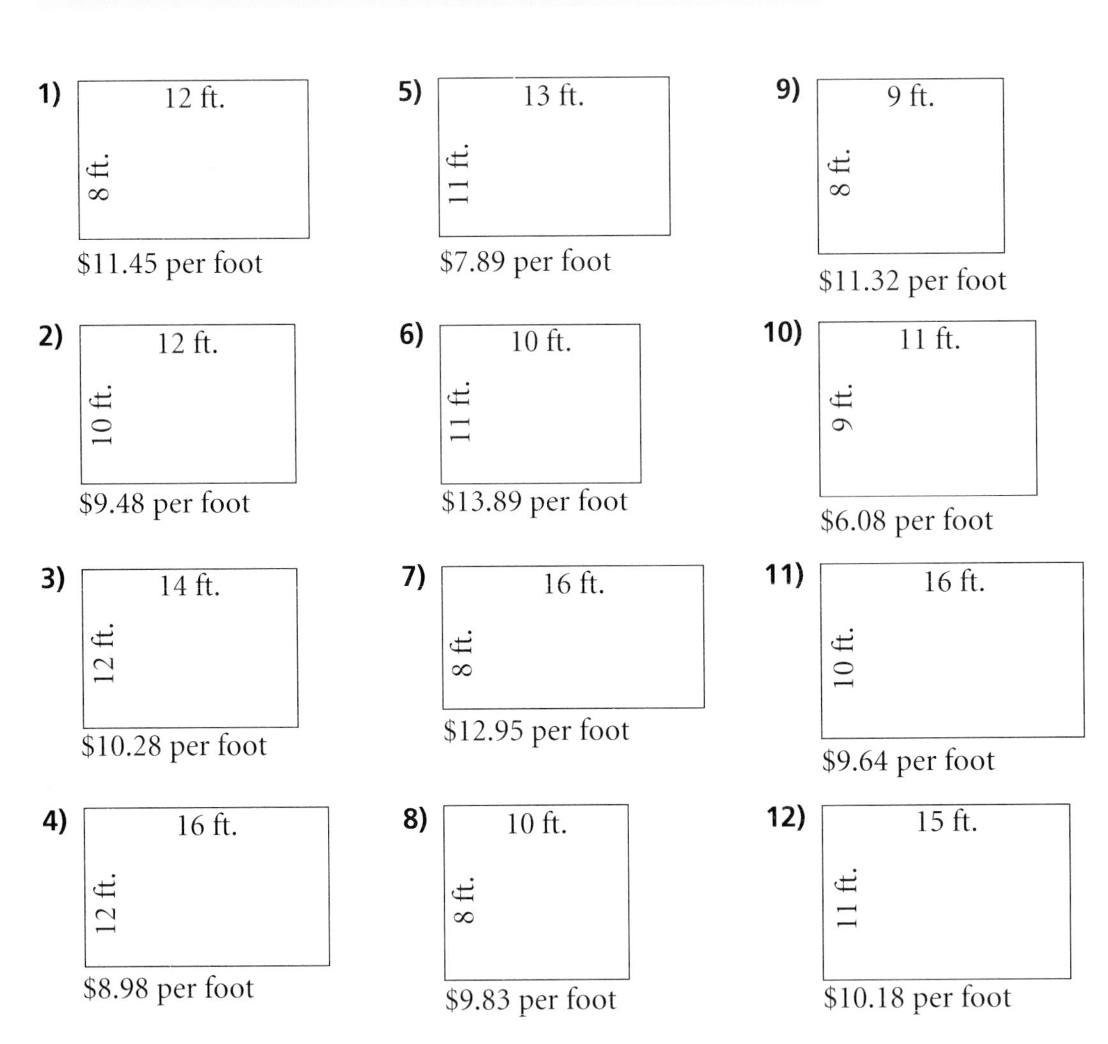

Lesson 3 Buying Floor Tiles

Width

The distance from side to side.

Floor tiles are usually sold in cartons of 45. Each tile covers one square foot. To determine how many tiles you need, multiply the length × **width** of the room. Divide that number by 45 to determine how many cartons you will need. Then multiply by the carton price to find a subtotal. Remember to multiply the remainder by the cost of a single tile to find the other subtotal. Then add the subtotals to find the total cost.

EXAMPLE A carton costs $15.30. Each single tile costs $.35. What is the cost to tile an 8 ft. by 16 ft. room?

An 8 ft. by 16 ft. room
8 × 16 = 128 tiles
128 ÷ 45 = 2 cartons and 38 single tiles
$15.30 × 2 = $30.60
$.35 × 38 = $13.30

$30.60	2 cartons
+13.30	38 singles
$43.90	Total cost

The cost is $43.90.

Exercise A If a carton of tiles costs $15.30 and a single tile costs 35¢, then find the cost of tiling each floor.

1) A 12 ft. by 14 ft. room
_____ cartons
_____ single tiles
_____ cost

2) A 12 ft. by 12 ft. room
_____ cartons
_____ single tiles
_____ cost

3) A room 9 ft. by 14 ft.
_____ cartons
_____ single tiles
_____ cost

4) A room 8 ft. by 12 ft.
_____ cartons
_____ single tiles
_____ cost

5) A room 7 ft. by 9 ft.
_____ cartons
_____ single tiles
_____ cost

6) A room 10 ft. by 12 ft.
_____ cartons
_____ single tiles
_____ cost

7) A room 8 ft. by 11 ft.
_____ cartons
_____ single tiles
_____ cost

8) A room 8 ft. by 14 ft.
_____ cartons
_____ single tiles
_____ cost

9) A room 10 ft. by 10 ft.
_____ cartons
_____ single tiles
_____ cost

10) A room 10 ft. by 15 ft.
_____ cartons
_____ single tiles
_____ cost

11) A room 10 ft. by 16 ft.
_____ cartons
_____ single tiles
_____ cost

12) A room 13 ft. by 15 ft.
_____ cartons
_____ single tiles
_____ cost

Lesson 4 Estimating the Amount of Wallpaper

Double roll

Wallpaper that covers twice the wall area of a single roll.

Round up

To round to the next highest number.

Wallpaper is often sold by the **double roll**. You can estimate the amount of wallpaper that is needed to paper a room by using this rule of thumb:

> **• How to Measure for Wallpaper •**
>
> Number of double rolls needed = distance around room × height of walls ÷ 60. Next, subtract one double roll for every four doors or windows. Always round up if you have a remainder after dividing by 60.

EXAMPLE One double roll of wallpaper costs $12.48.

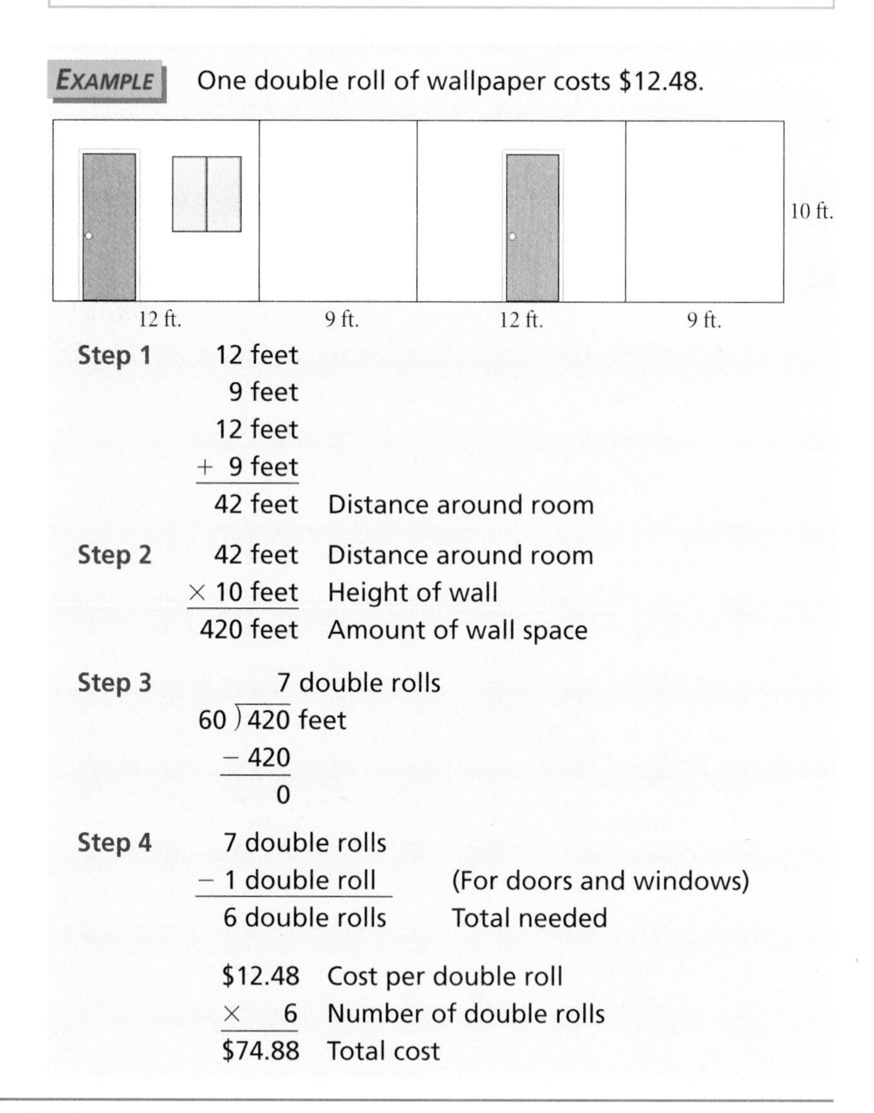

Step 1

$$\begin{array}{r l} 12 \text{ feet} & \\ 9 \text{ feet} & \\ 12 \text{ feet} & \\ + \ 9 \text{ feet} & \\ \hline 42 \text{ feet} & \text{Distance around room} \end{array}$$

Step 2

$$\begin{array}{r l} 42 \text{ feet} & \text{Distance around room} \\ \times \ 10 \text{ feet} & \text{Height of wall} \\ \hline 420 \text{ feet} & \text{Amount of wall space} \end{array}$$

Step 3

$$\begin{array}{r} 7 \text{ double rolls} \\ 60 \overline{)420} \text{ feet} \\ -420 \\ \hline 0 \end{array}$$

Step 4

$$\begin{array}{r l} 7 \text{ double rolls} & \\ - \ 1 \text{ double roll} & \text{(For doors and windows)} \\ \hline 6 \text{ double rolls} & \text{Total needed} \end{array}$$

$$\begin{array}{r l} \$12.48 & \text{Cost per double roll} \\ \times \quad 6 & \text{Number of double rolls} \\ \hline \$74.88 & \text{Total cost} \end{array}$$

Exercise A Find the cost of wallpapering each of these rooms. The cost of one double roll is given.

1) One double roll of wallpaper costs $11.98.

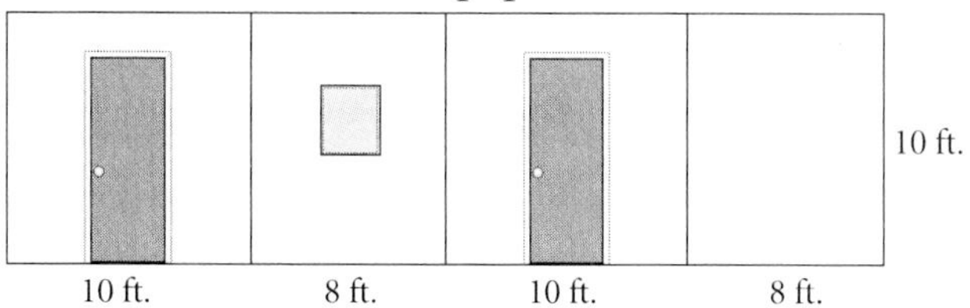

2) One double roll of wallpaper costs $9.95.

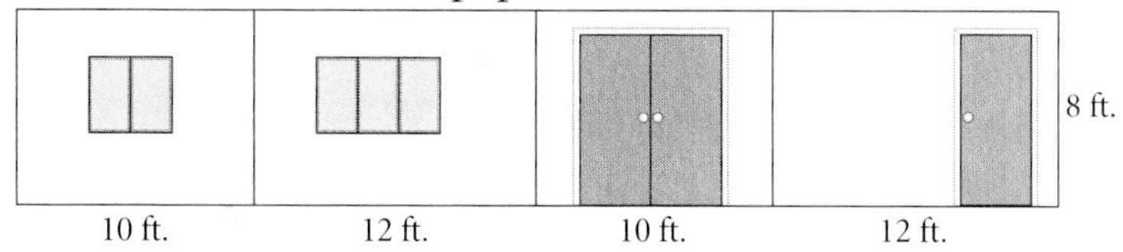

3) One double roll of wallpaper costs $15.45.

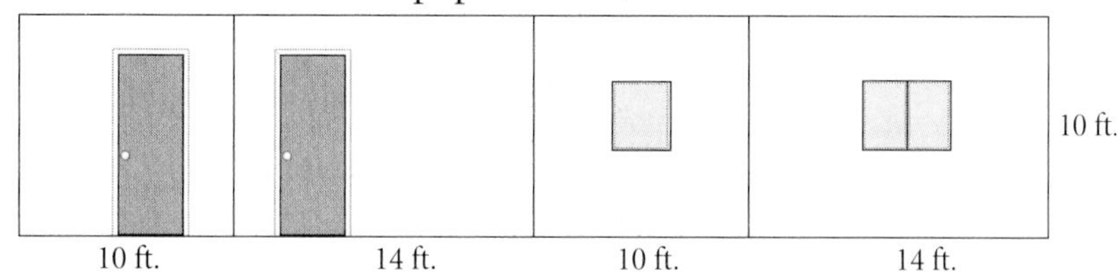

4) One double roll of wallpaper costs $13.28.

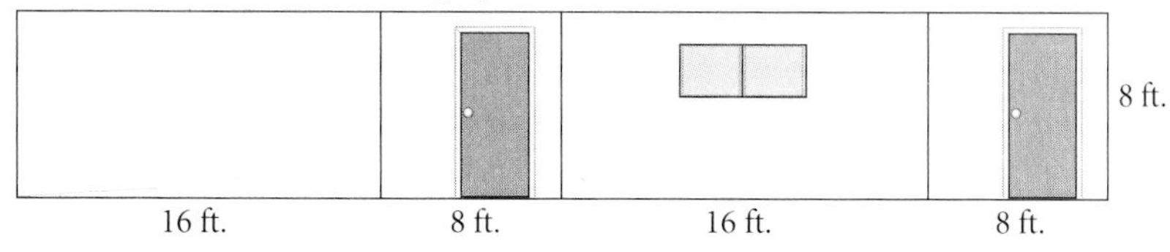

5) One double roll of wallpaper costs $17.49.

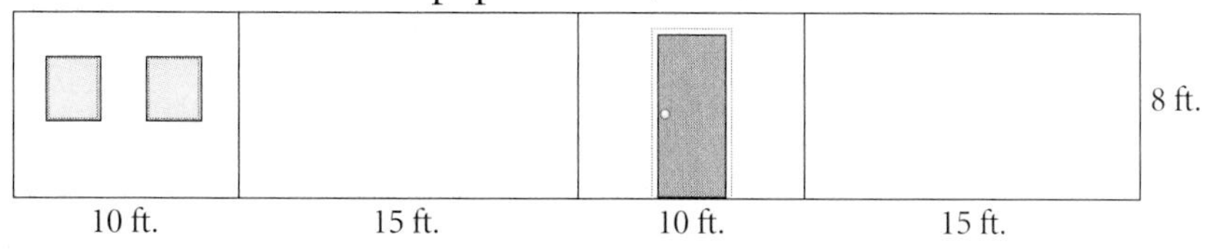

Calculator Practice

You can multiply quickly with a calculator. Key in each number. Check it on the calculator display before you key in the sign or the next number. Find the products of these numbers.

1) 2,706 × 412

2) 362 × 535

3) 8,711 × 305

4) 8,017 × 217

5) 6,153 × 8,715

6) 323 × 762

Chapter 2 Review

Find the answers.

1) $\begin{array}{r} 346 \\ \times \quad 7 \\ \hline \end{array}$

2) $7\,\overline{)\,5{,}292}$

3) $\begin{array}{r} 408 \\ \times \quad 37 \\ \hline \end{array}$

4) $14\,\overline{)\,639}$

5) $60\,\overline{)\,4{,}740}$

6) $\begin{array}{r} 823 \\ \times \quad 226 \\ \hline \end{array}$

7) $15\,\overline{)\,\$34.95}$

8) $\begin{array}{r} \$\ 154.32 \\ \times \qquad 38 \\ \hline \end{array}$

Find the surface area of the walls drawn below. Subtract the area of any doors or windows.

9)

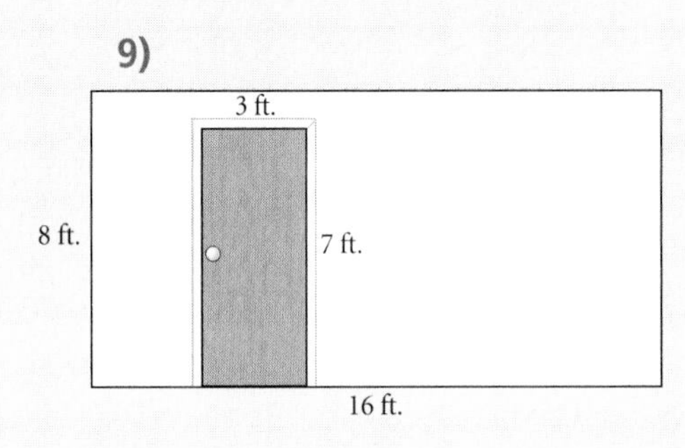

10)

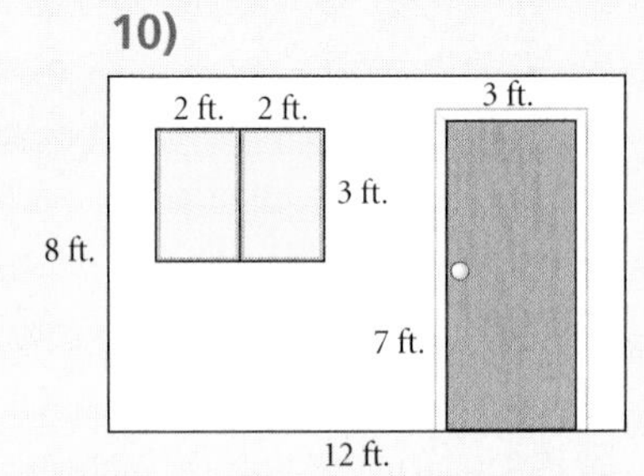

11)

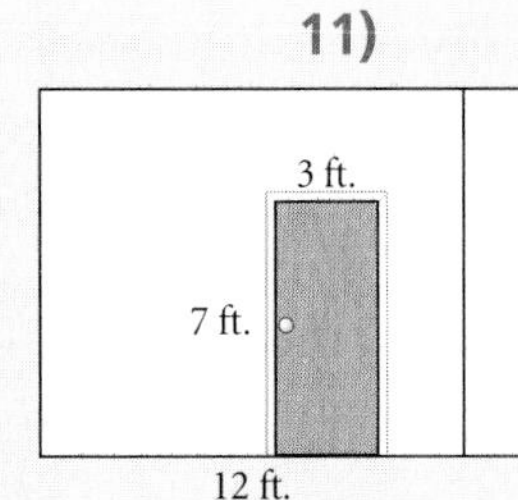

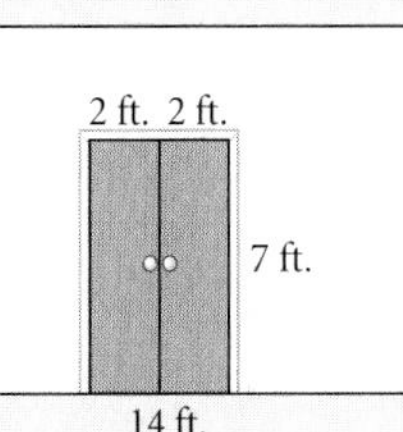

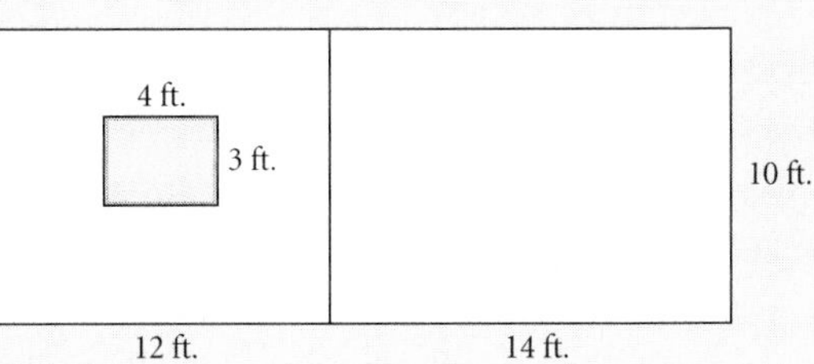

12) Find the number of double rolls of wallpaper needed to paper the room drawn in #11. Multiply the distance around the room by the wall height and divide by 60. Subtract one double roll for every four doors or windows.

Find the lowest cost of a carpet for each floor if 12-foot-wide carpeting costs $13.45 per foot.

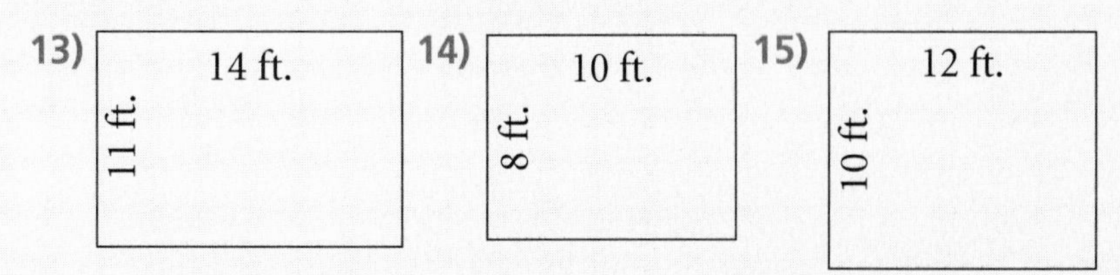

Find the number of square yards of carpet that are needed to carpet each floor.

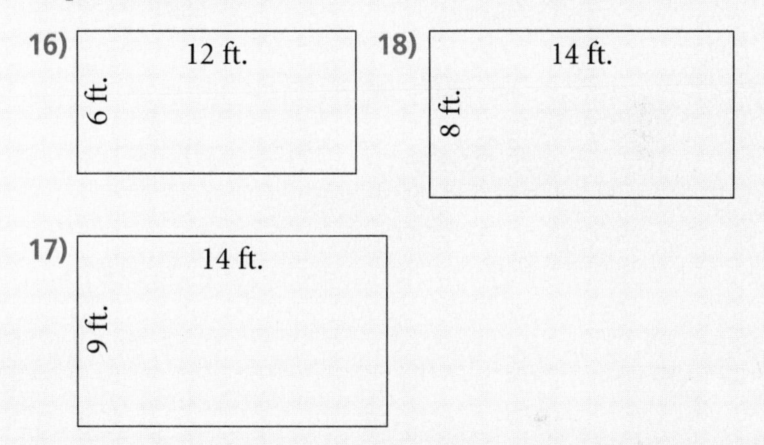

Find the lowest cost for tiling each floor described. Floor tiles that cover one square foot each are sold in cartons of 45 tiles for $17.00. Individual tiles cost $.38 each.

19) A 12 ft. by 15 ft. room

_______ cartons

_______ single tiles

_______ cost

20) A 10 ft. by 12 ft. room

_______ cartons

_______ single tiles

_______ cost

Test Taking Tip Drawing pictures or diagrams is one way to help you understand and solve problems.

Chapter 3

Using Math in Sports

Whether you are a member of a sports team, or follow sports in the newspaper, or enjoy channel surfing, you have experienced mathematics in sports. Baseball players keep track of batting averages, bowlers score their success, and Olympic records are broadcast on television. Next time you think about numbers, think about sports! Adding, subtracting, multiplying, and dividing are some of the mathematics you'll discover there.

In Chapter 3, you will learn how to score spares and strikes in bowling. You will challenge your problem-solving skills as you explore the mathematics in weight lifting.

Goals for Learning

- To compute bowling scores
- To compute with whole numbers in the context of weight lifting
- To find average scores

Lesson 1 Bowling

Mathematics is used in scoring a bowling game. When you fill in a score sheet, you are adding the number of pins knocked down.

Frame

In bowling, any of the divisions of a game in which all ten pins are set up anew.

The large squares on a score sheet are called **frames.** A bowler may roll two balls for each frame. The number of pins you knock down with each roll is written in a small box in the frame.

EXAMPLES Karen plays a 3-frame game. Look at her score sheet. Notice how the numbers are added.

1st frame:	1st roll	3
	2d roll	2

1		2		3	
3	2				
5					

2d frame:	1st roll	4
	2d roll	5

1		2		3	
3	2	4	5		
5		14			

3d frame:	1st roll	6
	2d roll	2
Total score:	**22**	

1		2		3	
3	2	4	5	6	2
5		14		22	

John bowls 3 frames with the following results.

1st frame:	1st roll	6
	2d roll	2
2d frame:	1st roll	5
	2d roll	2
3d frame:	1st roll	8
	2d roll	0
Total score:	**23**	

1		2		3	
6	2	5	2	8	–
8		15		23	

When John hits no pins, he writes a dash in the box.

Exercise A On separate paper, write the number of pins knocked down in each frame.

1)

2)

1	2	3	4
2 5	4 2	5 –	5 4
7	13	18	27

3)

1	2	3
4 1	1 6	5 3
5	12	20

4)

1	2	3	4	5
2 –	5 3	8 1	5 1	4 –
2	10	19	25	29

Exercise B On separate paper, add to find the score for each frame.

1)

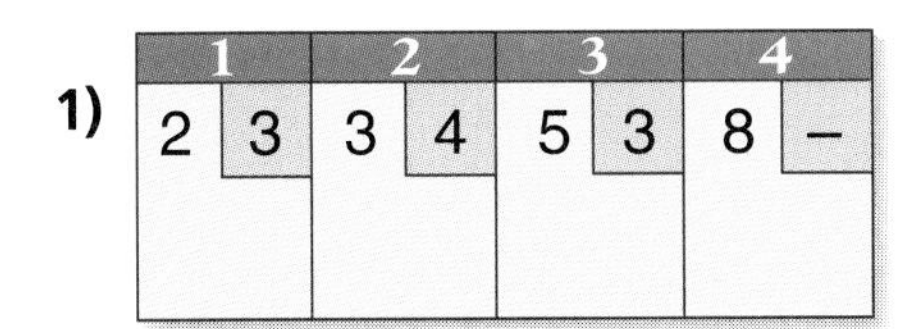

2)

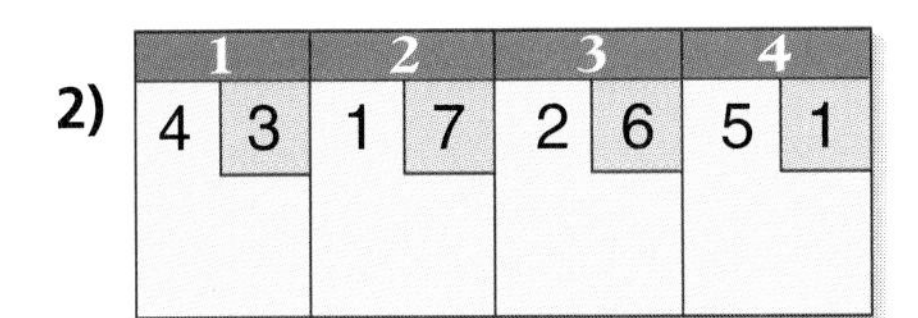

3)

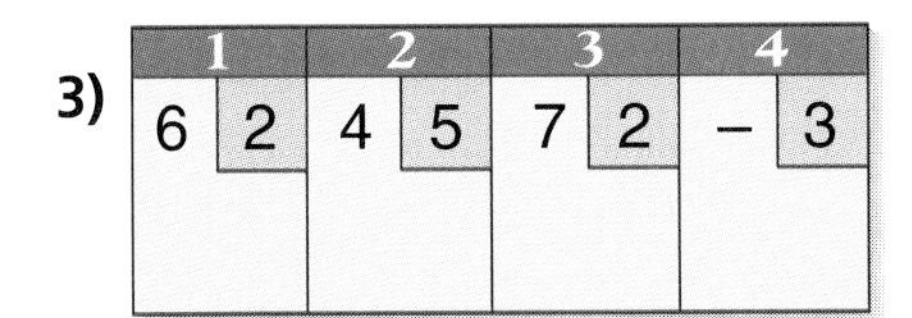

4)

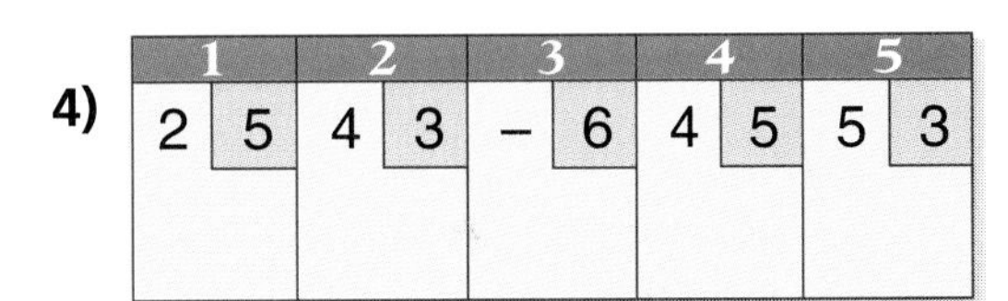

5)

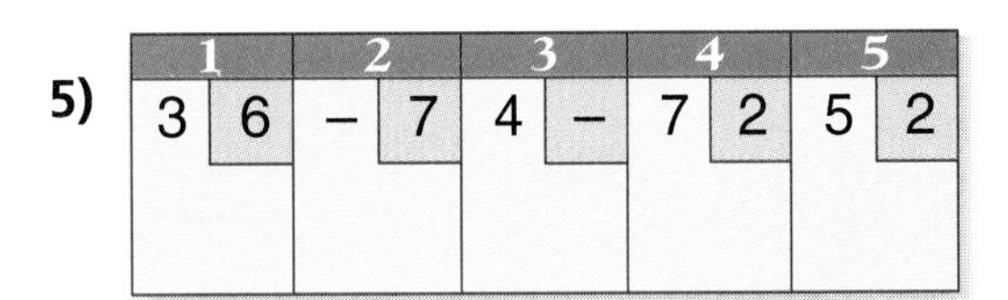

6)

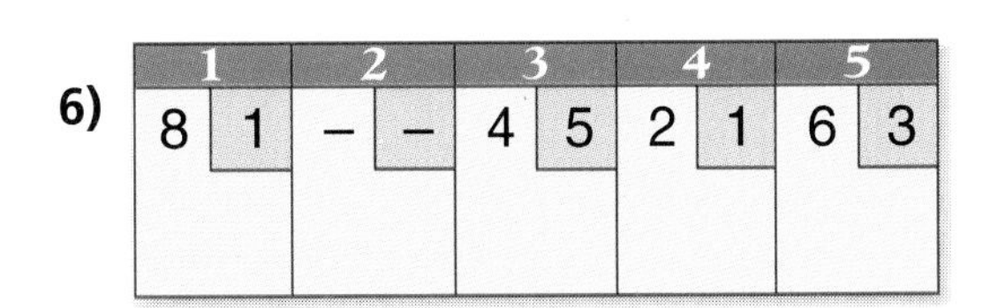

Exercise C Use the score sheet your teacher gives you. Fill in the frames with the scores for each game.

1) 1st frame: 1st roll 2; 2d roll 3
2d frame: 1st roll 5; 2d roll 4
3d frame: 1st roll 4; 2d roll 5

2) 1st frame: 1st roll 3; 2d roll 5
2d frame: 1st roll 6; 2d roll 2
3d frame: 1st roll 4; 2d roll 3

3) 1st frame: 1st roll 7; 2d roll 2
2d frame: 1st roll 5; 2d roll 4
3d frame: 1st roll 3; 2d roll 5

4) 1st frame: 1st roll 4; 2d roll 5
2d frame: 1st roll 5; 2d roll 2
3d frame: 1st roll 4; 2d roll 2

5) 1st frame: 1st roll 1; 2d roll 2
2d frame: 1st roll 1; 2d roll 5
3d frame: 1st roll 3; 2d roll 5

6) 1st frame: 1st roll 1; 2d roll 3
2d frame: 1st roll 1; 2d roll 7
3d frame: 1st roll 3; 2d roll 6

7) 1st frame: 1st roll 2; 2d roll 7
2d frame: 1st roll 3; 2d roll 4
3d frame: 1st roll 8; 2d roll 1

8) 1st frame: 1st roll 3; 2d roll 3
2d frame: 1st roll 5; 2d roll 4
3d frame: 1st roll 1; 2d roll 6

Scoring Spares With a little luck you may knock down all ten pins with two rolls of the ball. When you do this, you score a **spare**. Getting a spare helps you to increase your score.

> ***Spare***
> *In bowling, knocking down all the pins with two rolls of the ball.*

EXAMPLES

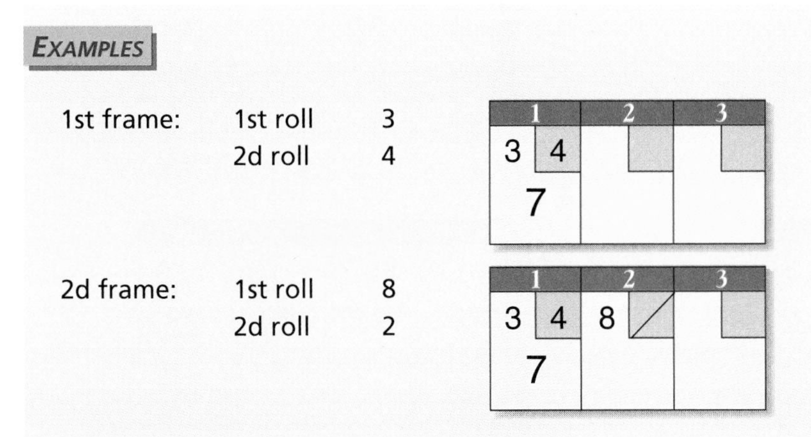

1st frame: 1st roll 3
2d roll 4

2d frame: 1st roll 8
2d roll 2

The spare mark (/) means that 10 pins are scored in the frame PLUS the number of pins on the first roll of the next frame.

3d frame: 1st roll 3
2d roll 6

1	2	3
3 4	8 /	3 6
7	20	29

When a spare occurs in a frame, the total for that frame is the result of adding the previous frame total, plus 10, plus the number of pins knocked down on the first roll of the next frame.

1	2	3
4 2	6 /	3 5
6	19	27

1st frame:	1st roll	4
	2d roll	2
2d frame:	1st roll	6
	2d roll	4
3d frame:	1st roll	3
	2d roll	5

Exercise D On separate paper, write the number of pins that were knocked down on each roll.

1) 

2) 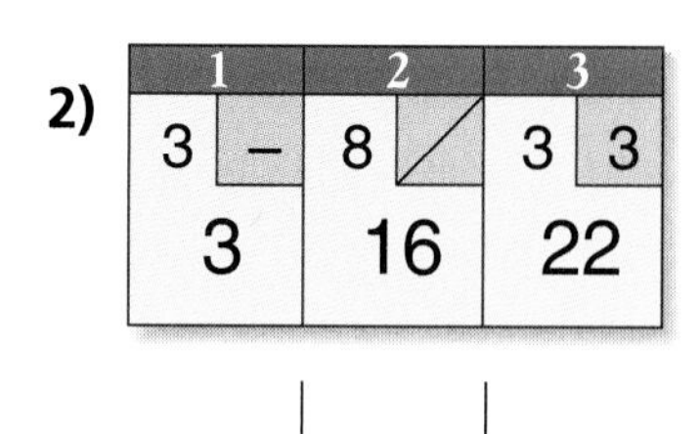

3)

1	2	3
4 /	5 /	5 2
15	30	37

4) 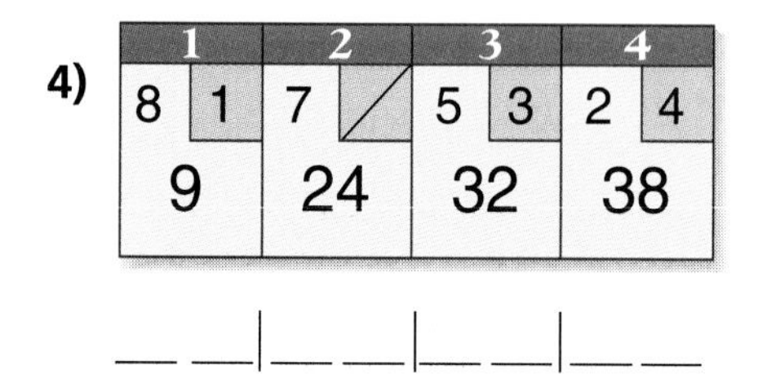

5) 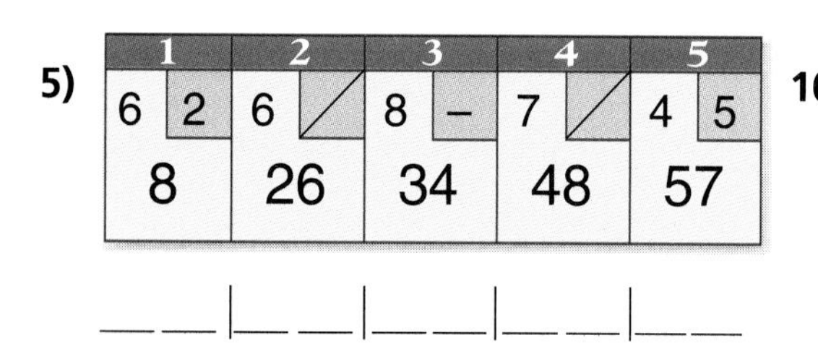

6)

1	2	3	4
4 1	2 /	5 –	4 3
5	20	25	32

7) 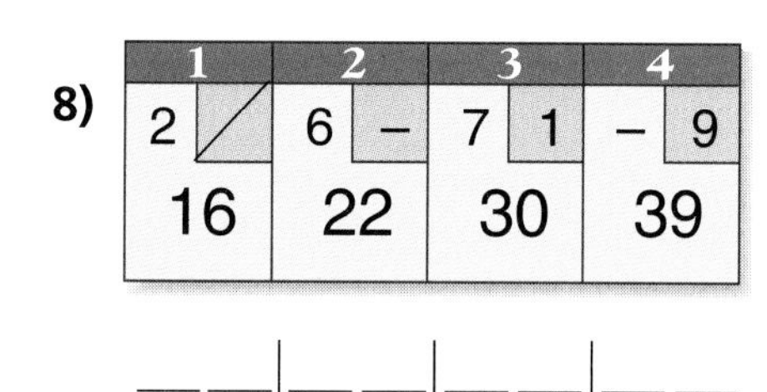

8)

1	2	3	4
2 /	6 –	7 1	– 9
16	22	30	39

9) 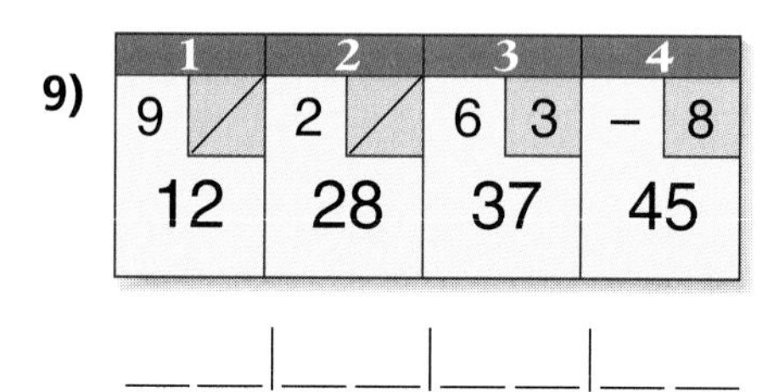

10) 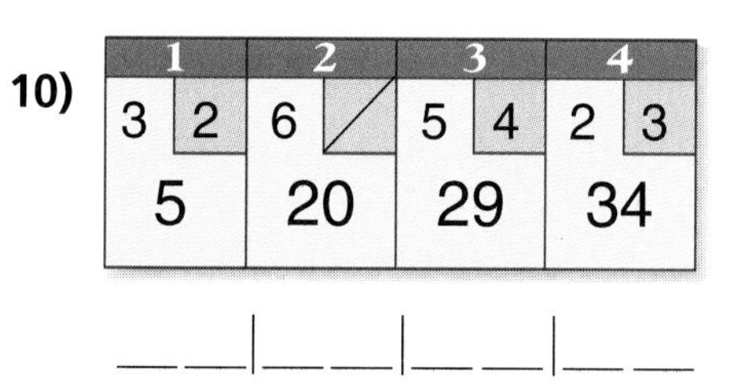

Exercise E Use the score sheet your teacher gives you. Fill in the frames with the scores for each game.

1)

Frame	Roll	Pins
1st frame:	1st roll	4
	2d roll	6
2d frame:	1st roll	6
	2d roll	3
3d frame:	1st roll	5
	2d roll	2

2)

Frame	Roll	Pins
1st frame:	1st roll	5
	2d roll	2
2d frame:	1st roll	5
	2d roll	5
3d frame:	1st roll	7
	2d roll	2

3)

Frame	Roll	Pins
1st frame:	1st roll	3
	2d roll	7
2d frame:	1st roll	5
	2d roll	3
3d frame:	1st roll	4
	2d roll	6
4th frame:	1st roll	8
	2d roll	0
5th frame:	1st roll	5
	2d roll	4

4)

Frame	Roll	Pins
1st frame:	1st roll	5
	2d roll	5
2d frame:	1st roll	4
	2d roll	6
3d frame:	1st roll	1
	2d roll	8
4th frame:	1st roll	3
	2d roll	4
5th frame:	1st roll	3
	2d roll	3

Scoring a Strike A **strike** occurs when a bowler knocks down all ten pins with the first roll of a frame.

The score for a strike is ten plus the total number of pins the bowler knocks down with the next two rolls. A strike in the tenth frame gives the bowler two extra rolls.

> ***Strike***
>
> *In bowling, knocking down all ten pins on one roll of the ball.*

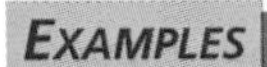

1st frame: 1st roll 4
2d roll 5

2d frame: 1st roll 10
2d roll —

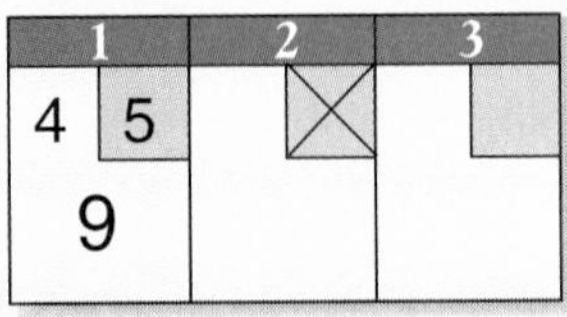

3d frame: 1st roll 7
2d roll 2

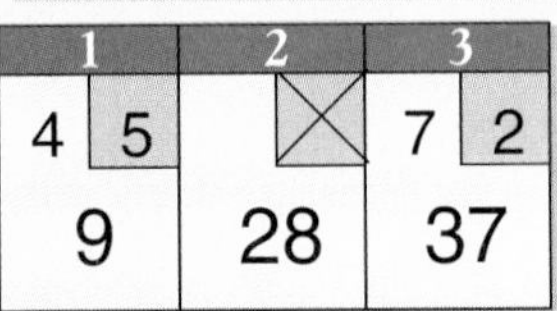

Felicia's score is 96 for the sixth frame. Her game continues as shown.

7th frame: 1st roll 10
2d roll —

8th frame: 1st roll 3
2d roll 7

9th frame: 1st roll 6
2d roll 3

10th frame: 1st roll 10
2d roll —

1st extra roll 10
2d extra roll 9

Exercise F Fill in the frame with the scores.

1) 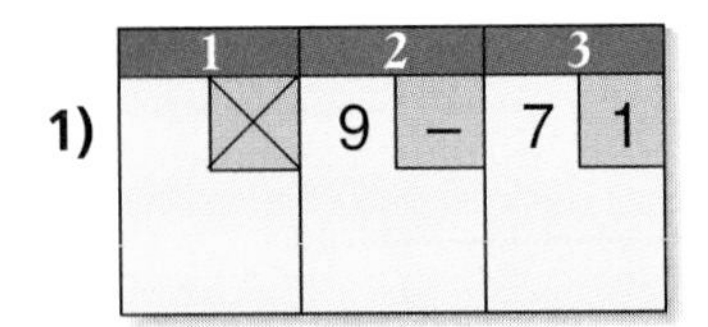

2) 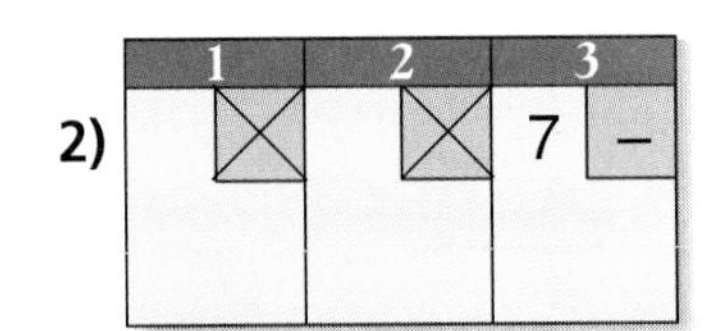

3) 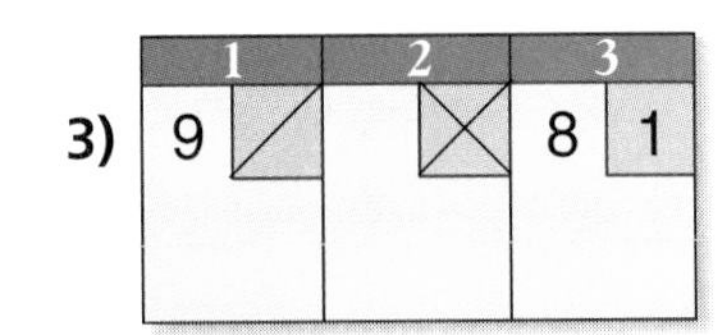

Exercise G Use the score sheet your teacher gives you. Fill in the frames with the scores for each game.

1)

Frame	Roll	Score
1st frame:	1st roll	9
	2d roll	1
2d frame:	1st roll	10
	2d roll	–
3d frame:	1st roll	8
	2d roll	1
4th frame:	1st roll	5
	2d roll	2

2)

Frame	Roll	Score
1st frame:	1st roll	5
	2d roll	3
2d frame:	1st roll	10
	2d roll	–
3d frame:	1st roll	–
	2d roll	10
4th frame:	1st roll	3
	2d roll	2

3)

Frame	Roll	Score
1st frame:	1st roll	–
	2d roll	10
2d frame:	1st roll	5
	2d roll	4
3d frame:	1st roll	10
	2d roll	–
4th frame:	1st roll	8
	2d roll	0

4)

Frame	Roll	Score
1st frame:	1st roll	8
	2d roll	2
2d frame:	1st roll	10
	2d roll	–
3d frame:	1st roll	10
	2d roll	–
4th frame:	1st roll	5
	2d roll	0

5) 7th frame total: 85

Frame	Roll	Score
8th frame:	1st roll	8
	2d roll	2
9th frame:	1st roll	10
	2d roll	–
10th frame:	1st roll	7
	2d roll	2

6) 7th frame total: 95

Frame	Roll	Score
8th frame:	1st roll	8
	2d roll	1
9th frame:	1st roll	8
	2d roll	2
10th frame:	1st roll	10
	2d roll	–
	1st extra roll:	10
	2d extra roll:	9

A Summary of Scoring A complete game has ten frames.

Ordinary play To determine a score for a frame, you add its pin count to the score of the previous frame.

Spare After knocking down all ten pins with two rolls, you take the previous frame total, plus 10, plus the number of pins on the first roll of the following frame.

Strike After knocking down all ten pins with the first roll, you take the previous frame total, plus 10, plus the number of pins knocked down on the next two rolls.

EXAMPLE Enrico bowls the following game. Study his score sheet for the correct scoring procedure.

Frame	Roll	Pins
1st frame:	1st roll	5
	2d roll	5
2d frame:	1st roll	6
	2d roll	2
3d frame:	1st roll	10
	2d roll	—
4th frame:	1st roll	9
	2d roll	1
5th frame:	1st roll	8
	2d roll	2
6th frame:	1st roll	3
	2d roll	6
7th frame:	1st roll	10
	2d roll	—
8th frame:	1st roll	0
	2d roll	10
9th frame:	1st roll	10
	2d roll	—
10th frame:	1st roll	10
	2d roll	—
	1st extra roll	10
	2d extra roll	9

1	2	3	4	5	6	7	8	9	10
5 /	6 2	X	9 /	8 /	3 6	X	– /	X	X X 9
16	24	44	62	75	84	104	124	154	183

Exercise H Use the score sheet your teacher gives you. Fill in the frames with the scores for each game.

1)

1	2	3	4	5	6	7	8	9	10
6 3	5 2	8 1	X	4 5	9 –	4 5	3 2	5 4	4 / 4

2)

1st frame:	1st roll	5
	2d roll	4
2d frame:	1st roll	6
	2d roll	2
3d frame:	1st roll	4
	2d roll	6
4th frame:	1st roll	3
	2d roll	5
5th frame:	1st roll	8
	2d roll	1
6th frame:	1st roll	2
	2d roll	8
7th frame:	1st roll	4
	2d roll	5
8th frame:	1st roll	3
	2d roll	7
9th frame:	1st roll	6
	2d roll	1
10th frame:	1st roll	10
	2d roll	—
	1st extra roll	9
	2d extra roll	1

3)

1st frame:	1st roll	8
	2d roll	2
2d frame:	1st roll	6
	2d roll	4
3d frame:	1st roll	10
	2d roll	—
4th frame:	1st roll	9
	2d roll	1
5th frame:	1st roll	8
	2d roll	1
6th frame:	1st roll	6
	2d roll	3
7th frame:	1st roll	8
	2d roll	0
8th frame:	1st roll	8
	2d roll	2
9th frame:	1st roll	10
	2d roll	—
10th frame:	1st roll	10
	2d roll	—
	1st extra roll	10
	2d extra roll	10

Lesson 2 Weight Lifting

Calculate
To find an answer by using mathematics.

Compute
To calculate or figure out.

Weight lifting helps develop the body and keeps a person physically fit. Mathematics is needed in weight lifting to **calculate** weight totals. When you use mathematics in weight lifting, you need to know how to **compute** with zeros.

EXAMPLES

Each member of the Martinsburg High weight lifting team lifts 200 pounds with barbells. Twenty-three members are on the team. What is the total weight the team lifts?

$$\begin{array}{rl} 200 & \text{Pounds each} \\ \times \quad 23 & \text{Members} \\ \hline 600 & \\ +4\,00 & \\ \hline 4{,}600 & \text{Total pounds} \end{array}$$

Qui uses two 10-pound dumbbells to help strengthen his upper arms. Qui's exercise schedule requires 15 lifts with the dumbbells. What is the total weight each arm lifts after 15 lifts?

$$\begin{array}{rl} 15 & \text{Lifts} \\ \times\ 10 & \text{Pounds per lift} \\ \hline 150 & \text{Total pounds} \end{array}$$

Marcell lifts 150 pounds on his first attempt. He increases the weight by 16 pounds on his second lift. What is the total weight he lifts on the second lift?

$$\begin{array}{rl} 150 & \text{Pounds} \\ +\ 16 & \text{Pounds increased} \\ \hline 166 & \text{Total pounds} \end{array}$$

Exercise A Practice your skill with zeros. Find the answer to each problem.

1) $\begin{array}{r} 200 \\ -\ 15 \\ \hline \end{array}$

2) $\begin{array}{r} 310 \\ -\ 182 \\ \hline \end{array}$

3) $\begin{array}{r} 670 \\ -\ 568 \\ \hline \end{array}$

4) $\begin{array}{r} 320 \\ -\ 196 \\ \hline \end{array}$

5) $\begin{array}{r} 200 \\ -\ 156 \\ \hline \end{array}$

6) $\begin{array}{r} 235 \\ -\ 216 \\ \hline \end{array}$

7) $\begin{array}{r} 200 \\ -\ 198 \\ \hline \end{array}$

8) $\begin{array}{r} 230 \\ -\ 62 \\ \hline \end{array}$

9) $310 + 296 + 400$

10) $506 + 23 + 915$

11) $7{,}101 \div 9$

12) $4{,}860 \div 12$

13) 320×50

14) $806 + 209 + 10$

15) $101 + 310 + 1{,}091$

16) $3{,}581 \div 10$

17) $2{,}500 \div 25$

18) $4{,}700 \times 70$

PROBLEM SOLVING

Exercise B Solve these problems.

1) Sergio lifts a 95-pound barbell six times during his workout. What is the total weight that Sergio lifts?

2) Danielle lifts 55 pounds on her first attempt. She increases the weight by 20 pounds for the second lift. How many pounds does she lift on the second attempt?

3) Melissa's weight lifting team lifts the following weights: 125, 90, 102, and 91 pounds. What is the total weight her team lifts?

4) José's barbell set includes a 45-pound handle, two 10-pound plates, two 5-pound collars, and two $2\frac{1}{2}$-pound plates. How much does the set weigh in all?

Lesson 3 Averages

Average

The number obtained by dividing the sum of two or more quantities by the number of quantities.

In comparing performances in sports, **average** scores are useful. An average is found by adding all of the single scores and dividing the sum by the number of single scores.

EXAMPLE The Silver Stingrays bowling team bowls 175, 182, 162, and 200. What is their average score?

Add.

$$\left.\begin{array}{r} 175 \\ 182 \\ 162 \\ +200 \end{array}\right\} \text{Score}$$

$$\begin{array}{r} 719 \end{array}$$

Divide.

$$\begin{array}{r} 179\frac{3}{4} \\ 4\,\overline{)\,719} \\ -4 \\ \hline 31 \\ -28 \\ \hline 39 \\ -36 \\ \hline 3 \end{array}$$

The average score is $179\frac{3}{4}$.

Cory lifts 108, 105, 100, 99, and 103 pounds during the weight lifting finals. What is the average weight Cory lifts?

Add.

$$\left.\begin{array}{r} 108 \\ 105 \\ 100 \\ 99 \\ +103 \end{array}\right\} \text{Weights}$$

$$\begin{array}{r} 515 \end{array}$$

Divide.

$$\begin{array}{r} 103 \\ 5\,\overline{)\,515} \\ -50 \\ \hline 15 \\ -15 \\ \hline 0 \end{array}$$

The average weight is 103 pounds.

Exercise A Find the average for each set of numbers. Write remainders as fractions.

1) 26, 35, 20

2) 80, 83, 90

3) 180, 296, 121

4) 126, 103, 110

5) 165, 203, 175

6) 162, 200, 178

7) 202, 213, 185

8) 106, 115, 125, 163, 152, 128

9) 163, 200, 417, 831

10) 170, 117, 168, 200, 315

PROBLEM SOLVING

Exercise B Find the averages.

1) The Lapton High School bowling team bowls 178, 186, 275, and 190. What is their average score?

2) Ngoc's bowling scores are 263, 200, 217, 225, and 195. What is Ngoc's average score?

3) For the first week of school, Anthony consumes 1,951; 2,065; 2,419; 2,315; and 2,661 calories. What is Anthony's average calorie consumption?

4) Coach Thompson's weight lifting team turns in the following presses: 125, 105, 150, 95, 150, 145, and 72 pounds. What is the average press?

5) During the week of the New Castle bowling tournament, spectators number 175, 180, 165, 180, 170, 175, and 192. What is the average attendance for spectators?

Calculator Practice

Estimation Before you use a calculator to find an average, estimate the sum of the numbers.

EXAMPLE Find the average of 270, 420, and 305.

Step 1 Estimate the sum first.

270	rounds to	300	
420	rounds to	400	
305	rounds to	+ 300	
		1,000	Estimated sum

The exact sum on the calculator is 995. Since 995 is very close to the estimated sum, 995 is a reasonable answer.

Step 2 Estimate the average.
1,000 divided by 3 is about 333.

Step 3 Divide. 995 [÷] 3 [=] 331.66666

The exact average on the calculator is 331.66666, which rounds to 332. Since 332 is very close to 333, 332 is a reasonable answer.

For this exercise we will use only whole numbers. The average of 270, 420, and 305 is 332.

You can find the average weight lifted. Just add all of the amounts lifted and divide by the number of lifts.

Calculator Exercise Use your calculator to find the averages. Estimate the sum of each set of numbers first. Use rounded numbers to estimate. Round your average to three decimal places. Write your answers on separate paper.

	Numbers	Estimated Sum	Estimated Average	Exact Sum	Average
1)	26, 28, 20	______	______	______	______
2)	38, 57, 31, 33	______	______	______	______
3)	58, 42, 48	______	______	______	______
4)	62, 69	______	______	______	______
5)	32, 36, 51, 20	______	______	______	______
6)	184, 108, 200, 190	______	______	______	______
7)	260, 221, 315	______	______	______	______
8)	3,001; 2,115; 2,815	______	______	______	______
9)	516, 786, 912, 492, 758	______	______	______	______
10)	9,984; 12,068; 11,496	______	______	______	______

Chapter 3 Review

Use the score sheet your teacher gives you. Fill in the frames.

1)

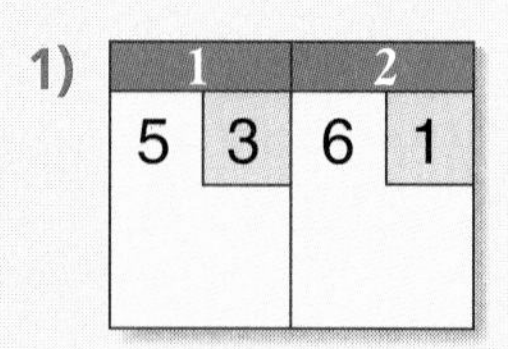

2)

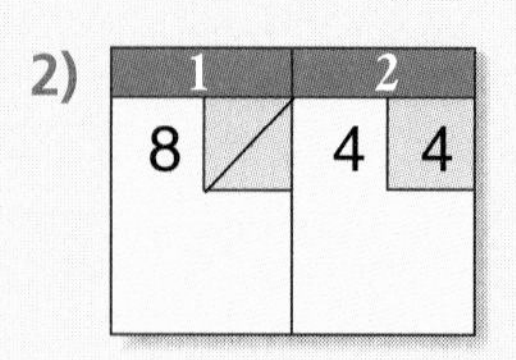

3)

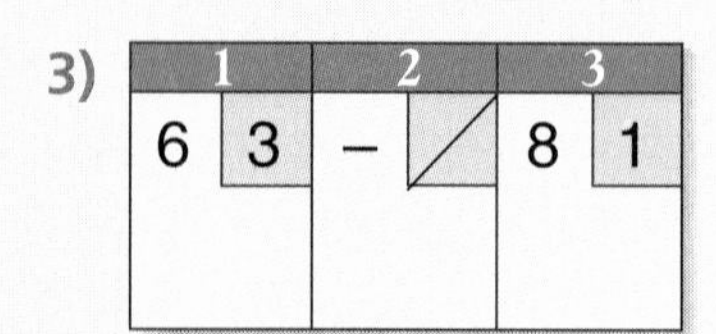

4)

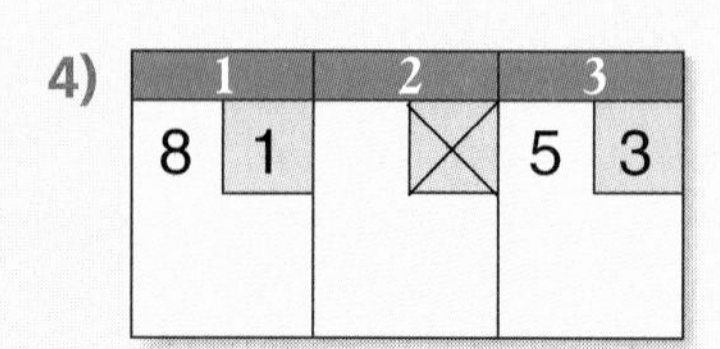

5)

Frame	Roll	Pins
1st frame:	1st roll	8
	2d roll	1
2d frame:	1st roll	0
	2d roll	5
3d frame:	1st roll	3
	2d roll	7
4th frame:	1st roll	6
	2d roll	4
5th frame:	1st roll	10
	2d roll	—
6th frame:	1st roll	6
	2d roll	1
7th frame:	1st roll	1
	2d roll	5
8th frame:	1st roll	7
	2d roll	0
9th frame:	1st roll	10
	2d roll	—
10th frame:	1st roll	6
	2d roll	3

6) Marco increases his 123-pound bench-press weight by 15 pounds. What is his new press weight?

Find the averages.

7) 39, 42, 65

8) 72, 83, 91, 39, 36

9) Kenny bowls 216, 195, and 190. What is his average score?

10) Zakiya lifts these weights: 100, 80, 110, 140, 120, and 115 pounds. What is the average weight Zakiya lifts?

Test Taking Tip Estimating answers to problems is one way to check whether your answers on tests are reasonable.

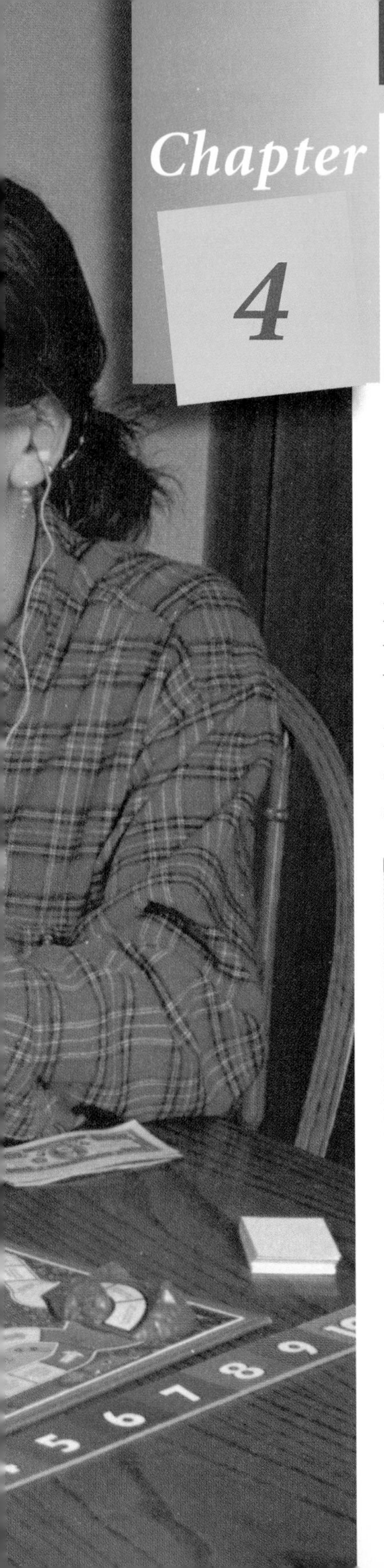

Chapter 4

Games of Chance

How many times have you played a game of cards or a board game? Did you wonder whether you could predict when you would beat your opponent? Mathematicians like yourself use probability to predict what will happen. Try it next time you play a game with your friends. You will have them wondering what's your secret.

In Chapter 4, you will use dice to explore probability. You will discover that experiments are done in mathematics, just as they are in science.

Goals for Learning

- To determine the total number of possible outcomes from flipping a coin
- To use probability to predict the possibility of an event occurring
- To predict the probability of drawing a given card from a 52-card deck

Lesson 1 Flipping Coins

> ***Possible outcomes***
> *Results that can happen.*

> ***Probability tree***
> *A diagram showing all possible outcomes.*

When you flip a coin, there are two **possible outcomes**. The coin will either land on heads or tails. We can use a **probability tree** to help us keep track of several flips of a coin.

EXAMPLE What are the possible outcomes of flipping a coin three times?

H = Coin lands heads up

T = Coin lands tails up

1st Flip	2d Flip	3d Flip	Outcomes
H	H	H	1. H H H
		T	2. H H T
	T	H	3. H T H
		T	4. H T T
T	H	H	5. T H H
		T	6. T H T
	T	H	7. T T H
		T	8. T T T

Eight different outcomes are possible.

PROBLEM SOLVING

Exercise A Use probability trees to answer the questions.

1) How many possible outcomes are there if you flip a coin two times?
2) If you flip a coin two times, how many outcomes give you a head and a tail?
3) Suppose you flip a coin four times. How many different possible outcomes are there?
4) With four coin flips, how many outcomes give two heads and two tails?
5) With four coin flips, how many outcomes give four tails?
6) With four coin flips, how many outcomes give three heads and one tail?
7) If you flip a coin five times, how many outcomes give three heads and two tails?
8) With five coin flips, how may outcomes give one tail and four heads?

Lesson 2 What Are the Chances?

Probability
The chances that an outcome will happen.

Formula
A rule or method of doing something.

Die
(plural: dice) Small cubes of bone, plastic, etc., marked on each side with from one to six spots and used usually in pairs.

Use **probability** to measure how likely an event is to happen. The probability of an event happening is the number of successful outcomes divided by the total number of possible outcomes. Probability is given in fractional form. In **formula** form this is:

$$\text{Probability} = \frac{\text{Number of successful outcomes}}{\text{Total number of possible outcomes}}$$

As an example, consider the **die** (singular form of **dice**). A die has six faces. Each face is equally likely to appear when you roll the die.

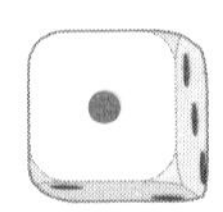 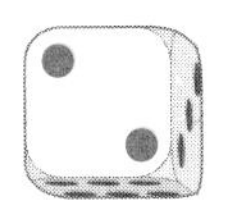    

What is the probability that you will roll a 5?

You can use probability to predict how many times an event is likely to happen.

EXAMPLE If Sam rolls a die 24 times, how many times can he expect to roll a 3?

The probability of rolling a 3 is $\frac{1}{6}$.

$\frac{1}{6} = \frac{\blacksquare}{24}$

Sam can expect to roll a 3 four times out of 24 rolls.

Exercise A Answer these questions about rolling one die. How many times can you expect to roll…

1) a 5 out of 18 rolls?

2) a 3 out of 24 rolls?

3) a 3 out of 30 rolls?

4) a 6 out of 30 rolls?

5) a 1 out of 12 rolls?

6) a 6 out of 54 rolls?

7) a 4 out of 36 rolls?

8) a 2 out of 48 rolls?

9) a 2 out of 42 rolls?

10) a 1 out of 72 rolls?

Lesson 3 Probability When Rolling Dice

Possibilities

Outcomes that can occur.

Dice sum

The total points shown on two or more dice.

When you roll two dice, the likely outcomes are not equal. This is because there are different numbers of **possibilities** of rolling each **dice sum**. You can roll a 5 by rolling 1 and 4, 2 and 3, 3 and 2, 4 and 1. You can roll a 4 by rolling 1 and 3, 2 and 2, and 3 and 1. You can roll a 5 four different ways, but you can roll a 4 only three different ways. Therefore, you will probably roll more 5s than 4s.

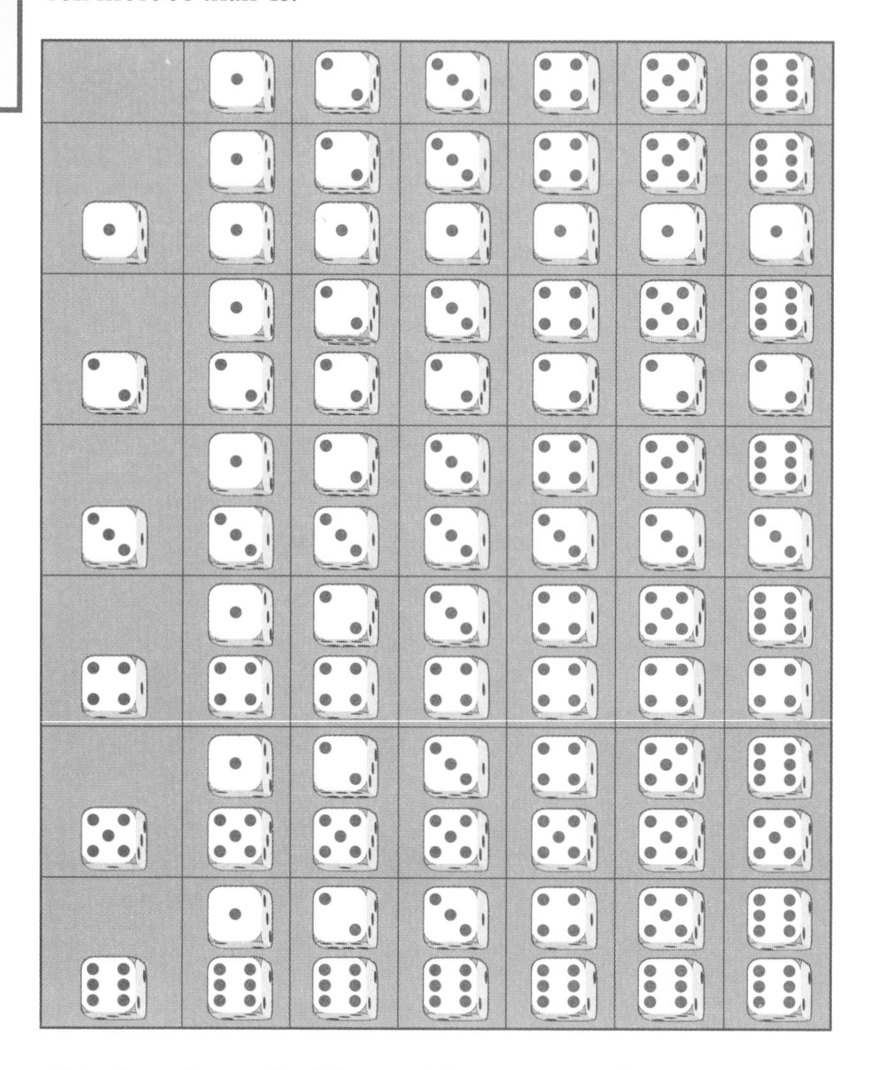

This chart shows all of the possible outcomes of rolling two dice.

Exercise A Answer these questions about rolling two dice.

1) How many outcomes are possible?

2) How many different ways are there to roll a six?

3) What are all of the ways that you can roll a 6?

4) What is the probability of rolling a 6?

5) What are all of the possible ways to roll a 9?

6) How many ways are there to roll a 9?

7) What is the probability of rolling a 9?

8) What is the least dice sum that you can roll with two dice?

9) What is the greatest dice sum that you can roll?

Exercise B Fill in this chart about the probability of rolling the given dice sum.

Dice Sum	Probability of Rolling
2	______
3	______
4	______
5	______
6	______
7	______
8	______
9	______
10	______
11	______
12	______

Using Probability

Advance

To move forward.

Many board games use the sum of two dice to determine how many spaces a player may **advance** on each turn. Below is the board for the game of *Journey.*

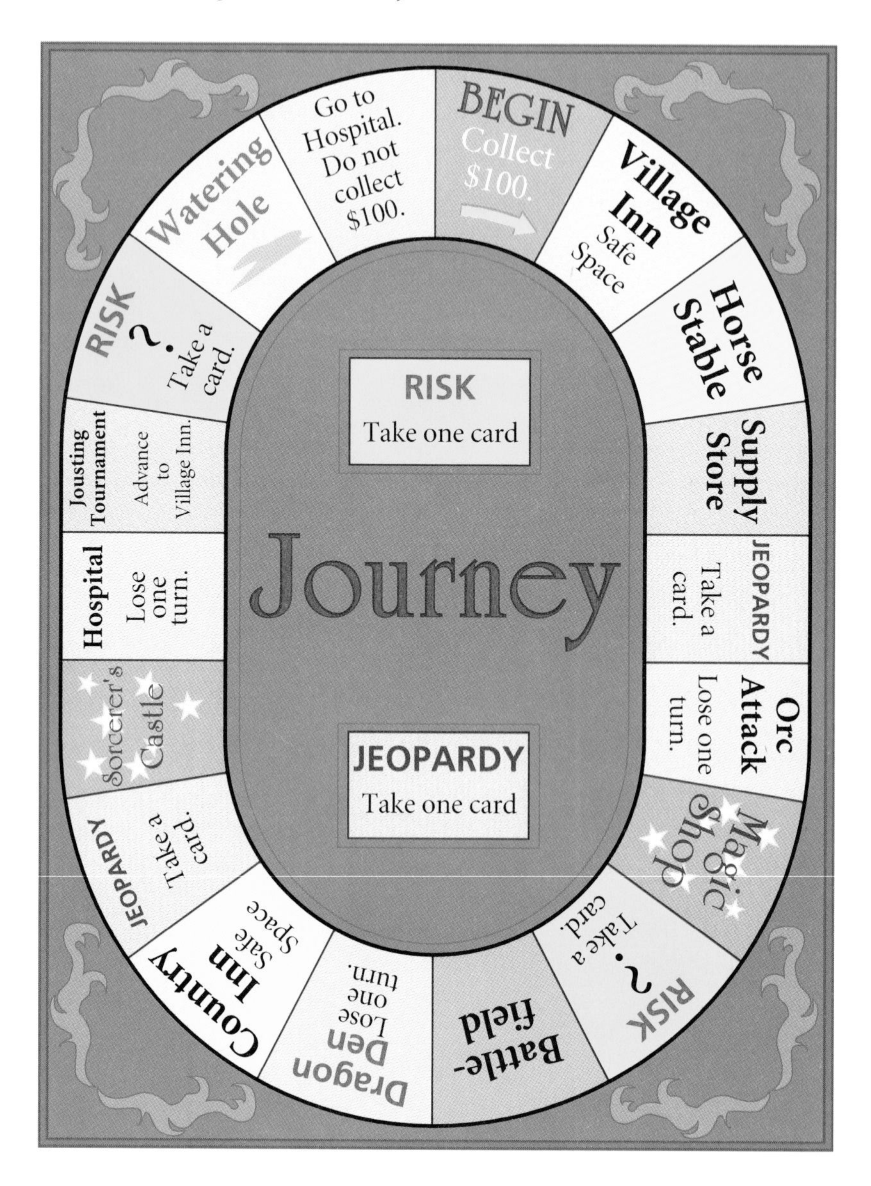

When it is your turn in the game of *Journey*, you roll two dice. Then you advance that number of spaces in a **clockwise** direction. You follow the directions printed in the space on which you land.

Clockwise

In the direction in which the hands of a clock rotate.

At each turn you are more likely to land on some spaces than on others. This is because there are more ways to roll the number that will place you on those spaces.

EXAMPLE If you are on the BEGIN space, what is the probability that you will land on the Magic Shop on your next turn? This information will help you find a solution:

- Magic Shop is six spaces away.
- There are five different ways to roll a 6.
- There are thirty-six different outcomes of rolling two dice.

Therefore, the probability of landing on the Magic Shop is $\frac{5}{36}$.

PROBLEM SOLVING

Exercise A Answer these questions about probability. You may need to simplify fractions to simplest terms.

1) You are at BEGIN. What is the probability of landing on Orc Attack on your next turn?

2) You are at Battlefield. What is the probability of landing on Risk on your next turn?

3) What is the probability of landing on Supply Store from Village Inn?

4) What is the probability of landing on Country Inn from Magic Shop?

5) What is the probability of landing on Dragon Den from Village Inn?

More than one number on the dice roll might place you on the same square. For example, suppose that you are on Country Inn and you roll a 9. You would land on Village Inn. What would have happened if you had rolled a 4? You would have advanced to Jousting Tournament.

The directions there say, "Advance to Village Inn." The game has two events that would allow you to advance to Village Inn. Those events are: rolling a 4 or rolling a 9. To figure the probability of landing on Village Inn from Country Inn, you need to know the following:

Probability of Event A or Event B =
Probability of Event A + Probability of Event B

EXAMPLE Look at the board game on page 54. What is the probability of landing on Village Inn from Country Inn?

This information will help you find a solution:

- Can land on Village Inn by rolling a 4 or a 9
- Probability of rolling a 4 is $\frac{3}{36}$
- Probability of rolling a 9 is $\frac{4}{36}$
- Probability of rolling a 4 or a 9 is $\frac{3}{36} + \frac{4}{36}$, or $\frac{7}{36}$

Therefore, the probability of landing on Village Inn is $\frac{7}{36}$.

Exercise B Answer these questions about the probability of landing on a space from a given space. There may be more than one way of landing on the space, or there may be more than one of the spaces. Use the board game on page 54.

1) From Horse Stable to Dragon Den

2) From Dragon Den to Hospital

3) From Orc Attack to Risk

4) From Sorcerer's Castle to Village Inn

5) From Orc Attack to Village Inn

Lesson 5 Experimental Probability

Expect
To look foward to.

Experiment
A procedure used to test a theory.

When you roll two dice, you can **expect** to roll a 7 six times out of thirty-six rolls, or one-sixth of the time. This is expected. This may or may not be what happens.

Try this **experiment**. Get two dice. Get a copy of the chart from your teacher. Each time that you roll the dice, make a mark on your chart next to the number that you rolled. Do this 36 times.

Number on Dice	Number of Times Rolled	Number of Times Expected
2		1
3		2
4		3
5		4
6		5
7		6
8		5
9		4
10		3
11		2
12		1

PROBLEM SOLVING

Exercise A Answer these questions about your chart.

1) Was the number of times rolled the same as the number of times expected for any of the dice sums?

2) Was the number of times rolled different from the number of times expected for any of the dice sums?

3) Why do you suppose the number of times that you rolled some numbers was different from the number of times that you expected to roll those numbers?

Lesson 6 Making Predictions

Predict
To state what will happen.

You can determine how many times you can expect to roll a given number with two dice. The probability of rolling each number is different for each dice sum. You can **predict** how many times you can expect to roll a given number if you remember the formula for finding probability:

$$\text{Probability} = \frac{\text{Number of successful outcomes}}{\text{Total number of possible outcomes}}$$

EXAMPLES

How many times can you expect to roll an 8 out of 72 rolls?

$$\frac{5}{36} = \frac{■}{72}$$

You can expect to roll ten 8s.

How many times can you expect to roll a 4 out of 60 rolls?

3 chances out of 36, or
1 chance out of 12 $\frac{1}{12} = \frac{■}{60}$

You can expect to roll five 4s.

Exercise A Answer these questions about rolling two dice. How many times can you expect to roll…

1) a 7 out of 24 rolls?

2) a 7 out of 18 rolls?

3) a 5 out of 36 rolls?

4) a 5 out of 18 rolls?

5) a 10 out of 60 rolls?

6) a 3 out of 54 rolls?

7) an 8 out of 108 rolls?

8) a 13 out of 24 rolls?

9) a 2 out of 36 rolls?

10) a 6 out of 36 rolls?

11) an 11 out of 54 rolls?

12) a 12 out of 72 rolls?

13) a 4 out of 72 rolls?

14) a 5 out of 63 rolls?

15) a 9 out of 27 rolls?

16) a 10 out of 48 rolls?

Cards

Suit

Any of the four sets of thirteen playing cards.

Draw

To pick at random.

A standard deck of playing cards has 52 cards in four **suits**: hearts, clubs, diamonds, and spades. Thirteen cards are in each suit.

Given that information, what is the probability that if you **draw** one card, it will be a 7?

$$\text{Probability} = \frac{\text{Number of successful outcomes}}{\text{Total number of possible outcomes}}$$

$$\text{Probability} = \frac{4}{52} = \frac{1}{13}$$

There are four 7s out of 52 possible cards, so the probability of drawing a 7 is $\frac{4}{52} = \frac{1}{13}$.

EXAMPLE What is the probability of drawing a red 10?

$$\text{Probability} = \frac{\text{Number of successful outcomes}}{\text{Total number of possible outcomes}}$$

$$\text{Probability} = \frac{2}{52} = \frac{1}{26}$$

There are only two red 10s: the 10 of hearts and the 10 of diamonds.

Exercise A Answer these questions about the probability of drawing certain cards. What is the probability of drawing…

1) a jack?

2) a black 3?

3) a club?

4) a 5 of hearts?

5) a red 8?

6) a king or a queen?

7) a black card?

8) a face card (king, queen, jack)?

9) a 10 of spades?

10) a card less than a 7? (Do not include aces.)

Rummy In the game of **rummy**, players are dealt seven cards. Then they draw cards and try to get three of a kind (such as three 7s) or a run in the same suit (such as the 3, 4, and 5 of spades). Because some of the 52 cards are already dealt, the probability of drawing a particular card is figured differently.

Rummy

Card games in which the object is to match cards into sets of the same denomination or sequences of the same suit.

EXAMPLES Study this seven-card hand:

What is the probability that this player will draw a 9?

52 cards − 7 = 45

Probability = $\frac{3}{45} = \frac{1}{15}$

(There are four 9s, but one is already in the player's hand.)

What is the probability that this player will draw a 3 of clubs?

Probability = $\frac{1}{45}$

(There is only one 3 of clubs.)

In both examples the total number of outcomes is 45 instead of 52 because seven cards are already in the hand (52 − 7 = 45).

Exercise B Answer these questions about the probability of drawing the card described. Remember to consider the cards that are already in the hand.

1) What is the probability of drawing a jack?

2) What is the probability of drawing a 5?

3) What is the probability of drawing the 6 of diamonds?

4) What is the probability of drawing a 2?

5) What is the probability of drawing a 4 or an 8?

6) What is the probability of drawing a queen?

7) What is the probability of drawing a 2, a 6, or a 7?

8) What is the probability of drawing the 6 of hearts or a 3?

9) What is the probability of drawing a club?

10) What is the probability of drawing a 3 or an ace?

Calculator Practice

Changing fractions to decimal equivalents can be easy on your calculator. Use the division function.

EXAMPLE Calculate $\frac{5}{7}$ as a decimal.

Solution Press these buttons in order:

5 [÷] 7 [=]

Answer 0.7142857

Calculator Exercise Use your calculator to change each fraction to a decimal.

1) $\frac{5}{8}$ ____________

2) $\frac{3}{7}$ ____________

3) $\frac{1}{6}$ ____________

4) $\frac{3}{4}$ ____________

5) $\frac{2}{9}$ ____________

6) $\frac{1}{3}$ ____________

7) $\frac{5}{6}$ ____________

8) $\frac{4}{12}$ ____________

9) $\frac{10}{11}$ ____________

10) $\frac{15}{17}$ ____________

11) $\frac{20}{21}$ ____________

12) $\frac{18}{19}$ ____________

13) $\frac{16}{17}$ ____________

14) $\frac{28}{29}$ ____________

15) $\frac{5}{13}$ ____________

16) $\frac{3}{16}$ ____________

Chapter 4 Review

Write your answers in simplest form.

1) $\frac{15}{36} =$

2) $\frac{39}{52} =$

Fill in the missing numerator.

3) $\frac{5}{6} = \frac{■}{42}$

4) $\frac{7}{36} = \frac{■}{72}$

When you are rolling one die, how many times…

5) can you expect to roll a 4 out of 18 rolls?

6) can you expect to roll a 2 out of 54 rolls?

7) can you expect to roll a 5 out of 42 rolls?

When you are rolling two dice, how many times…

8) can you expect to roll a 4 out of 24 rolls?

9) can you expect to roll a 9 out of 45 rolls?

What is the probability of…

10) rolling a 10?

11) rolling a 6?

This is part of a board game. Answer these questions about your next turn. For each question, start on the GO space.

For each turn, you roll two dice, advance the number of spaces that you rolled, and follow the directions on the space that you land on. The cards that you draw give you special favors, but do not tell you to move to any other spaces.

What is the probability that...

12) you will land on Battlefield?

13) you will land on Risk?

14) you will land on Dungeon?

A deck of 52 cards is mixed. You draw one card. What is the probability that...

15) the card is a 6?

16) the card is a club?

17) the card is a king or a queen?

18) the card is a 4 or a red 6?

Answer these questions about playing rummy with a 52-card deck. Remember that seven cards are already in your hand.

19) What is the probability of drawing a 6?

20) What is the probability of drawing a 3?

Test Taking Tip If you are having trouble solving a problem on a test, then go on to the next problem and come back to any skipped problems.

Chapter 5

Adjusting Recipes

Can you think of a time when you multiplied or divided with fractions and whole numbers? Maybe you were planning a menu and shopping list, or cooking and baking. Most recipes list ingredients as fractions or mixed numbers. Chefs in restaurants, bakers in factories, and cooks in their kitchens all multiply and divide with fractions to help them determine amounts of ingredients for their special recipes.

In Chapter 5, you will learn ways to increase recipes to feed more people and to reduce recipes to serve fewer.

Goals for Learning

- To rename an improper fraction to a mixed number in simplest form
- To convert units of measure to equivalent measures
- To adjust recipes by multiplying and dividing fractions and mixed numbers

Lesson 1 Equivalent Measurements

Recipe

Directions for making something.

Equivalent

A thing that is equal to another in a particular way.

Convert

To change to something of equal value.

Ingredients in **recipes** are written many ways. It is helpful to know what the **equivalent** measurement is in case you need to adjust a recipe. Working with equivalents can simplify many recipe adjustments. These equivalents should be a part of a cook's working knowledge.

2 tablespoons	=	1 ounce
3 teaspoons	=	1 tablespoon
16 tablespoons	=	1 cup
2 cups	=	1 pint
2 pints	=	1 quart
4 quarts	=	1 gallon

EXAMPLES 4 tablespoons = ■ teaspoons

Rule When you **convert** large units to small units, you multiply.

From the table, 3 teaspoons = 1 tablespoon.

$4 \times 3 = 12$ teaspoons

Solution 4 tablespoons = 12 teaspoons

5 gallons = ■ quarts

From the table, 4 quarts = 1 gallon.

$5 \times 4 = 20$ quarts

Solution 5 gallons = 20 quarts

6 pints = ■ quarts

Rule When you convert small units to large units, you divide.

From the table, 2 pints = 1 quart.

$6 \div 2 = 3$ quarts

Solution 6 pints = 3 quarts

Exercise A Convert the larger units to smaller units. Multiply to find the answers.

1) 3 ounces = ______ tablespoons

2) 2 tablespoons = ______ teaspoons

3) 2 cups = ______ tablespoons

4) 5 pints = ______ cups

5) 2 gallons = ______ quarts

6) 3 quarts = ______ pints

7) 7 ounces = ______ tablespoons

8) 3 cups = ______ tablespoons

9) 5 tablespoons = ______ teaspoons

10) 2 quarts = ______ pints

11) 56 ounces = ______ tablespoons

12) 15 tablespoons = ______ teaspoons

Exercise B Convert the smaller units to larger units. Divide to find the answers.

1) 8 tablespoons = ______ ounces

2) 6 teaspoons = ______ tablespoons

3) 64 tablespoons = ______ cups

4) 8 pints = ______ quarts

5) 16 quarts = ______ gallons

6) 20 quarts = ______ gallons

7) 6 tablespoons = ______ ounces

8) 10 tablespoons = ______ ounces

9) 12 teaspoons = ______ tablespoons

10) 8 cups = ______ pints

11) 36 tablespoons = ______ ounces

12) 16 pints = ______ quarts

Lesson 2 Increasing a Recipe by Multiplying

Factors

Numbers that when multiplied together form a product.

Improper fraction

A fraction whose numerator is equal to or greater than its denominator.

To increase a recipe, multiply the amount of each ingredient by the same **factor.** All mixed numbers must be expressed as **improper fractions** before multiplying.

Elsa's recipe for a frozen dessert will serve 8 people, but she wants to serve 16. What should she do?

EXAMPLE

Step 1 $\frac{16}{8}$ $\frac{\text{Amount to serve}}{\text{Amount in recipe}} = 2$ Factor

Step 2 Multiply each ingredient by the factor 2.

Frozen Smoothie (serves 8)	New Amount
$\frac{2}{3}$ cup mashed bananas	$\frac{2}{3} \times \frac{2}{1} = \frac{4}{3}$
$\frac{2}{3}$ cup low-fat milk	$\frac{2}{3} \times \frac{2}{1} = \frac{4}{3}$
2 cups orange sherbet	$2 \times 2 = 4$
$\frac{1}{2}$ teaspoon vanilla	$\frac{1}{2} \times \frac{2}{1} = 1$
$\frac{1}{4}$ cup chopped nuts	$\frac{1}{4} \times \frac{2}{1} = \frac{2}{4}$

Now let's take a closer look at the results of Elsa's multiplication.

New Adjusted Recipe
(serves 16)

$\frac{4}{3}$ cup mashed bananas

$\frac{4}{3}$ cup low-fat milk

4 cups orange sherbet

1 teaspoon vanilla

$\frac{2}{4}$ cup chopped nuts

Many recipes can be increased to serve more people. Multiply the amount of each ingredient by the same factor.

Renaming Improper Fractions Elsa will have to simplify her fractions before she can begin to measure because some of the answers are improper fractions. They need to be **renamed.** To change an improper fraction to a **proper fraction**, divide the numerator by the denominator.

> ***Rename***
> *To express in another form equal to the original.*

> ***Proper fraction***
> *A fraction in which the numerator is less than the denominator.*

EXAMPLE Change $\frac{4}{3}$ to a proper fraction.

Numerator: 4
Denominator: 3

$$\begin{array}{r} 1 \\ 3\overline{)4} \\ -3 \\ \hline 1 \end{array}$$ Remainder

$1\frac{1}{3}$ $\frac{\text{Remainder}}{\text{Old denominator}}$

Simplifying Fractions to Simplest Form Think of the largest number that you can divide into both the numerator and the denominator with a zero remainder.

For example, to simplify $\frac{2}{4}$ to simplest form, the largest number that can be divided into both numbers is 2.

$$\frac{2}{4} = \frac{2 \div 2}{4 \div 2} = \frac{1}{2}$$

EXAMPLE Increase this recipe to serve 24 people.

Potatoes Royal
(serves 6)

6 baking potatoes

2 cups boiled cabbage

$\frac{1}{4}$ cup melted margarine

$\frac{1}{3}$ cup diced onions

Step 1 Divide the new number of servings by the old number of servings to find the conversion factor.

$$\frac{\text{New servings}}{\text{Old servings}} = \frac{24}{6} = \frac{4}{1}$$

The conversion factor is 4.

Step 2 Multiply each ingredient by the factor.

$6 \times 4 = 24$ baking potatoes

$2 \times 4 = 8$ cups boiled cabbage

$\frac{1}{4} \times 4 = 1$ cup melted margarine

$\frac{1}{3} \times 4 = \frac{4}{3} = 1\frac{1}{3}$ cups diced onions

Exercise A Increase these recipes to serve 12.

1) Polenta (Serves 6)

1 cup corn meal

3 cups water

$\frac{2}{3}$ tsp. salt

$\frac{1}{3}$ cup grated cheese

1 tbsp. margarine

2) Red Sauce (Serves 4)

1 diced onion

2 serrano chilies

$2\frac{1}{2}$ cups tomatoes

$\frac{1}{2}$ tsp. cumin seed

$\frac{1}{3}$ tsp. oregano

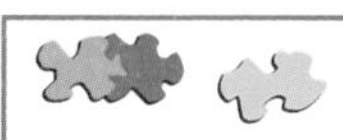

PROBLEM SOLVING

Exercise B Increase each recipe to serve the number of people shown.

1) Harry's Poppy-Seed Cake serves 8 people. Rewrite the recipe so it serves 24.

$\frac{1}{3}$ cup poppy seeds

$\frac{3}{4}$ cup milk

$\frac{3}{4}$ cup butter

$1\frac{1}{2}$ cups sugar

$1\frac{1}{2}$ tsp. vanilla

2 cups flour

$2\frac{1}{2}$ tsp. baking powder

$\frac{1}{4}$ tsp. salt

4 egg whites, beaten

2) Rosa's recipe for Hard Rolls serves 12. Convert the recipe to serve 24.

1 pkg. dry yeast

$1\frac{1}{4}$ cups water

$1\frac{1}{2}$ tsp. salt

$3\frac{3}{4}$ cups flour

1 egg, beaten

3) Lorena's favorite cookie recipe makes 4 dozen (48) cookies. Convert her recipe to make 12 dozen (144).

1 cup granulated sugar

1 cup brown sugar

1 cup shortening

2 eggs, beaten

$2\frac{1}{2}$ cups flour

1 tsp. baking soda

$\frac{1}{2}$ tsp. baking powder

3 cups whole bran flakes cereal

4) Jason's Banana Enrolada (banana rolled in pastry) serves 4. Rewrite the recipe to serve 20.

$1\frac{1}{2}$ cups flour

2 tbsp. granulated sugar

$\frac{1}{2}$ tsp. salt

6 tbsp. butter, softened but not melted

5) Bruno is preparing Escoveitch Fish (pickled fish) for a dinner party of 12. The recipe serves 4. Rewrite it to serve 12.

2 lb. fresh catfish

juice of 2 limes

$\frac{1}{2}$ tsp. salt

1 tsp. black pepper

2 onions, sliced

2 hot peppers

2 tbsp. pimiento

1 cup vinegar

Exercise C Increase each ingredient by using the factor given.

1) $\frac{3}{4}$ tablespoons sugar × 12

2) $2\frac{1}{2}$ cups shortening × 20

3) 9 teaspoons vanilla × 30

4) 12 whole apples × 10

5) 10 pounds ice × 3

6) 7 cups milk × 20

7) 8 cups flour × 10

8) $\frac{3}{4}$ cup flour × 20

9) $\frac{2}{3}$ cup brown sugar × 21

10) $3\frac{3}{4}$ cups sliced apples × 8

11) 5 tablespoons cream × 30

12) $\frac{3}{5}$ cups diced onions × 15

Exercise D Multiply these mixed numbers by the whole numbers.

1) $5\frac{4}{5} \times 10$

2) $20\frac{1}{2} \times 10$

3) $9\frac{4}{7} \times 14$

4) $12\frac{1}{2} \times 12$

5) $1\frac{2}{5} \times 15$

6) $22\frac{1}{3} \times 30$

7) $1\frac{5}{6} \times 18$

8) $3\frac{4}{7} \times 2$

9) $2\frac{4}{5} \times 15$

10) $1\frac{4}{9} \times 2$

11) $3\frac{1}{6} \times 24$

12) $4\frac{5}{6} \times 6$

13) $2\frac{3}{4} \times 8$

14) $10\frac{1}{6} \times 12$

15) $4\frac{5}{6} \times 18$

16) $10\frac{2}{5} \times 25$

17) $3\frac{6}{7} \times 21$

18) $22\frac{1}{7} \times 7$

Lesson 3 Decreasing a Recipe by Dividing

You may decrease a recipe by dividing the amount of each ingredient by the same factor.

EXAMPLE Roland's recipe for vanilla pudding serves 8 people. How can this recipe be adjusted so that it serves only 4 people?

Step 1 Divide the old number of servings by the new number of servings to find the conversion factor.

$$\frac{\text{Old servings}}{\text{New servings}} = \frac{8}{4} = \frac{2}{1}$$

The factor is $\frac{2}{1}$.

Step 2 Divide each of the ingredients by the conversion factor. Roland's recipe calls for $3\frac{1}{3}$ cups milk.

$$3\frac{1}{3} \div \frac{2}{1} = \frac{10}{3} \div \frac{2}{1} = \frac{10}{3} \times \frac{1}{2} = \frac{10}{6} = 1\frac{2}{3}$$

$1\frac{2}{3}$ cup milk is needed for the adjusted recipe to serve only 4 people.

Exercise A Practice dividing with mixed numbers.

1) $2\frac{1}{2} \div 4$

2) $3\frac{1}{2} \div 2$

3) $1\frac{1}{3} \div \frac{1}{2}$

4) $4\frac{1}{4} \div \frac{1}{2}$

5) $3\frac{2}{5} \div 5$

6) $2\frac{2}{3} \div \frac{1}{2}$

7) $4\frac{2}{3} \div 3$

8) $1\frac{1}{5} \div 1\frac{1}{2}$

9) $2\frac{3}{4} \div 2$

10) $5 \div 2\frac{1}{2}$

11) $1\frac{1}{6} \div \frac{2}{3}$

12) $2\frac{5}{6} \div 2\frac{1}{2}$

13) $3\frac{2}{5} \div 1\frac{1}{2}$

14) $1\frac{2}{3} \div 1\frac{1}{3}$

15) $5\frac{2}{5} \div 2\frac{1}{3}$

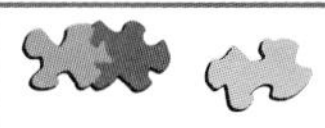

PROBLEM SOLVING

Exercise B Decrease these recipes to serve the number of people shown.

1) Decrease to serve 8:

Special Rolls (Makes 40)

5 pkgs. dry yeast

$3\frac{3}{4}$ cups warm water

$12\frac{1}{2}$ cups biscuit mix

5 tsp. poultry seasoning

$2\frac{1}{2}$ tsp. celery seed

2) Decrease to serve 6:

Best Green Beans (Serves 24)

$1\frac{1}{3}$ cups chopped onion

$5\frac{1}{3}$ tbsp. salad oil

1 cup chili sauce

$1\frac{1}{3}$ tsp. salt

8 cups green beans

3) Decrease to serve 8:

Super Meatballs (Serves 32)

6 lb. ground beef

2 cups uncooked rice

4 tsp. salt

1 tsp. pepper

1 cup chopped onion

4 cans tomato soup

2 cups water

4) Decrease to serve 12:

Real Good Muffins (Makes 84)

$12\frac{1}{4}$ cups sifted flour

14 tbsp. sugar

$17\frac{1}{2}$ tsp. baking powder

$5\frac{1}{4}$ tsp. salt

7 well-beaten eggs

$5\frac{1}{4}$ cups milk

$2\frac{1}{3}$ cups salad oil

5) Decrease to serve 8:

Nut-Orange Bread (Serves 56)

$15\frac{3}{4}$ cups sifted flour

$5\frac{1}{4}$ cups sugar

$15\frac{3}{4}$ tsp. baking powder

$5\frac{1}{4}$ tsp. salt

$1\frac{3}{4}$ tsp. soda

$5\frac{1}{4}$ cups chopped nuts

7 tbsp. grated orange peel

7 beaten eggs

$5\frac{1}{4}$ cups orange juice

14 tbsp. salad oil

Calculator Practice

A calculator can help you **compare** fractions. First, calculate the decimal equivalent of each fraction. Then, compare the two decimals. Finally, write the correct **symbol** ($<$, $>$, or $=$). Remember that “$<$” means “less than” and “$>$” means “greater than.”

> ***Compare***
> *To examine two numbers to determine which is larger.*

> ***Symbol***
> *A character that stands for something else.*

EXAMPLE Compare $\frac{5}{7}$ and $\frac{4}{11}$

$\frac{5}{7}$ ■ $\frac{4}{11}$

5 ÷ 7 ■ 4 ÷ 11

0.7142857 $>$ 0.3636363

$\frac{5}{7} > \frac{4}{11}$

Calculator Exercise Use a calculator to help you compare the fractions in each set. Use $>$ or $<$ to show your comparison.

1) $\frac{5}{6}$ and $\frac{4}{9}$

2) $\frac{7}{10}$ and $\frac{6}{11}$

3) $\frac{15}{17}$ and $\frac{18}{23}$

4) $\frac{13}{15}$ and $\frac{3}{4}$

5) $\frac{6}{13}$ and $\frac{7}{15}$

6) $\frac{8}{13}$ and $\frac{7}{12}$

7) $\frac{2}{35}$ and $\frac{5}{72}$

8) $\frac{15}{19}$ and $\frac{2}{3}$

9) $\frac{34}{35}$ and $\frac{61}{62}$

10) $\frac{4}{5}$ and $\frac{7}{9}$

11) $\frac{10}{11}$ and $\frac{11}{12}$

12) $\frac{6}{17}$ and $\frac{5}{18}$

13) $\frac{9}{10}$ and $\frac{11}{12}$

14) $\frac{10}{13}$ and $\frac{12}{17}$

15) $\frac{6}{13}$ and $\frac{7}{17}$

16) $\frac{13}{15}$ and $\frac{8}{9}$

17) $\frac{15}{22}$ and $\frac{14}{23}$

18) $\frac{9}{20}$ and $\frac{8}{21}$

19) $\frac{11}{35}$ and $\frac{21}{35}$

20) $\frac{1}{20}$ and $\frac{2}{31}$

Chapter 5 Review

Find the answers.

1) After adjusting a recipe, Omar needs $\frac{8}{24}$ cup flour. Which is the simplest form of the fraction $\frac{8}{24}$?

a) $\frac{2}{6}$

b) $\frac{1}{8}$

c) $\frac{1}{3}$

2) Saritha's new cookie recipe calls for $2\frac{4}{12}$ cups sugar. Which is the simplest form of $2\frac{4}{12}$?

a) $2\frac{1}{2}$

b) $2\frac{1}{3}$

c) $2\frac{1}{12}$

3) What is $\frac{2}{3}$ cup chopped nuts multiplied by 6?

4) Which is $\frac{1}{2}$ of $3\frac{1}{2}$ tablespoons diced peppers?

a) $3\frac{1}{4}$ tbsp.

b) 7 tbsp.

c) $1\frac{3}{4}$ tbsp.

5) Rename $\frac{5}{3}$ teaspoons cream as a mixed number.

6) Rename $3\frac{4}{5}$ cups flour as an improper fraction.

7) How many ounces do 8 tablespoons equal?

8) How many gallons do 8 quarts equal?

9) Lauren and Bruce's bread recipe calls for 6 cups sifted flour. How much flour will they use if they make only $\frac{2}{3}$ of the recipe?

10) Rick's cake recipe serves 6 people. It requires $2\frac{1}{4}$ cups flour. How much flour does he need for cake to serve 18 people?

Test Taking Tip

Become familiar with where to locate, then study, tables and charts showing measurement conversions. They can usually be found in the back of recipe books, dictionaries, and mathematics textbooks.

Chapter 6

Math and Crafts

What are your hobbies? Do they involve fabric, or string, or wood, or other materials? If they do, then you use mathematics to help you. Patterns often give important mathematical information about what materials are required. When you draw diagrams to help you build something, you use mathematics. Hobbies are only one example of where you can discover mathematics in your everyday life.

In Chapter 6, you will learn how to work with fractions to help you solve problems involving projects.

Goals for Learning

- To use a fabric guide to help find the amount of fabric a project requires
- To compute total lengths by adding fractional parts of a finished project
- To use measurement with fractions as it applies to repeating patterns

Lesson 1 Working With a Fabric Guide

Fabric guide

Chart showing the amount of material needed to make garments.

People who sew their own clothes can select the exact style and type of fabric. When they buy a pattern, a **fabric guide** on the back of the pattern tells them how much fabric they need. The amount of fabric depends on the width of the fabric.

Garment	Fabric Width in Inches	Misses' Sizes 10	12	14	16	18	20	
Top	36″	$1\frac{7}{8}$	$2\frac{1}{8}$	$2\frac{1}{8}$	$2\frac{1}{8}$	$2\frac{1}{8}$	$2\frac{1}{4}$	Yards
	45″	$1\frac{1}{4}$	$1\frac{3}{8}$	$1\frac{3}{8}$	$1\frac{5}{8}$	$1\frac{5}{8}$	$1\frac{3}{4}$	Yards
	60″	$1\frac{1}{8}$	$1\frac{1}{8}$	$1\frac{1}{8}$	$1\frac{1}{4}$	$1\frac{1}{4}$	$1\frac{1}{4}$	Yards
Skirt	36″	$1\frac{5}{8}$	$1\frac{3}{4}$	$1\frac{3}{4}$	$1\frac{3}{4}$	$1\frac{3}{4}$	$1\frac{3}{4}$	Yards
	45″	$1\frac{1}{8}$	$1\frac{3}{8}$	$1\frac{1}{2}$	$1\frac{3}{4}$	$1\frac{3}{4}$	$1\frac{3}{4}$	Yards
	60″	$\frac{7}{8}$	$\frac{7}{8}$	1	1	1	1	Yards
Pants	36″	$2\frac{1}{2}$	$2\frac{1}{2}$	$2\frac{5}{8}$	$2\frac{5}{8}$	$2\frac{5}{8}$	$2\frac{5}{8}$	Yards
	45″	$2\frac{1}{4}$	$2\frac{3}{8}$	$2\frac{5}{8}$	$2\frac{5}{8}$	$2\frac{5}{8}$	$2\frac{5}{8}$	Yards
	60″	$1\frac{3}{8}$	$1\frac{3}{8}$	$1\frac{1}{2}$	$1\frac{3}{4}$	$2\frac{1}{4}$	$2\frac{1}{4}$	Yards
Jacket	36″	$2\frac{3}{8}$	$2\frac{3}{8}$	$2\frac{1}{2}$	$2\frac{1}{2}$	$2\frac{5}{8}$	$2\frac{3}{4}$	Yards
	45″	$1\frac{7}{8}$	$1\frac{7}{8}$	$2\frac{1}{8}$	$2\frac{1}{8}$	$2\frac{1}{8}$	$2\frac{1}{4}$	Yards
	60″	$1\frac{1}{2}$	$1\frac{1}{2}$	$1\frac{1}{2}$	$1\frac{5}{8}$	$1\frac{5}{8}$	$1\frac{5}{8}$	Yards

EXAMPLE How much 45″ fabric is needed to make a size 12 top and a size 14 skirt?

$$\begin{array}{rcr} 1\frac{3}{8} & = & 1\frac{3}{8} \\ +\ 1\frac{1}{2} & = & +\ 1\frac{4}{8} \\ \hline & & 2\frac{7}{8} \end{array}$$

You need $2\frac{7}{8}$ yards of 45″ fabric.

Exercise A Use the fabric guide to find the amount of fabric needed to make the garments listed. Remember to check for fabric width.

1) 45″ fabric
size 16 top
size 16 skirt

2) 60″ fabric
size 18 jacket
size 16 pants

3) 36″ fabric
size 20 top
size 18 pants

4) 45″ fabric
size 14 pants
size 12 jacket

5) 45″ fabric
size 18 top
size 20 skirt
size 18 jacket

6) 60″ fabric
size 14 top
size 12 pants
size 14 jacket

7) 60″ fabric
size 18 top
size 18 jacket
size 18 skirt

8) 45″ fabric
size 18 pants
size 16 top
size 16 jacket

9) 36″ fabric
size 16 top
size 16 jacket
size 18 pants
size 18 skirt

10) 60″ fabric
size 12 top
size 14 skirt
size 12 jacket
size 14 pants

11) 45″ fabric
size 12 top
size 12 skirt
size 12 jacket
size 12 pants

12) 36″ fabric
size 14 pants
size 16 top
size 14 skirt
size 16 jacket

Lesson 2 Macramé

Geometric

Formed of straight lines, triangles, circles, etc., as a pattern.

Macramé

A coarse fringe or lace of cord knotted into designs.

Many people make decorative items by tying knots in **geometric** patterns. This is called **macramé.** Careful measuring is needed for a successful and attractive project.

Exercise A Add the lengths to find the total length of each macramé project.

1) 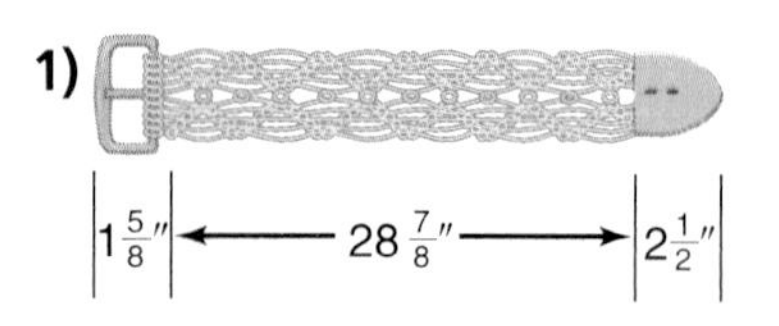

4) 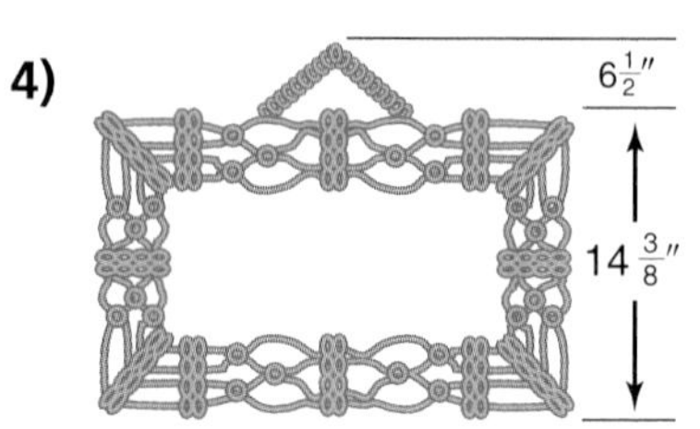

2) 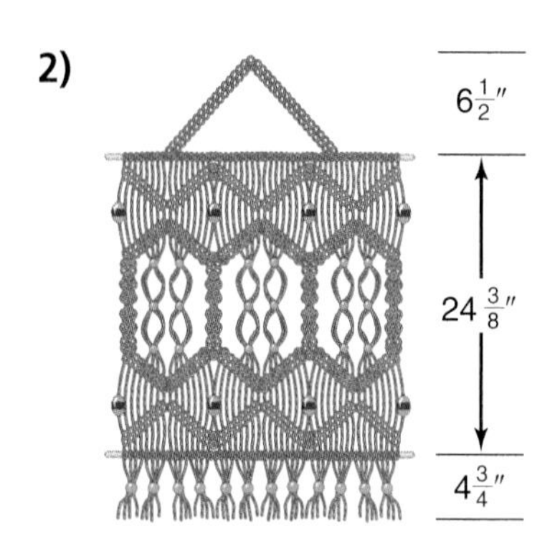

5) 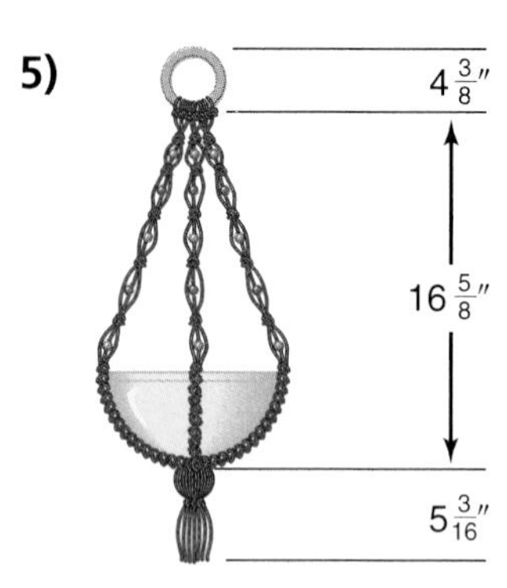

3) 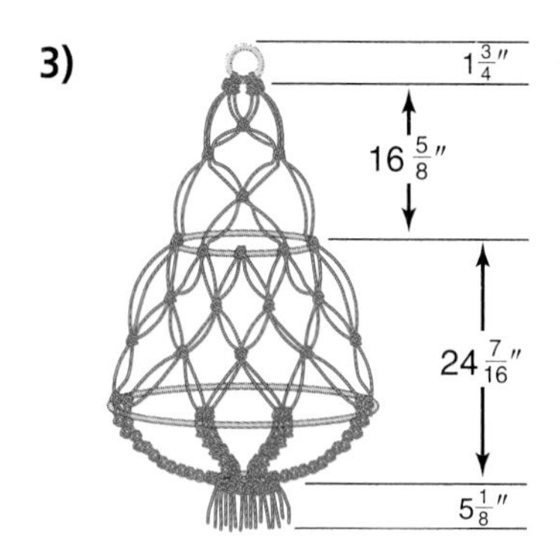

6) 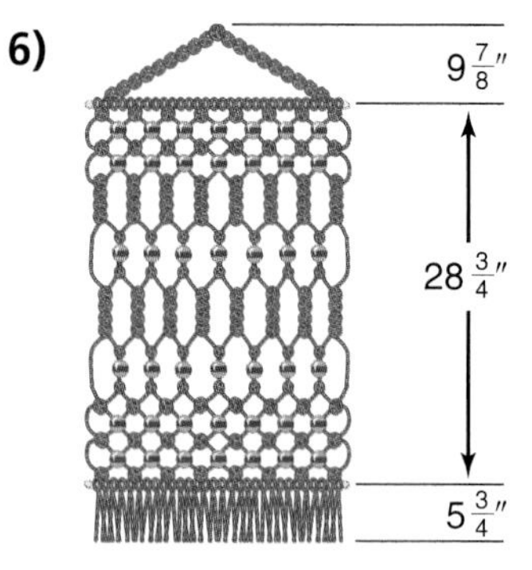

You need to subtract mixed numbers for some craft or sewing projects. In subtraction, just as in addition, you must have like denominators.

EXAMPLE

$12\frac{7}{8} - 3\frac{5}{8} = \blacksquare$

$$\begin{array}{r} 12\frac{7}{8} \\ -\ 3\frac{5}{8} \\ \hline 9\frac{2}{8} \end{array} = 9\frac{1}{4} \text{ Difference}$$

$14\frac{3}{4} - 6\frac{2}{3} = \blacksquare$

$$\begin{array}{r} 14\frac{3}{4} \\ -\ 6\frac{2}{3} \\ \hline \end{array} = \begin{array}{r} 14\frac{9}{12} \\ -\ 6\frac{8}{12} \\ \hline 8\frac{1}{12} \end{array} \text{ Difference}$$

Exercise B Rewrite each problem in vertical form and find the difference. Write your answers in simplest form.

1) $4\frac{7}{8} - 1\frac{3}{4}$

2) $6\frac{2}{3} - 1\frac{1}{4}$

3) $15\frac{3}{8} - 7\frac{1}{16}$

4) $15\frac{15}{16} - 2\frac{3}{8}$

5) $6\frac{3}{4} - 2$

6) $17\frac{7}{8} - 9\frac{1}{2}$

7) $21\frac{5}{6} - 13\frac{3}{4}$

8) $4\frac{3}{4} - \frac{5}{16}$

9) $12\frac{7}{8} - 5\frac{3}{8}$

10) $24\frac{3}{8} - 17$

11) $15\frac{4}{5} - 8\frac{3}{10}$

12) $9\frac{2}{3} - 6\frac{1}{2}$

13) $29\frac{5}{6} - 3\frac{1}{3}$

14) $32\frac{4}{5} - \frac{1}{2}$

15) $23\frac{7}{8} - 16\frac{1}{6}$

16) $23\frac{7}{8} - 9\frac{3}{4}$

17) $25\frac{1}{2} - 18\frac{1}{7}$

18) $45\frac{3}{16} - 32\frac{1}{8}$

19) $58\frac{5}{8} - 6\frac{1}{4}$

20) $9\frac{13}{15} - 5\frac{3}{10}$

After you have changed to common denominators, you may find that the top numerator is smaller than the bottom numerator. Then you must **regroup** before you subtract. Look at these examples.

Regroup
To reorganize.

EXAMPLES

$25\frac{3}{4} - 2\frac{7}{8} = \blacksquare$

$$\begin{array}{rcrcr} 25\frac{3}{4} & = & 25\frac{6}{8} & = & 24\frac{14}{8} \\ -\ 2\frac{7}{8} & = & -\ 2\frac{7}{8} & = & -\ 2\frac{7}{8} \\ \hline & & & & 22\frac{7}{8} \end{array}$$

$28 - 4\frac{3}{5} = \blacksquare$

$$\begin{array}{rcr} 28 & = & 27\frac{5}{5} \\ -\ 4\frac{3}{5} & = & -\ 4\frac{3}{5} \\ \hline & & 23\frac{2}{5} \end{array}$$

Exercise C Find the differences. Write your answers in simplest form.

1) $13\frac{1}{8} - 9\frac{1}{2}$

2) $15 - 6\frac{7}{12}$

3) $28\frac{3}{4} - 6\frac{5}{6}$

4) $17\frac{3}{8} - 9\frac{3}{4}$

5) $17\frac{3}{5} - 9$

6) $42\frac{7}{16} - 38\frac{5}{8}$

7) $21\frac{3}{4} - 9\frac{5}{6}$

8) $42 - 17\frac{5}{9}$

9) $32\frac{3}{4} - 17\frac{5}{8}$

10) $21\frac{1}{2} - 17\frac{7}{8}$

11) $48 - 8\frac{7}{9}$

12) $33\frac{3}{5} - 12\frac{1}{2}$

13) $26\frac{1}{8} - 3\frac{3}{4}$

14) $15\frac{1}{3} - 9\frac{1}{2}$

15) $25 - 14\frac{7}{12}$

16) $29\frac{5}{8} - 19\frac{5}{6}$

17) $9\frac{5}{12} - 2\frac{3}{4}$

18) $29\frac{7}{8} - 13\frac{5}{6}$

19) $42\frac{2}{3} - 26\frac{7}{8}$

20) $11\frac{3}{4} - \frac{7}{8}$

Lesson 3 Saving Scraps

Whenever you work with fabric, you have some scrap material left over. Careful placement of the pattern pieces may mean that the scraps will be large enough to use for some other project.

> Allow the length to be the longer measurement.

EXAMPLE Find the length and width of the two rectangular pieces of scrap material A and B.

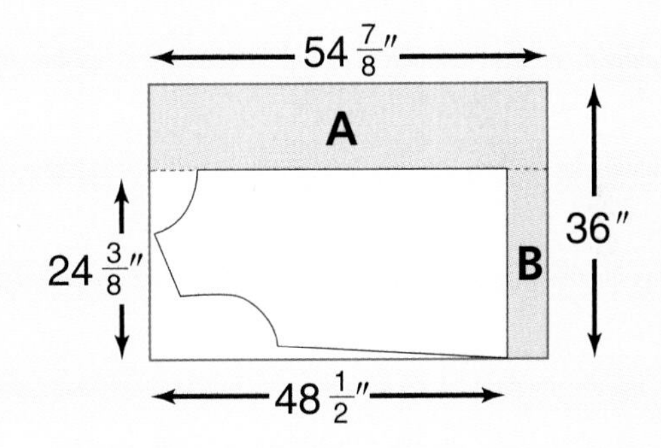

Piece A

$$\begin{array}{rcr} 36 & = & 35\frac{8}{8} \\ -\,24\frac{3}{8} & = & -\,24\frac{3}{8} \\ \hline & & 11\frac{5}{8} \end{array}$$

Piece B

$$\begin{array}{rcr} 54\frac{7}{8} & = & 54\frac{7}{8} \\ -\,48\frac{1}{2} & = & -\,48\frac{4}{8} \\ \hline & & 6\frac{3}{8} \end{array}$$

Piece A

Length $= 54\frac{7}{8}''$

Width $= 11\frac{5}{8}''$

Piece B

Length $= 24\frac{3}{8}''$

Width $= 6\frac{3}{8}''$

Exercise A Find the length and width of the two rectangular pieces of scrap material in each of these patterns.

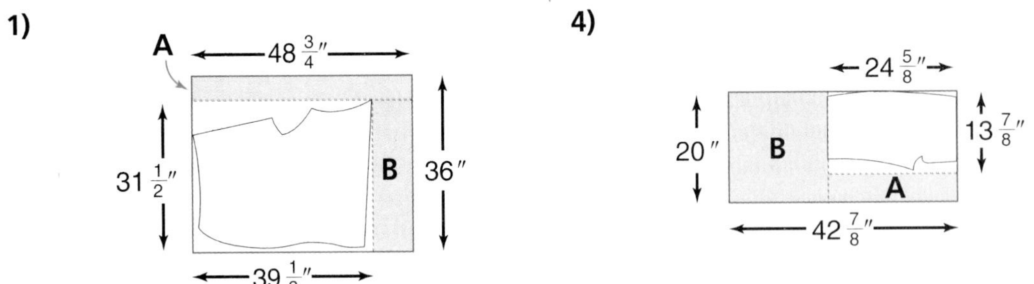

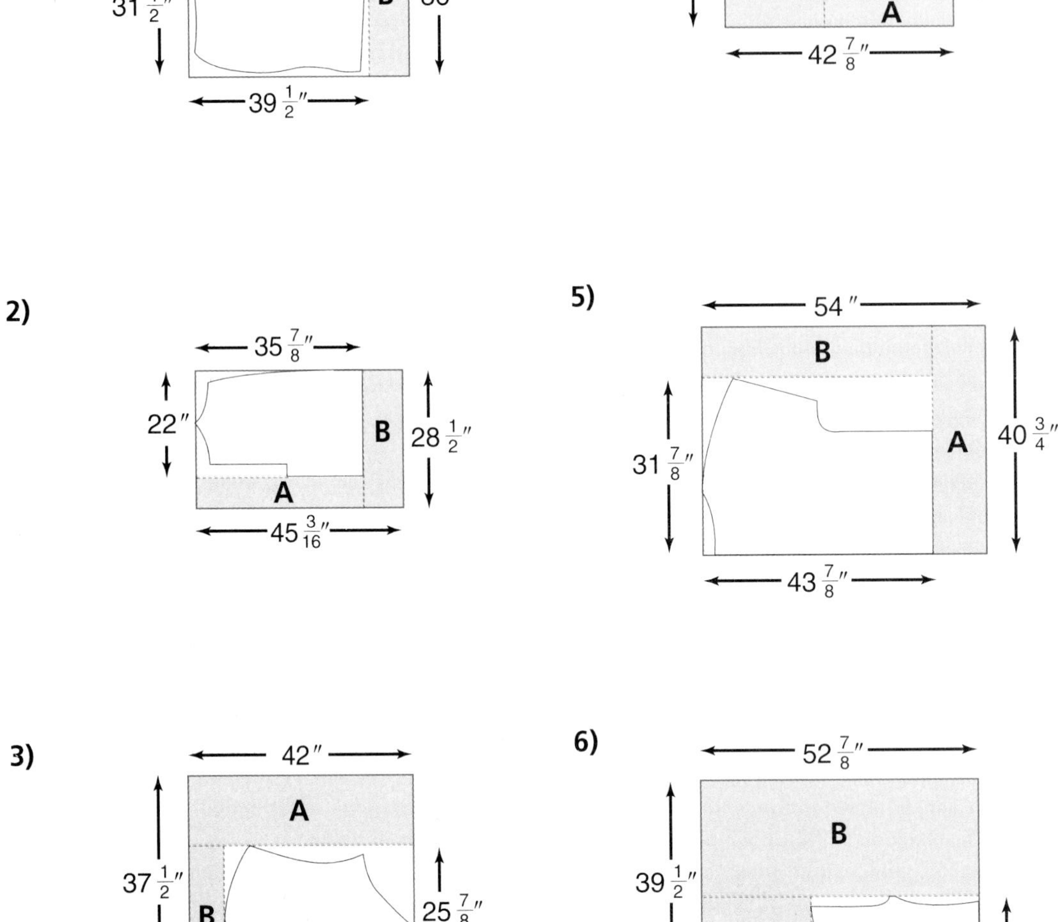

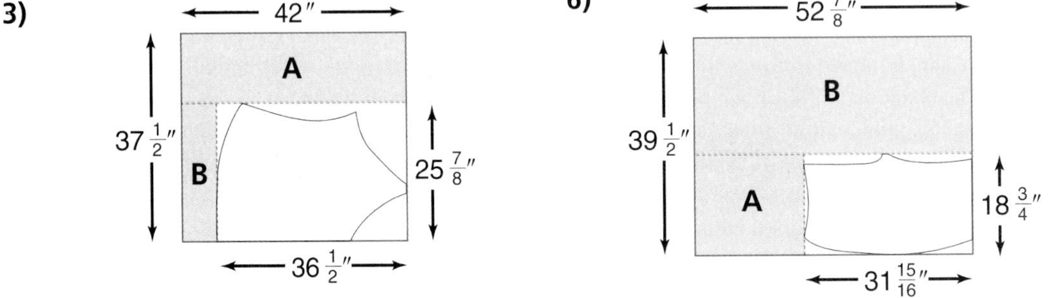

7)

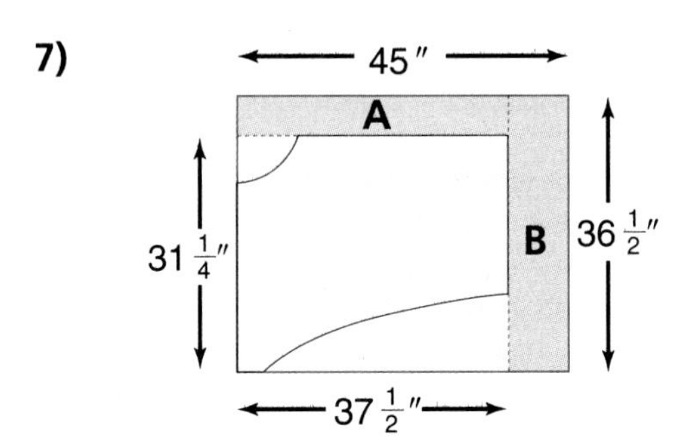

45″
A
B
31 1/4″
36 1/2″
37 1/2″

8)

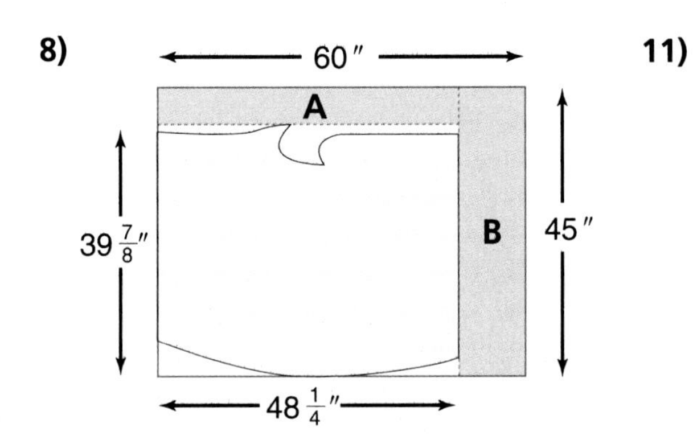

60″
A
B
39 7/8″
45″
48 1/4″

9)

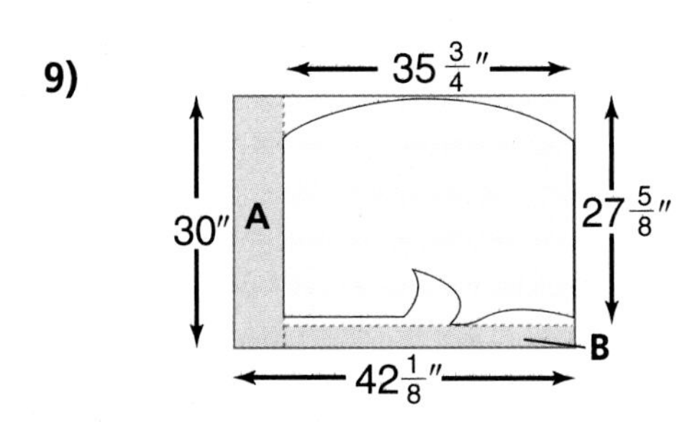

35 3/4″
30″
A
27 5/8″
B
42 1/8″

10)

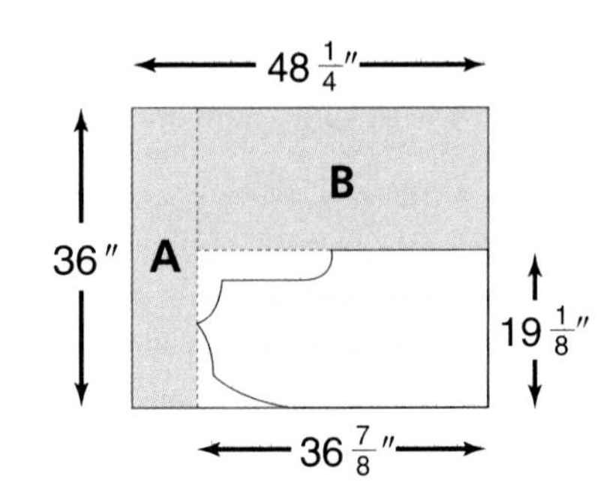

48 1/4″
B
36″
A
19 1/8″
36 7/8″

11)

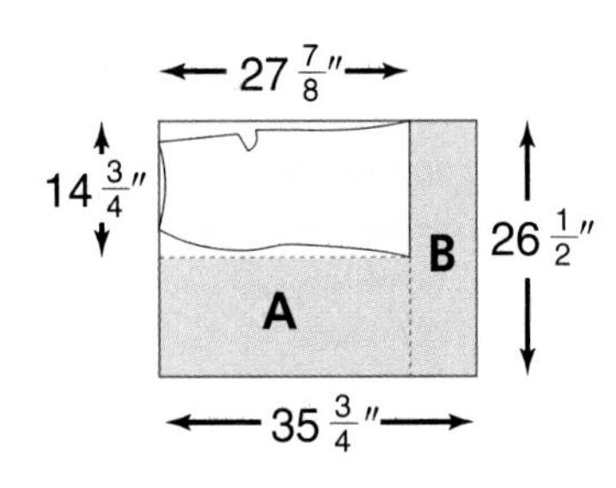

27 7/8″
14 3/4″
B
26 1/2″
A
35 3/4″

Lesson 4 Repeating Patterns

Repeat
To do or to make again.

On some projects the same design unit is repeated over and over. This design unit is called a **repeat**. The repeat is the same length throughout the design. A repeat is measured from one design to the same position on the next design.

EXAMPLE The pattern below repeats every $3\frac{1}{4}$ inches. How long will 20 repeats be?

$$3\frac{1}{4} \times 20 = \frac{13}{4} \times \frac{20}{1} = 65''$$

Twenty repeats will be 65 inches long.

PROBLEM SOLVING

Exercise A Answer these questions about repeating patterns.

1) A pattern repeats every $2\frac{3}{4}$ inches. How long are 16 repeats?

2) Another pattern repeats every $1\frac{7}{8}$ inches. How long are 20 repeats?

3) A belt is to have 18 repeats of $1\frac{3}{4}$ inches, plus $2\frac{3}{4}$ inches for a buckle. How long will the belt be?

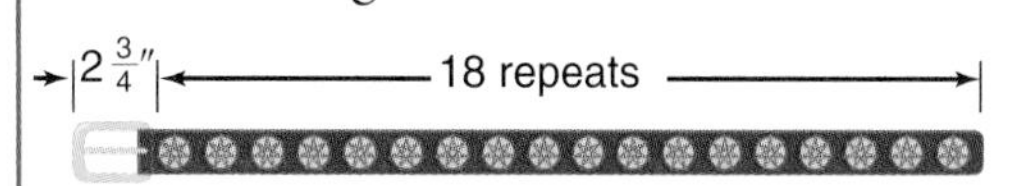

4) The repeat in a pattern is $2\frac{1}{4}$ inches long. How many repeats are in 36 inches?

5) How many $1\frac{3}{8}$-inch repeats are there in $27\frac{1}{2}$ inches?

6) This camera strap is to be 38 inches long. It will have 20 repeats of $1\frac{3}{4}$ inches each with equal borders at each end. How long will each border be?

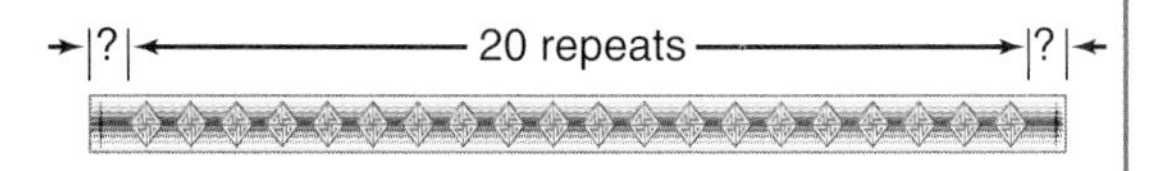

7) How long are 44 repeats if each is $\frac{7}{8}$ inches long?

8) How many $2\frac{3}{4}$-inch repeats are there in 33 inches?

Calculator Practice

Use your calculator to help you rename a mixed number as an improper fraction.

EXAMPLE Rename $25\frac{3}{4}$ as an improper fraction.

Step 1 Multiply the whole number by the denominator.

25 [×] 4 [=] 100

Step 2 Add the product to the numerator.

100 [+] 3 [=] 103

Step 3 Write the sum, 103, as the new numerator, and use the original denominator.

Solution $25\frac{3}{4} = \frac{103}{4}$

Calculator Exercise A Write these mixed numbers as improper fractions.

1) $12\frac{11}{25}$

2) $9\frac{11}{34}$

3) $10\frac{6}{11}$

4) $20\frac{6}{13}$

5) $13\frac{5}{18}$

6) $57\frac{5}{14}$

7) $12\frac{11}{13}$

8) $16\frac{5}{11}$

9) $16\frac{15}{16}$

10) $24\frac{16}{17}$

11) $8\frac{6}{11}$

12) $8\frac{1}{15}$

13) $49\frac{12}{13}$

14) $15\frac{23}{34}$

15) $19\frac{2}{12}$

16) $7\frac{1}{10}$

Calculator Exercise B Write the mixed numbers as improper fractions.

1) $26\frac{2}{3}$

2) $15\frac{16}{19}$

3) $29\frac{6}{7}$

4) $11\frac{9}{10}$

5) $16\frac{10}{20}$

6) $12\frac{5}{11}$

7) $16\frac{15}{16}$

8) $12\frac{13}{14}$

9) $28\frac{5}{11}$

10) $39\frac{10}{13}$

11) $20\frac{10}{11}$

12) $19\frac{6}{7}$

13) $14\frac{12}{13}$

14) $22\frac{5}{7}$

15) $18\frac{10}{11}$

16) $18\frac{12}{13}$

17) $10\frac{11}{12}$

18) $18\frac{7}{8}$

19) $8\frac{11}{12}$

20) $13\frac{8}{9}$

21) $4\frac{12}{15}$

Chapter 6 Review

Find the answers and write them in simplest form.

1) $\begin{array}{r} 6\frac{3}{4} \\ +18\frac{1}{8} \\ \hline \end{array}$

2) $\begin{array}{r} 9\frac{7}{8} \\ +4\frac{1}{2} \\ \hline \end{array}$

3) $\begin{array}{r} 12\frac{3}{4} \\ -5\frac{1}{3} \\ \hline \end{array}$

4) $\begin{array}{r} 17\frac{3}{4} \\ -11\frac{7}{8} \\ \hline \end{array}$

Use this fabric guide to answer the questions.

Garment	Fabric Width in Inches	Misses' Sizes 10	12	14	16	18	20	
Top	36″	$1\frac{3}{4}$	$1\frac{7}{8}$	$1\frac{7}{8}$	$1\frac{7}{8}$	$2\frac{1}{8}$	$2\frac{1}{4}$	Yards
	45″	$1\frac{1}{4}$	$1\frac{3}{8}$	$1\frac{3}{8}$	$1\frac{5}{8}$	$1\frac{5}{8}$	$1\frac{3}{4}$	Yards
	60″	$1\frac{1}{8}$	$1\frac{1}{8}$	$1\frac{1}{8}$	$1\frac{1}{4}$	$1\frac{1}{4}$	$1\frac{1}{4}$	Yards
Skirt	36″	$1\frac{5}{8}$	$1\frac{3}{4}$	$1\frac{3}{4}$	$1\frac{3}{4}$	$1\frac{3}{4}$	$1\frac{3}{4}$	Yards
	45″	$1\frac{1}{8}$	$1\frac{3}{8}$	$1\frac{1}{2}$	$1\frac{3}{4}$	$1\frac{3}{4}$	$1\frac{3}{4}$	Yards
	60″	$\frac{7}{8}$	$\frac{7}{8}$	1	1	1	1	Yards

How many yards of fabric are needed for each project?

5) 45″ fabric
size 14 top
size 14 skirt

6) 60″ fabric
size 12 top
size 12 skirt

7) 36″ fabric
size 10 top
size 12 skirt

8) 60″ fabric
size 14 top
size 16 skirt

9) 36″ fabric
size 10 top
size 10 skirt

Find the total length of each macramé project.

10) 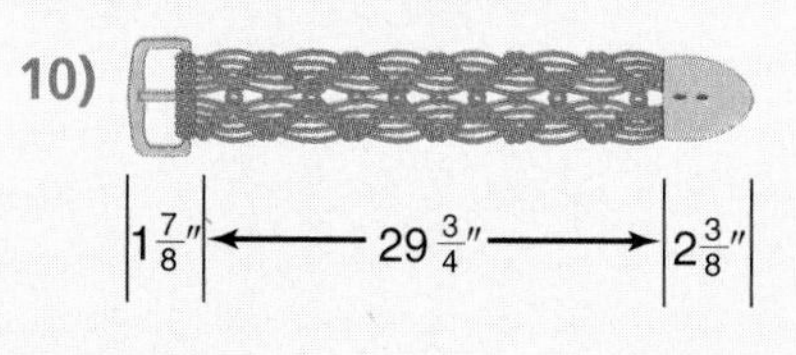

11) 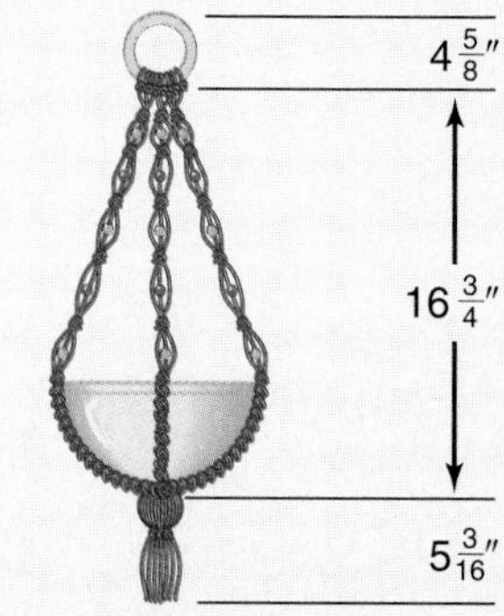

Find the length and width of these pieces of scrap material A and B.

12) **13)**

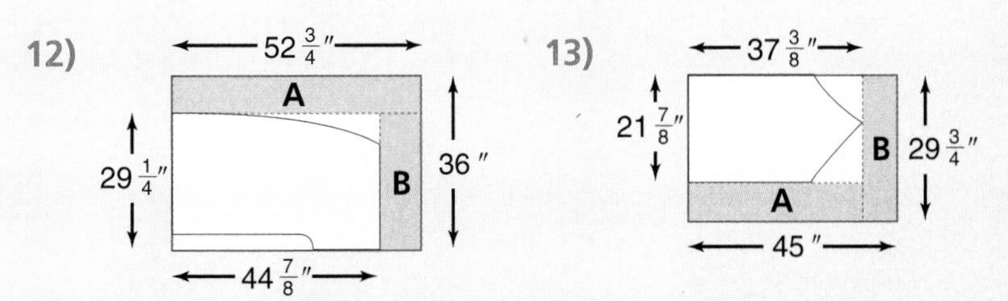

Answer these questions about repeating patterns.

14) Anna is making a border that has a repeating pattern. The pattern repeats every $1\frac{3}{4}$ inches. How long are 14 repeats?

15) Carlo's belt is to have 15 repeats of $1\frac{7}{8}$ inches plus $3\frac{5}{8}$ inches for the buckle. How long will the finished belt be?

16) Diane is making a camera strap that is to be 38 inches long. It will have 12 repeats of $2\frac{3}{4}$ inches each with equal borders at each end. How long will each of the two borders be?

17) How long are 23 repeats if each is $3\frac{1}{8}$ inches long?

Find the missing numerators.

18) $14\frac{5}{8} = 13\frac{\blacksquare}{8}$ **19)** $8 = 7\frac{\blacksquare}{3}$ **20)** $25\frac{3}{4} = 24\frac{\blacksquare}{8}$

Test Taking Tip Drawing a picture or diagram can help you solve a problem.

Chapter 7 Fractions in the Home

Recycling scraps of fabric can show your creative abilities. Scrap quilts were ways that early settlers first recycled cloth. They cut and sewed together old socks, leftover bedding, and scraps from dressmaking to make colorful, warm quilts. Next time you work on a project, think of how you might use mathematics to conserve your materials and challenge your creativity!

In Chapter 7, you will explore some of the many ways we use measurement with fractions in our daily lives.

Goals for Learning

- To add fractions to find totals
- To subtract fractions to find amounts of leftover materials
- To multiply fractions to find area
- To divide mixed numbers and fractions

Lesson 1 Addition of Fractions

When you are finding the total measurement of two or more items, you may have to add fractions. Be careful to keep the same unit of measure within the same problem.

EXAMPLES

Lisa wants to combine $2\frac{3}{4}$ cups of flour and one pint of milk. How many cups in all does that make? Remember, one pint equals two cups.

$$\begin{array}{ll} 2\frac{3}{4} \text{ cups of flour} & = \quad 2\frac{3}{4} \text{ cups of flour} \\ \underline{+1 \quad \text{pint of milk}} & = \quad \underline{+2 \quad \text{cups of milk}} \\ & \qquad 4\frac{3}{4} \text{ cups} \end{array}$$

Answer: $4\frac{3}{4}$ cups in all

Lori buys $2\frac{1}{2}$ yards of green material and $3\frac{2}{3}$ yards of red material. How many yards of material does Lori buy?

$$\begin{array}{ll} 2\frac{1}{2} \text{ yards} & = \quad 2\frac{3}{6} \text{ yards} \\ \underline{+\,3\frac{2}{3} \text{ yards}} & = \quad \underline{+3\frac{4}{6} \text{ yards}} \\ & \qquad 5\frac{7}{6} = 6\frac{1}{6} \text{ yards} \end{array}$$

Answer: $6\frac{1}{6}$ yards

Remember: $5\frac{7}{6} = 5 + \frac{7}{6}$

$= 5 + 1\frac{1}{6}$

$= 6\frac{1}{6}$

Exercise A Practice adding fractions. Write your answers in simplest form.

1) $2\frac{3}{4} + 1\frac{1}{5}$

2) $5\frac{2}{5} + 1\frac{4}{6}$

3) $4\frac{3}{7} + 2\frac{5}{6}$

4) $2 + 9\frac{1}{8}$

5) $12 + 2\frac{5}{6}$

6) $8 + 3\frac{1}{4}$

7) $5 + 3\frac{7}{8}$

8) $3\frac{1}{8} + 5\frac{1}{6}$

PROBLEM SOLVING

Exercise B Solve these problems. Include the units in your answers.

1) $2\frac{1}{3}$ yards + $1\frac{1}{2}$ ft.

2) $2\frac{1}{2}$ pints + $3\frac{3}{4}$ cups

3) Carlos buys $6\frac{1}{2}$ feet of blue webbing and $3\frac{4}{5}$ feet of yellow webbing to fix his lawn chairs. What is the total number of feet he buys?

4) Jacob measures the distance around his patio and makes the following measurements: $12\frac{1}{4}$ feet, $16\frac{2}{3}$ feet, $12\frac{1}{4}$ feet, and $16\frac{2}{3}$ feet. Find the perimeter of the patio. (The perimeter equals the sum of the sides.)

5) Victor is to bake two cakes and one batch of cookies for the school bake sale. His flour needs are $2\frac{1}{2}$ cups, 3 cups, and $2\frac{1}{3}$ cups. Find the total number of cups he needs.

6) Tess's notebook paper measures $7\frac{15}{16}$ inches wide and $10\frac{7}{8}$ inches long. Find the perimeter of Tess's notebook paper.

Lesson 2 Subtraction of Fractions

When you measure items, you may need to subtract quantities with fractions.

EXAMPLES Maria buys a quart of mayonnaise. She uses $2\frac{1}{3}$ cups in a large salad. How many cups of mayonnaise are left? (One quart = 4 cups)

$$\begin{array}{rcr} 4 \text{ cups} & = & 3\frac{3}{3} \text{ cups} \\ -2\frac{1}{3} \text{ cups} & = & -2\frac{1}{3} \text{ cups} \\ \hline & & 1\frac{2}{3} \text{ cups} \end{array}$$

$$\begin{aligned} 4 &= 3 + 1 \\ &= 3 + \frac{3}{3} \\ &= 3\frac{3}{3} \end{aligned}$$

Answer: $1\frac{2}{3}$ cups of mayonnaise are left.

Warren uses $6\frac{3}{4}$ feet of a $12\frac{1}{8}$-foot board. How much of the board is left?

$$\begin{array}{rcrcr} 12\frac{1}{8} \text{ feet} & = & 12\frac{1}{8} \text{ feet} & = & 11\frac{9}{8} \text{ feet} \\ -6\frac{3}{4} \text{ feet} & = & -6\frac{6}{8} \text{ feet} & = & -6\frac{6}{8} \text{ feet} \\ \hline & & & & 5\frac{3}{8} \text{ feet} \end{array}$$

$$\begin{aligned} 12\frac{1}{8} &= 11 + 1 + \frac{1}{8} \\ &= 11 + \frac{8}{8} + \frac{1}{8} \\ &= 11 + \frac{9}{8} \\ &= 11\frac{9}{8} \end{aligned}$$

Answer: $5\frac{3}{8}$ feet are left.

Lumber is generally sold in standard lengths. When you plan a building project, double-check your addition and subtraction so that you purchase the right amount of materials.

Exercise A Practice subtracting fractions. Write your answers in simplest form.

1) $13 - 5\frac{2}{3}$

2) $6\frac{5}{8} - 2\frac{1}{3}$

3) $3\frac{1}{6} - 2\frac{3}{8}$

4) $18\frac{5}{6} - 2\frac{4}{11}$

5) $4\frac{6}{11} - \frac{3}{4}$

6) $15 - 2\frac{1}{10}$

7) $5\frac{2}{3} - \frac{8}{9}$

8) $13\frac{2}{7} - 3\frac{13}{14}$

PROBLEM SOLVING

Exercise B Solve these problems. Include the units in your answers.

1) 1 yard $-$ $16\frac{1}{4}$ inches

2) 2 quarts $-$ $5\frac{1}{2}$ cups

3) Seamus uses $2\frac{5}{8}$ yards of a 6-yard piece of canvas to patch his tent. How many yards are left?

4) Lelia needs a shade for a window that is $48\frac{3}{4}$ inches long. She finds a shade that is 72 inches long. How much longer is the shade than the window?

5) Micah has $6\frac{3}{4}$ gallons of white paint and 7 quarts of green paint. How much more white paint than green paint does he have?

6) Russ buys 6 feet of picture wire. He uses $29\frac{1}{2}$ inches to hang a mirror. How much does he have left?

Lesson 3 Multiplication of Fractions

Frequently you need to use measurements in home projects. If one measurement is repeated many times, then you can multiply to find the total length.

EXAMPLE Miranda wants to make a bookcase with four shelves to fit between two windows. Each shelf is to be $23\frac{1}{2}$ inches long. How many inches of shelving does she need? To find the total length of shelving needed, she can multiply $23\frac{1}{2}''$ times 4.

$23\frac{1}{2} \times 4 = \blacksquare$

Write mixed numbers as improper fractions.

$$\frac{47}{\cancel{2}_{1}} \times \frac{\cancel{4}^{2}}{1} = \blacksquare$$

$\frac{47}{1} \times \frac{2}{1} = \frac{94}{1} = 94$ inches of shelving

Exercise A Find the inches of shelving needed for each project. Give your answers in inches.

1) $16\frac{1}{4}'' \times 7$

2) $13\frac{3}{4}'' \times 4$

3) $24\frac{7}{8}'' \times 6$

4) $28\frac{1}{4}'' \times 16$

5) $38\frac{1}{8}'' \times 10$

6) $60\frac{1}{4}'' \times 10$

7) $13\frac{1}{2}'' \times 5$

8) $16\frac{7}{8}'' \times 3$

9) $30\frac{4}{5}'' \times 2$

10) $6\frac{1}{8}'' \times 22$

11) $5\frac{3}{4}'' \times 20$

12) $9\frac{2}{7}'' \times 16$

Finding the Area To find the area of a surface, you can multiply.

EXAMPLE Charlie's hobby is gardening. He is getting ready to plant flowers in a raised flower bed. The bed is $13\frac{1}{2}$ feet long, and $12\frac{3}{4}$ feet wide. What is the area? Remember, the area equals the length times the width. Write your answer in square feet.

Length $\times$ Width = Area

$13\frac{1}{2} \times 12\frac{3}{4} = ■$

$\frac{27}{2} \times \frac{51}{4} = \frac{1,377}{8} = 172\frac{1}{8}$ square feet

Exercise B Find the area of each. Write your answer in square units.

1) $2\frac{1}{3}$ ft. $\times$ 3 ft.

2) $2\frac{3}{5}$ in. $\times$ 20 in.

3) $\frac{4}{7}$ miles $\times$ 5 miles

4) $4\frac{2}{3}$ yd. $\times$ 30 yd.

5) $1\frac{1}{2}$ ft. $\times$ $2\frac{5}{6}$ ft.

6) 3 miles $\times$ $\frac{3}{4}$ miles

7) $5\frac{3}{8}$ in. $\times$ $5\frac{2}{3}$ in.

8) $3\frac{7}{8}$ yd. $\times$ $\frac{4}{5}$ yd.

9) 8 yd. $\times$ $16\frac{2}{9}$ yd.

10) $6\frac{3}{4}$ in. $\times$ 12 in.

11) 14 in. $\times$ $5\frac{4}{7}$ in.

12) $13\frac{4}{9}$ yd. $\times$ $\frac{5}{8}$ yd.

13) $9\frac{1}{2}$ ft. $\times$ 6 ft.

14) $8\frac{1}{3}$ miles $\times$ $2\frac{1}{2}$ miles

Exercise C Practice multiplying with fractions. Find these lengths. Write your answers in the units given.

1) $3\frac{1}{2}$ ft. × 3

2) $6\frac{2}{3}$ in. × $\frac{1}{2}$

3) $2\frac{3}{4}$ yd. × 5

4) $1\frac{1}{5}$ yd. × 6

5) $1\frac{2}{5}$ in. × $1\frac{1}{2}$

6) $5\frac{2}{5}$ ft. × $1\frac{1}{3}$

7) 21 in. × $\frac{2}{3}$

8) $3\frac{2}{9}$ in. × $2\frac{1}{12}$

9) $1\frac{1}{3}$ ft. × $1\frac{1}{5}$

10) $2\frac{1}{6}$ yd. × $1\frac{1}{6}$

11) $2\frac{3}{4}$ in. × $1\frac{1}{2}$

12) $7\frac{2}{5}$ ft. × $2\frac{2}{3}$

PROBLEM SOLVING

Exercise D Solve these problems. Write your answers in the correct units of measure.

1) Diego's gravy recipe calls for $2\frac{1}{2}$ tablespoons cornstarch. How much will he need if he makes only $\frac{2}{3}$ of the recipe?

2) Helena's bookshelf plan calls for 5 shelves, each measuring $25\frac{1}{2}$ inches. Find the total length of shelving in inches.

3) J. Ellis is installing wall-to-wall carpeting in his den. If the room measures 13 by $14\frac{1}{2}$ feet, how many square feet of carpeting will he need?

4) Tehron's kitchen measures 16 by $12\frac{1}{4}$ feet. If she is installing one-square-foot tiles, how many tiles will she need?

5) Brian purchases $20\frac{1}{2}$ feet of hall carpet and has $\frac{2}{3}$ of this left. How many feet does he have left?

Lesson 4 Division of Mixed Numbers and Fractions

Invert

To change to the direct opposite.

To divide a mixed number, first change the mixed number to a fraction. Then **invert** the divisor and multiply.

EXAMPLES Eve buys $25\frac{1}{3}$ feet of shelf paper. How many 5-foot shelves can she cover with this? Eve can use division to solve this problem.

$$25\frac{1}{3} \div 5 = \blacksquare$$

$$\frac{76}{3} \div \frac{5}{1} = \blacksquare$$

$$\frac{76}{3} \times \frac{1}{5} = \frac{76}{15} = 5\frac{1}{15}$$

Eve can cover five shelves. The remainder of $\frac{1}{15}$ is not enough to cover a complete shelf.

Tony's apartment has a balcony that is $2\frac{1}{3}$ yards wide. Its area is $9\frac{1}{3}$ square yards. What is the length of the balcony?

Area ÷ Width = Length

$$9\frac{1}{3} \div 2\frac{1}{3} = \blacksquare$$

$$\frac{28}{3} \div \frac{7}{3} = \blacksquare$$

$$\frac{\overset{4}{\cancel{28}}}{\underset{1}{\cancel{3}}} \times \frac{\overset{1}{\cancel{3}}}{\underset{1}{\cancel{7}}} = \frac{4}{1} = 4 \text{ yards}$$

The balcony is 4 yards long.

Knowing the length, width, and area of your balcony will help you plan for outdoor furniture. You may even have room for a gas grill!

Exercise A Practice dividing with fractions and mixed numbers.

1) $\frac{5}{6} \div \frac{2}{3}$

2) $\frac{4}{5} \div 8$

3) $2\frac{3}{4} \div \frac{6}{7}$

4) $5\frac{1}{7} \div \frac{2}{5}$

5) $6\frac{2}{5} \div 1\frac{1}{2}$

6) $5\frac{2}{3} \div 2\frac{1}{2}$

7) $4\frac{1}{3} \div 12$

8) $6\frac{2}{9} \div 3$

9) $5\frac{2}{8} \div \frac{5}{6}$

10) $7\frac{1}{7} \div 10$

11) $5 \div \frac{2}{5}$

12) $3\frac{4}{5} \div 3\frac{1}{8}$

13) $4\frac{1}{3} \div 1\frac{1}{2}$

14) $6 \div 2\frac{6}{7}$

15) $6\frac{2}{5} \div 1\frac{1}{5}$

16) $2\frac{7}{8} \div 1\frac{1}{4}$

PROBLEM SOLVING

Exercise B Solve these problems. Write your answers in the correct units.

1) If the area of a cabinet top is $3\frac{1}{2}$ square feet, and the length is $1\frac{1}{4}$ feet, then what is the width?

2) Jeff's recipe for barbecue sauce calls for $2\frac{1}{3}$ tablespoons vinegar. How much vinegar will he use if he divides the recipe by 4?

3) Hai's project calls for $15\frac{1}{3}$ feet of rope. If the $15\frac{1}{3}$ feet are divided into 4 equal pieces, how long is each piece?

4) Bo is cutting rubber floor mats for the basement. He has $25\frac{1}{4}$ feet of matting. Each mat is to be $5\frac{1}{4}$ feet long. How many mats can he cut?

Calculator Practice You can use a calculator to help you express improper fractions as mixed numbers.

EXAMPLE Write $\frac{115}{25}$ as a mixed number.

Step 1 Divide the numerator by the denominator.
115 [÷] 25 [=] 4.6

Step 2 Multiply the whole number portion, 4, by the denominator, 25.
25 [×] 4 [=] 100

Step 3 Subtract the product, 100, from 115 for the new numerator.
115 [−] 100 [=] 15

Solution $\frac{115}{25} = 4\frac{15}{25} = 4\frac{3}{5}$

Calculator Exercise A Express these improper fractions as mixed numbers. Use your calculator to help you. Write your answer in simplest form.

1) $\frac{18}{3}$
2) $\frac{93}{35}$
3) $\frac{23}{4}$
4) $\frac{42}{13}$
5) $\frac{89}{5}$
6) $\frac{109}{10}$
7) $\frac{20}{8}$
8) $\frac{30}{11}$
9) $\frac{34}{17}$
10) $\frac{45}{9}$
11) $\frac{80}{21}$
12) $\frac{66}{30}$

Calculator Exercise B Express these improper fractions as mixed numbers. Use your calculator to help you. Write your answers in simplest form.

1) $\frac{128}{15}$
2) $\frac{135}{17}$
3) $\frac{253}{51}$
4) $\frac{47}{5}$
5) $\frac{63}{8}$
6) $\frac{72}{7}$
7) $\frac{132}{34}$
8) $\frac{27}{8}$
9) $\frac{18}{5}$
10) $\frac{178}{10}$
11) $\frac{75}{6}$
12) $\frac{291}{28}$
13) $\frac{103}{15}$
14) $\frac{216}{3}$
15) $\frac{129}{15}$
16) $\frac{623}{45}$

Chapter 7 Review

Perform the following operations. Write your answers in simplest form.

1) $12\frac{4}{5} + 6\frac{2}{3}$

2) $16 - 3\frac{2}{5}$

3) $8\frac{12}{15} - 5\frac{1}{5}$

4) $9\frac{2}{7} - 3\frac{4}{9}$

Find the answers.

5) $5\frac{1}{5}$ ft. $\times 1\frac{1}{2} =$

6) 7 sq. ft. $\div 1\frac{2}{5} =$

Solve these problems. Write your answers in simplest form. Include the units of measure in your answers.

7) Marco uses $\frac{3}{4}$ of an old shelf that is 22 inches long. How much is left over?

a) $\frac{3}{88}$ inches

b) $16\frac{1}{2}$ inches

c) $5\frac{1}{2}$ inches

8) Fran measures the distance around his desk. The measurements are 26 inches, $30\frac{1}{2}$ inches, 26 inches, and $30\frac{1}{2}$ inches. Find the perimeter of Fran's desk.

9) Otto has a board $6\frac{1}{2}$ feet long. If he divides the board into shelves $\frac{2}{3}$ foot long, how many shelves can he cut?

10) Find the area of Cara's kitchen. The length equals $12\frac{1}{2}$ feet, and the width equals 10 feet.

11) If Bridget's room is 11 feet by $8\frac{3}{4}$ feet, then how many square feet of flooring should she buy?

12) Sun Li needs curtains for her window. She buys curtains that are 60″ long. How much should she shorten them if her window is $49\frac{7}{8}$″ long?

13) Satha buys $1\frac{5}{8}$ yards of braid trim and $\frac{3}{8}$ yard of lace trim. How many yards of trim does she buy?

14) Matthew is digging a flower bed around three sides of his patio. If one side of the patio is $8\frac{3}{4}$ feet, and the other two sides are each $5\frac{7}{8}$ feet, then how many feet long will his new flower bed be?

15) Kyle plans to cover his kitchen shelves. He buys a roll of shelf paper that is $25\frac{1}{2}$ feet long. How many shelves can he fully cover if each shelf is 4 feet long?

Test Taking Tip

Try to get in the habit of reviewing your corrected tests. You can learn from your mistakes.

UNITED STATES OF AMERICA
E·PLU RIB US·U NUM
ONE DIME
UNITED STATES OF AMERICA
E·PLURIBUS UNUM
ONE CENT
IN GOD WE TRUST
LIBERTY
IN GOD WE TRUST

Chapter 8

Spending Money

As consumers, we spend money for goods and services. A smart shopper knows how much a purchase will be, finds the better buy, and calculates what amount of change is due. But money is not always expressed as whole numbers, or dollars. Why? Because our money system has parts of dollars called *cents.* You'll save your pennies when you know how to apply mathematics to decimals, such as money.

In Chapter 8, you will learn how to add and subtract with money and other decimals.

Goals for Learning

- To compare decimals
- To read prices and write them in decimal form
- To find the total amount of a purchase of several items
- To compute the amount of change due

Lesson 1 Addition of Decimals

Decimal

A whole number followed by a dot and places to the right. The numbers to the dot's right equal less than one.

Decimal places

Positions to the right of the decimal point.

When you add **decimals,** keeping the **decimal places** in the same column is important so that you will not add tenths to hundredths. You can do this easily if you place the decimals in vertical form and line up the decimal points. For example, to add 2.3 + .06 + 5, you would write in a column. Putting in zeros will help keep numbers in the correct column.

EXAMPLES

Add 2.3 + .06 + 5

```
  2.3            2.30
   .06           0.06
 +5      OR    + 5.00
 ----          ------
                 7.36
```

Add 5 + .09 + .7

```
  5              5.00
   .09           0.09
 +  .7   OR     +0.70
 -----          -----
                 5.79
```

Exercise A Write these problems in vertical form, then add. Remember to line up the decimals points.

1) 6 + .35 + 2.6
2) 5.8 + 16 + .45
3) 15.61 + 1.2 + 9
4) 2 + .008 + .25
5) 3.6 + 8 + 2.35
6) 14.1 + 2 + .506
7) 8.2 + .07 + 11
8) 13.62 + 1.2 + .309

Adding Prices Stavros goes shopping for a camping trip and buys the following items. How much money does he spend for them? Remember, prices do not always have a decimal point or dollar sign. Solve this by placing the decimal point two places from the right.

EXAMPLE

Stavros's List	Price Shown	Actual Price
Baked beans	45	$ .45
Dry cereal	195	$1.95
Beef stew	250	$2.50
Tomatoes	95	$ .95
Coffee	458	+ $4.58
		$10.43

Stavros spends $10.43 for the items.

Supermarket

Everyday PRICES

Item	Size	Price	Item	Size	Price
Green Beans....	16-oz. can	3/155	Apple Juice	46-oz. can	2/219
Tea Bags	box of 50	279	Eggs..............	dozen	125
Orange Juice....	16-oz. can	109	Corn	pkg. of 6 ears	98
Onions	3-lb. bag	99	Macaroni	8-oz. box	75
Cat Food........	6-oz. can	58	Detergent......	24-oz. box	189

Exercise B Add the prices to find the total for each order.

1) 3 cans of green beans
1 package of corn
3 pounds of onions

2) 1 dozen eggs
1 box of detergent
1 box of tea bags

3) 1 can of orange juice
1 box of detergent
1 can of cat food

4) 1 box of tea bags
3 packages of corn
3 pounds of onions

5) 1 package of corn
1 dozen eggs
2 cans of apple juice

6) 1 can of cat food
4 cans of apple juice
1 can of orange juice

7) 1 box of detergent
1 box of tea bags
3 cans of green beans
1 can of cat food

8) 1 box of macaroni
3 pounds of onions
1 dozen eggs
1 can of orange juice

Calculator Practice

When you add decimals on a calculator, remember to include any decimal points. Press the + button after each addend except the last one. You press the = button after the last addend.

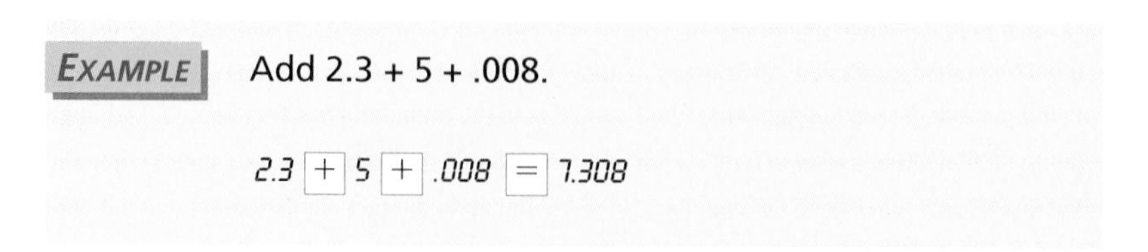

Calculator Exercise Add these numbers on your calculator.

1)
```
    235.06
  1,238.091
    462.923
  2,630.105
+    62.188
```

2)
```
   50.638
    1.1093
  175.2063
  361.189
+ 201.892
```

3)
```
  2.23402
   .081152
  1.120803
   .18165
+ 3.5176
```

4)
```
   .136
  1.4892
 12.6
  9.82
+  .965
```

5)
```
     1.60606
      .234
     1.5678
    92.4
     5.8
+16,348.59
```

6)
```
   530.61
    15.8
     9.004
      .005
     6.8
    14.50963
+ 2,368.52
```

Lesson 2 Subtraction With Decimals

When you subtract decimals, first line up the decimal points. You may have to write zeros before you can subtract.

EXAMPLE Ms. Lawson buys a jacket for $87.92. How much change will she receive if she gives the salesclerk $100?

```
  $ 100            $100.00
 −  87.92         − 87.92
                  $ 12.08
```

Write a decimal point and two zeros here.

Ms. Lawson will receive $12.08 change.

Exercise A Write these subtraction problems in vertical form, then subtract. Remember to line up the decimal points. Add any zeros that are needed.

1) $23 − $2.67

2) 4 − 2.09

3) 2.1 − .92

4) 6 − .721

5) 1 − .34

6) 2.4 − .024

7) 5.03 − .223

8) 89.1 − .2

9) $50 − $1.93

10) 3 − .04

11) 24.93 − 3.4

12) 9.2 − .334

13) 56 − 2.33

14) 1.1 − .11

15) 30 − .093

16) .234 − .092

17) 2.03 − .8

18) 67.9 − .341

19) 1 − .3

20) 4 − .4

21) 12.5 − 3.4

22) 107 − .51

23) 7.1 − .77

24) 2.4 − 1.34

Exercise B Find the amount of change due for each purchase.

	Cost	Paid With		Cost	Paid With
1)	$79.60	$100	**13)**	$0.54	$20
2)	$18.75	$20	**14)**	$39	$50
3)	$42.50	$50	**15)**	$567.09	$1,000
4)	$39.36	$40	**16)**	$73.15	$100
5)	$1.59	$2	**17)**	$15.65	$75
6)	$42.70	$50	**18)**	$4.76	$10.76
7)	$11.95	$20	**19)**	$1.23	$2
8)	$11.76	$20	**20)**	$2.41	$10.01
9)	$17.36	$20.01	**21)**	$39.23	$50.03
10)	$9.78	$50	**22)**	$1.11	$20
11)	$11.90	$40	**23)**	$203	$500
12)	$4.02	$10.02	**24)**	$8.98	$20

Adding and Subtracting Money Both addition and subtraction with money take place when you buy more than one item at a time.

EXAMPLE Amy buys a blouse for $11.95, a skirt for $17.50, and socks for $1.95. If she gives the salesclerk $50, then how much change will she receive?
First you add the items together. Then you subtract to find the amount of change due.

Step 1 Add to find the total.

$$\begin{array}{r} \$11.95 \\ 17.50 \\ +\ 1.95 \\ \hline \$31.40 \end{array} \longleftarrow \text{Total}$$

Step 2 Subtract to find the change due.

$$\begin{array}{r} \$\ 50.00 \\ -31.40 \\ \hline \$\ 18.60 \end{array} \longleftarrow \text{Change due.}$$

Exercise C Find the amount of change due each purchase.

	Items Bought	Paid With
1)	Coat, $189.95 Hat, $28.99	$300
2)	Shirt, $19.99 Coat, $92.00	$200
3)	Sandals, $29.95 Scarf, $12.00	$50
4)	Gloves, $23.50 Dress, $52.75	$100
5)	Belt, $26.50 Pants, $49.00	$100
6)	Sweater, $38.25 Blouse, $52.00	$200

	Items Bought	Paid With
7)	Skirt, $21.50 Belt, $12.50 Shoes, $44.99 Hat, $16.00	$100
8)	Shorts, $24.80 Blouse, $48.75 Socks, $6.00 Shoes, $69.10	$200
9)	Slippers, $19.50 Socks, $3.50 Skirt, $23.90 Blouse, $25.99	$100
10)	Suit, $395.00 Vest, $49.95 Belt, $28.00 Shirt, $50.00	$1,000

As you shop, keep the prices in mind. You may be able to afford more items if you shop wisely.

Chapter 8 Review

Ten Thousands	Thousands	Hundreds	Tens	Ones		Tenths	Hundredths	Thousandths	Ten Thousandths
				2	.	6	3	1	
			2	1	.	9	5		

What is the place value of each underlined digit?

1) $21.65

2) 3.015

3) .35

4) $1.6035

5) $26.72

6) $231.72

7) $12.096

8) $36.21

Write *True* or *False* for each of these comparisons.

9) .091 > 1.1
10) .035 < .10
11) .01 > .0098

Write these prices correctly with decimal points.

12) Tomatoes, can 2/87
13) Peanut butter, jar 179

Find the total amount of each purchase.

14) Cooking oil 175
Baked beans 45
10 lb. potatoes 279

15) Frozen dinner 159
Canned corn 55
Lettuce 75

Find the amount of change due.

16) Coat, $29.95—Paid $50
17) Shoes, $19.11—Paid $25

Solve each problem.

18) $2.50 + $.85 + $30
19) 5.6 + .28 + 5 + .6
20) $29 − $.89
21) 1.1 − .063

Find the total cost and the amount of change due for each set of purchases.

	Items Bought	Paid With
22)	Hat, $49.00 Gloves, $29.95 Shoes, $88.95	$200
23)	Slippers, $35.00 Shirt, $31.99 Ribbon, $6.00	$100

	Items Bought	Paid With
24)	Sweater, $55.60 Vest, $32.00 Scarf, $22.00	$150
25)	Suit, $250.00 Belt, $19.00 Shoes, $42.00	$400

Test Taking Tip

When you read true-false questions, the statement must be absolutely correct. Words like *always* or *never* tell you the question is probably false.

Welcome

Chapter 9

Earning Money

How are people paid for the work they do? Are they paid a weekly or yearly salary? Are their paychecks based upon an hourly wage? When you read advertisements for jobs, it is important to know how to convert the pay that is offered to the amount you can expect in your paycheck. Let mathematics help you!

In Chapter 9, you will learn how to multiply and divide with decimals.

Goals for Learning

- To multiply to find gross pay
- To divide to find hourly pay, if the weekly pay is known
- To divide to find weekly salary, if the yearly salary is known
- To compute overtime pay

Lesson 1 Multiplication of Decimals

Gross pay
Pay before deductions.

Per
For each; for every.

We multiply decimals to compute the **gross pay** that a worker who is paid by the hour earns.

EXAMPLES Ho works part time as a bricklayer's helper and earns $5.75 **per** hour. If he works 35 hours during a one-week period, how much is his gross pay for that week?

Multiply the hourly wage by the number of hours worked.

```
  $  5.75  ◄—  2 places
  ×    35  ◄—  0 places
  -------
    28 75
  +172 5
  -------
  $201.25  ◄—  2 + 0 places = 2 places
```

Since two decimal places are in the factors, count off two decimal places in the product.

Ho's gross pay is $201.25.

Marti earns $6.50 per hour with her part-time job after school. If she works 8 hours during a one-week period, how much does she earn?

```
  $ 6.50
  ×    8
  ------
  $52.00
```

The total number of places to the right of a decimal determines the number of places in the answer.

Marti earns $52.00.

Exercise A Find the gross pay for these workers.

1) 32 hours at $5.75 per hour.

2) 17 hours at $5.19 per hour.

3) 22 hours at $6.25 per hour.

4) 18 hours at $6.38 per hour.

5) 23 hours at $7.10 per hour.

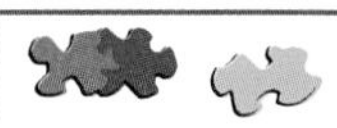

PROBLEM SOLVING

Exercise B Find the answers by multiplying.

1) Heather works part time as a shoe salesperson and earns $6.40 per hour. She works an 11-hour week. Find her weekly gross earnings.

2) Nelson works an 8-hour week earning $5.90 per hour as a carpenter's helper. What is Nelson's gross pay each week?

3) Cammy's part-time job earns her $6.55 per hour as a stock clerk. How much does Cammy earn if she works 22 hours?

4) The Super Food Market pays $6.10 per hour for a person to stock shelves. How much will a person earn at this job, working 15 hours?

5) Jamal tutors after school and earns $9.75 per hour. If he works 6 hours a week, how much does he earn per week?

Exercise C Find the gross pay.

1) 30 hours at $4.50 per hour
2) 22 hours at $5.60 per hour
3) 15 hours at $5.75 per hour
4) 28 hours at $4.50 per hour
5) 16 hours at $4.00 per hour
6) 19 hours at $5.65 per hour
7) 23 hours at $7.75 per hour
8) 36 hours at $8.25 per hour
9) 12 hours at $4.95 per hour
10) 17 hours at $5.00 per hour
11) 11 hours at $4.65 per hour
12) 28 hours at $7.16 per hour
13) 32 hours at $4.00 per hour
14) 23 hours at $4.95 per hour
15) 31 hours at $7.18 per hour
16) 42 hours at $4.25 per hour
17) 25 hours at $4.25 per hour
18) 16 hours at $5.50 per hour
19) 15 hours at $7.50 per hour
20) 8 hours at $5.60 per hour
21) 5 hours at $2.20 per hour
22) 38 hours at $6.50 per hour
23) 36 hours at $7.60 per hour
24) 40 hours at $8.00 per hour
25) 9 hours at $3.10 per hour
26) 42 hours at $9.20 per hour
27) 40 hours at $4.60 per hour
28) 5 hours at $4.95 per hour
29) 29 hours at $4.95 per hour
30) 19 hours at $6.75 per hour

Multiplying Decimals by Decimals When you multiply decimals, lining up the decimal points is not necessary. The total number of places to the right of the decimal point in each factor determines the placement of the decimal point in the answer.

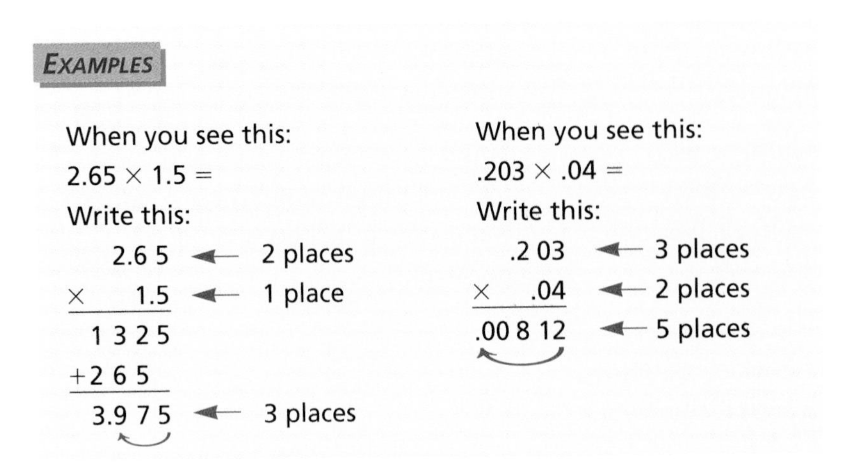

EXAMPLES

When you see this:
2.65 × 1.5 =
Write this:

```
   2.6 5  ◄— 2 places
×    1.5  ◄— 1 place
  1 3 2 5
 +2 6 5
  3.9 7 5 ◄— 3 places
```

When you see this:
.203 × .04 =
Write this:

```
  .2 03   ◄— 3 places
×   .04   ◄— 2 places
.00 8 12  ◄— 5 places
```

Exercise D Multiply these decimals. Count the decimal places in each factor before you place the decimal point in the answer.

1) \$ 3.25 × 1.5

2) \$ 4.20 × 16

3) \$ 1.95 × .28

4) 5.56 × 3.2

5) .063 × 2.9

6) 1.03 × .99

7) \$ 2.06 × 1.5

8) .68 × 2.5

9) 735 × 5.2

10) 1.69 × 13

11) 52.33 × 2.3

12) .263 × .09

13) .087 × .06

14) 7.31 × 1.06

15) .2106 × .35

16) .0528 × .003

17) .002 × .03

18) 1.006 × 1.07

19) 3.15 × .16

20) .819 × 23

21) 5.1 × .06

22) .205 × .01

23) 2.68 × 10

24) \$ 4.78 × 100

Multiplying With Decimal Parts of an Hour The number of hours an employee works may not always be a whole number. The worker may get paid for $\frac{1}{4}$, $\frac{1}{2}$, or $\frac{3}{4}$ of an hour.

Examples

Nilor works $11\frac{1}{2}$ hours after school, earning $5.25 per hour. How much is his gross pay? (Remember: $11\frac{1}{2} = 11.5$)

$$
\begin{array}{rl}
\$ \quad 5.25 & \leftarrow \text{2 places} \\
\times \quad 11.5 & \leftarrow \text{1 place} \\
\hline
2625 & \\
525 & \\
+525 & \\
\hline
\$60.375 & \leftarrow \text{3 places}
\end{array}
$$

Since only 2 decimal places are needed for money, round off the gross pay to the nearest cent. Nilor's gross pay is $60.38.

Alice works as a server and earns $4.57 per hour. If she works $12\frac{1}{4}$ hours for one week, how much is her gross pay? (Remember: $12\frac{1}{4} = 12.25$)

$$
\begin{array}{rl}
12.25 & \text{Hours} \\
\times \quad \$4.57 & \text{Per hour} \\
\hline
85\,75 & \\
6\,12\,5 & \\
+49\,00 & \\
\hline
\$55.98\,25 & \text{Gross pay}
\end{array}
$$

Remember, only two places are used for money.
$\$55.9825 \approx \$55.98$

Alice's gross pay is $55.98.

EXAMPLE An employee works $10\frac{3}{4}$ hours for an hourly pay of $6.29. Find the gross pay.
(Remember: $10\frac{3}{4} = 10.75$)

$$\begin{array}{r l}
10.75 & \leftarrow \text{2 places} \\
\times \quad \$6.29 & \leftarrow \text{2 places} \\
\hline
96\ 75 & \\
2\ 15\ 0 & \\
+64\ 50 & \\
\hline
\$67.61\ 75 & \approx \$67.62
\end{array}$$

The employee's gross pay is $67.62.

PROBLEM SOLVING

Exercise E Find the gross pay.

1) Anthony works $11\frac{1}{2}$ hours earning $5.25 per hour. Find Anthony 's gross pay.

2) José earns $10.00 per hour as a tutor after school. Find his gross pay if he works $9\frac{1}{4}$ hours.

3) Kim is an assistant clerk at City Hospital. She earns $6.20 an hour. She works $36\frac{3}{4}$ hours in one week. How much is her gross pay?

4) Mandy works as an electrician's helper, earning $5.25 per hour. If she works $28\frac{3}{4}$ hours in one week, how much is her gross pay?

5) The Pizza Parlor pays the pizza maker $7.86 per hour. Find the gross pay if the workweek is $38\frac{1}{4}$ hours.

6) Keiko earns $3.25 per hour with a babysitting service. Find her gross pay if she works 17 hours.

7) Casey worked as a part-time housecleaner 7 hours on Friday and $7\frac{1}{2}$ hours on Saturday. Find her gross pay if she earns $6.15 per hour.

Exercise F Find the gross pay.

1) $30\frac{1}{2}$ hours at $5.65 per hour

2) $15\frac{1}{2}$ hours at $5.92 per hour

3) $6\frac{3}{4}$ hours at $7.25 per hour

4) $12\frac{1}{2}$ hours at $6.12 per hour

5) $13\frac{1}{2}$ hours at $6.25 per hour

6) $10\frac{3}{4}$ hours at $7.00 per hour

7) 5 hours at $6.13 per hour

8) $27\frac{1}{2}$ hours at $5.70 per hour

9) $4\frac{3}{4}$ hours at $6.10 per hour

10) $15\frac{1}{2}$ hours at $8.70 per hour

11) $23\frac{1}{2}$ hours at $4.36 per hour

12) $26\frac{1}{2}$ hours at $6.90 per hour

13) $39\frac{1}{4}$ hours at $6.75 per hour

14) $25\frac{3}{4}$ hours at $7.62 per hour

15) $10\frac{1}{4}$ hours at $7.93 per hour

16) $22\frac{1}{2}$ hours at $6.50 per hour

17) $19\frac{1}{4}$ hours at $8.50 per hour

18) $32\frac{1}{4}$ hours at $7.25 per hour

19) $8\frac{3}{4}$ hours at $9.73 per hour

20) $40\frac{1}{4}$ hours at $6.95 per hour

21) $40\frac{1}{4}$ hours at $7.76 per hour

22) $14\frac{3}{4}$ hours at $6.75 per hour

23) $21\frac{1}{4}$ hours at $4.35 per hour

24) $28\frac{1}{4}$ hours at $7.25 per hour

Child care can be a part-time job or a full-time occupation for people who want to work with children.

Overtime Earnings Workers earn more than their hourly rate of pay when their employer asks them to work longer than the agreed-upon, or "straight," time. **Overtime** may be paid at the rate of **time and one-half** or **double time**.

Overtime
Time beyond the estimated limit.

Time and one-half
Payment of 1.5 times the hourly rate for work.

Double time
Payment of two times the hourly rate.

EXAMPLE Gary works 43 hours at $6.19 per hour with time and one-half for all time worked over 40 hours. What is his gross pay?

Step 1 Separate straight time from overtime.

43	Total time
− 40	Agreed straight time
3	Overtime

Step 2 Convert 3 hours to time and one-half. To do so, multiply by 1.5.

1.5	1.5 equals $1\frac{1}{2}$
× 3	Hours to be converted
4.5	Time and one-half

Step 3 Add straight time to time and one-half.

40.0	
+ 4.5	
44.5	Time used to compute gross pay

Step 4 Multiply the total time by the rate per hour.

44.5	Hours
× 6.19	Rate per hour
$275.455 ≈ $275.46	

Gary's gross pay is $275.46.

Working overtime can shorten the time you spend with your family, unless you bring your family to work with you.

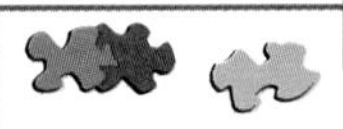

PROBLEM SOLVING

Exercise G Find the gross pay, including time and one-half.

1) Carol works 44 hours at $5.20 per hour with time and one-half for all time over 40 hours. Find Carol's gross pay.

2) Ricardo works 44 hours at $10.00 per hour with time and one-half for all time over 40 hours. Find Ricardo's gross pay.

3) Alexandra works 9 hours at $5.25 per hour with time and one-half for all time over 8 hours. Find Alexandra's gross pay.

4) Compute the gross pay for Cindy's 46-hour workweek if she gets $4.60 per hour and time and one-half for all time over 40 hours.

5) Twelve hours at $7.50 per hour with overtime after 8 hours.

6) Forty-five hours at $6.00 per hour with overtime after 40 hours.

7) Fifteen hours at $6.25 per hour with overtime after 8 hours.

8) Thirty-seven hours at $7.00 per hour with overtime after 3 hours.

9) Forty-one and one-half hours at $6.80 per hour with overtime after 40 hours.

10) Forty-two and three-fourths hours at $6.50 per hour with overtime after 40 hours.

11) Twelve hours at $11.75 per hour with time and one-half after 8 hours.

12) Sixteen hours at $9.50 per hour with time and one-half after 10 hours.

13) Forty-three hours at $14.00 per hour with time and one-half after 40 hours.

14) Eighteen hours at $6.50 per hour with time and one-half after 16 hours.

15) Forty-three hours at $5.60 per hour with time and one-half after 40 hours.

16) Fifty-two hours at $5.20 per hour with time and one-half after 40 hours.

17) Forty-six hours at $6.12 per hour with time and one-half after 40 hours.

Double Time Earnings To find double time earnings, first multiply the overtime hours by 2.

EXAMPLE Hatsue works 43 hours at a rate of $6.75 per hour for one week. She is paid straight time for 40 hours and double time for the time over 40 hours. What is her gross pay?

Step 1 Separate straight time from double time.

43	Total time
− 40	Agreed straight time
3	Hours at the double time rate

Step 2 Convert 3 hours to double time. To double, multiply by 2.

3	Hours to be converted
× 2	
6	Hours double time

Step 3 Add straight time to double time.

40	Hours straight time
+ 6	Hours double time
46	Total hours

Step 4 Multiply the rate per hour and the total.

$ 6.75	Per hour
× 46	Total hours
$310.50	Gross pay

Hatsue's gross pay is $310.50.

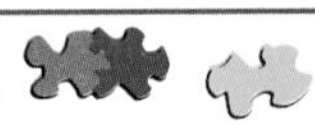

PROBLEM SOLVING

Exercise H Find the gross pay, including double time.

1) Find Luke's pay for 48 hours if he earns $8.20 per hour with double time for any hours over 40.

2) Marconi, a plumber's helper, works 45 hours one week. He earns $6.78 an hour, with five of the 45 hours at double time. Find Marconi's gross pay.

3) Pam earns $2.75 an hour babysitting. If she works 16 hours per week and charges double time for any time over 10 hours, then how much is her gross pay?

4) Thirteen hours at $6.26 per hour with double time over 10 hours.

5) Eighteen hours at $7.30 per hour with double time over 10 hours.

6) Forty-seven hours at $6.10 per hour with double time over 40 hours.

7) Fifty-two hours at $9.00 per hour with double time over 40 hours.

8) Twenty-six hours at $6.95 per hour with double time over 20 hours.

9) Forty-nine hours at $6.75 per hour with double time over 40 hours.

10) Nine and one-half hours at $8.00 per hour with double time over 8 hours.

11) Forty and one-half hours at $10.50 per hour with double time over 40 hours.

12) Ten and one-half hours at $9.00 per hour with double time over 8 hours.

13) Thirteen and one-half hours at $10.25 per hour with double time over 8 hours.

14) Forty-eight hours at $10.75 per hour with double time after 40 hours.

15) Ten hours at $4.67 per hour with double time after 8 hours.

16) Eleven hours at $6.15 per hour with double time after 8 hours.

17) Fifteen hours at $7.20 per hour with double time after 16 hours.

18) Forty-five hours at $6.38 per hour with double time after 40 hours.

Lesson 2 Division of Decimals

When you divide a decimal by a whole number, you divide as though you were dividing whole numbers. After you have found the quotient, you bring the decimal point straight up into the quotient.

EXAMPLE $136.80 ÷ 30 = ■

```
        $4.56
30 ) $136.80
     −120
        1 68
      − 1 50
         180
       − 180
           0
```

If the divisor is a decimal, then follow these steps:

Step 1 Move the decimal point in the divisor to the right of the number.

Step 2 Move the decimal point in the dividend the same number of places to the right.

Step 3 Divide and bring the decimal point up into the quotient.

.0945 ÷ 1.5 =

```
          .063
1.5. ) .0.945
        − 90
          45
        − 45
           0
```

Exercise A Find the quotients.

1) 157.5 ÷ 42

2) 35.28 ÷ 18

3) 11.256 ÷ 2.8

4) 88 ÷ 3.2

5) .08052 ÷ .61

6) .23427 ÷ .57

7) .00558 ÷ .06

8) .00736 ÷ .008

9) 156.4 ÷ 34

10) .01943 ÷ .67

11) 5.848 ÷ 8.5

12) 15.75 ÷ .35

Calculator Practice You can use a calculator to divide decimals by whole numbers.

EXAMPLE 2.75 ÷ 18 = ■

2.75 [÷] 18 [=] .1527777

Calculator Exercise Find the quotients.

1) .0016 ÷ 43

2) 117.3 ÷ 5

3) 88.556 ÷ 19

4) 1,111 ÷ 523

5) 12,039 ÷ 4,000

6) 1.57 ÷ 89

7) 456.98 ÷ 796

8) 24.153 ÷ 55

9) .341 ÷ 7

10) 3.41 ÷ 70

Dividing the Yearly Salary Sometimes the yearly **salary** for a job is mentioned in a want ad or in a job description. To find the weekly salary, divide the yearly salary by the number of weeks worked.

> *Salary*
> *A fixed amount of money paid to a worker regularly.*

EXAMPLE Monica is paid \$12,754 per year working as a word processor. Find Monica's weekly salary if she works 52 weeks per year.

$$\begin{array}{r} \$245.269 \approx \$245.27 \\ 52\overline{)\$12{,}754.000} \\ -10\,4 \\ \hline 2\,35 \\ -2\,08 \\ \hline 274 \\ -260 \\ \hline 14\,0 \\ -10\,4 \\ \hline 3\,60 \\ -3\,12 \\ \hline 480 \\ -468 \\ \hline 12 \end{array}$$

Divide to 3 decimal places and round to the nearest cent. Monica works 52 weeks a year. She is paid \$245.27 per week.

People who work for large finance companies are paid an annual salary.

Exercise B For each yearly salary below, find the amount paid weekly. There are 52 weeks in a year.

1) $12,938

2) $12,850

3) $15,652

4) $20,084

5) $21,372

6) $16,744

7) $14,482

8) $20,920

9) $29,100

10) $14,981

11) $29,777

12) $10,868

13) $15,226

14) $16,412

15) $21,856

16) $12,750

17) $25,655

18) $20,852

19) $31,672

20) $14,312

21) $22,880

22) $13,670

23) $17,151

24) $17,524

25) $14,222

26) $20,000

27) $33,468

28) $15,575

29) $18,710

30) $19,623

31) $13,405

32) $14,260

33) $15,486

34) $16,810

35) $10,676

36) $18,582

Dividing Gross Pay You can find the hourly rate when you know the gross pay. Divide the gross pay by the number of hours worked.

EXAMPLE Vernon's weekly gross pay is \$350. If he works 40 hours, then what is his hourly rate?

$$\begin{array}{r} \$8.75 \\ 40\,\overline{)\,\$350.00} \\ -\,320 \\ \hline 30\,0 \\ -\,28\,0 \\ \hline 2\,00 \\ -\,2\,00 \\ \hline 0 \end{array}$$

Vernon's hourly rate is \$8.75.

Exercise C Find the hourly rates.

	Gross Pay	Hours Worked
1)	\$180.00	30
2)	\$38.40	8
3)	\$39.68	8
4)	\$90.00	15
5)	\$77.00	11
6)	\$131.25	15
7)	\$86.25	15
8)	\$74.16	9
9)	\$108.40	20
10)	\$102.80	16
11)	\$85.68	12
12)	\$93.75	15
13)	\$78.54	14
14)	\$200.00	32
15)	\$45.98	11
16)	\$161.28	24
17)	\$45.60	8
18)	\$152.64	12

	Gross Pay	Hours Worked
19)	\$44.99	11
20)	\$65.44	8
21)	\$77.40	15
22)	\$72.00	12
23)	\$116.80	16
24)	\$79.20	12
25)	\$78.50	10
26)	\$77.00	7
27)	\$67.26	19
28)	\$133.65	22
29)	\$39.60	8
30)	\$81.00	12
31)	\$145.20	20
32)	\$104.00	16
33)	\$174.80	19
34)	\$46.80	6
35)	\$43.20	6
36)	\$95.85	18

Calculator Practice

You can use a calculator to convert a weekly salary to yearly salary.

EXAMPLE $225 weekly for 52 weeks = ■ yearly salary

225 [×] 52 [=] 11700 or $11,700.00 yearly salary

Calculator Exercise Convert each weekly salary to a yearly salary.

1) $255.00

2) $289.50

3) $305.00

4) $270.00

5) $256.79

6) $273.39

7) $250.00

8) $279.00

9) $401.00

10) $258.00

11) $299.96

12) $323.35

Chapter 9 Review

Find the products.

1) $2.78 \times .36$

2) $.076 \times .09$

3) $2.9 \times .19$

Find the gross pay.

4) Thirty-five hours at $9.25 per hour.

5) Six hours at $8.75 per hour.

6) Three hours at $4.15 per hour.

7) Ten and one-fourth hours at $3.75 per hour.

8) Twelve and one-half hours at $5.20 per hour.

9) Eighteen and three-fourths hours at $4.10 per hour.

10) Forty-four hours at $7.10 an hour with time and one-half after 40 hours.

11) Forty-five hours at $7.25 per hour with time and one-half after 40 hours.

12) Eighteen hours at $15.00 per hour with double time after 40 hours.

13) Forty-six hours at $8.90 an hour with double time after 40 hours.

Divide. Round the quotient to the nearest hundredth.

14) $72.96 \div 48$

15) $.1152 \div 6.4$

16) $.00144 \div .08$

Convert each annual salary to a weekly salary.

17) $15,083

18) $21,215.50

Convert each weekly gross pay to an hourly rate.

19) $142.20 for 18 hours

20) $161.85 for 39 hours

Test Taking Tip

When you are asked to compute numbers, always check the problem to find decimal numbers. Then, double-check your placement of the decimal point in your answer.

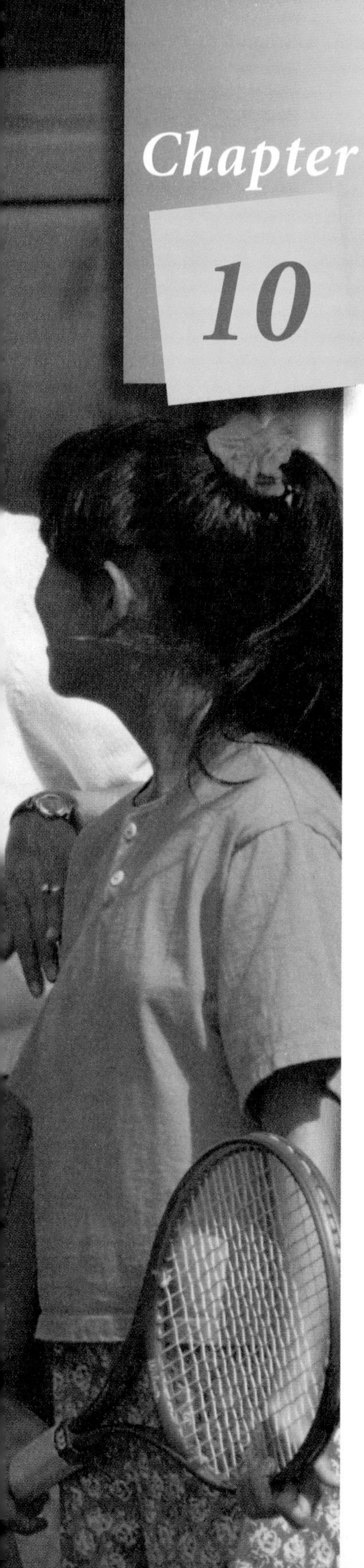

Chapter 10

Traveling

People travel on vacation. Businesspeople travel for work. Students travel to social events and school. There will be times in your life when you will be glad that you know how to use mathematics in your travels. Reading maps, determining mileage, even booking a cruise, all use mathematics in ways you may not have considered until now.

In Chapter 10, you will learn how decimals are used in traveling and discover how mathematics can make decimals work for you.

Goals for Learning

- To compute mileage with the aid of an odometer
- To compute the cost of a rental car
- To use a map to compute mileage
- To multiply with a conversion factor to convert currency

Lesson 1 Odometer Reading

Odometer

An instrument for measuring the distance traveled by a vehicle.

Speedometer

An instrument that measures how fast a car is traveling.

An **odometer** measures how far a car has traveled. It measures this distance in tenths of a mile. The odometer is found on the **speedometer** of the car.

EXAMPLE At the beginning of the trip, the odometer reads:

5 2 8 7 6 3

At the end of the trip, the odometer reads:

5 3 9 1 0 1

Subtract to find how many miles have been driven.

$$\begin{array}{r} 53{,}910.1 \\ -\ 52{,}876.3 \\ \hline 1{,}033.8 \end{array}$$

The total distance traveled is 1,033.8 miles.

Calculator Practice

Use your calculator to help you find the miles traveled. Write your answers on a separate sheet of paper.

	Trip Begins With:	Trip Ends With:	Miles Traveled
1)	72155.7	72389.2	______
2)	69016.1	69143.0	______
3)	28823.8	29002.0	______
4)	31057.8	33850.4	______
5)	89163.1	90014.3	______
6)	30062.5	32145.9	______
7)	29915.1	31304.5	______

People who commute to and from work in large cities add many miles on their odometers every day.

PROBLEM SOLVING

Exercise A Answer these questions about odometer readings.

1) At the beginning of Susan's vacation, she notices that the odometer in her car reads 468925. When she returns the odometer reads 473257. How far has she driven?

2) When Sam leaves home, his odometer reads 067292. It reads 100408 when Sam arrives in Macon, Georgia. How far has he driven?

3) While driving, Kabuo sees a sign that says, "Dallas—189 miles." He glances at his odometer and sees that it reads 388763. What will it read when Kabuo gets to Dallas?

4) Todd is going to the beach for the day. The beach is 48.7 miles away. If the odometer reads 629845 when he leaves, what will it read when Todd arrives at the beach?

5) When Barbara leaves for work in the morning, her odometer reads 379283. It reads 379531 when she arrives. How far has she driven to work?

Lesson 2 Gas Mileage

You can use your odometer to help compute your gas mileage. This is the number of miles that you can expect to travel on one gallon of gas.

EXAMPLE To compute your gas mileage, follow these steps:

Step 1 Fill your gas tank and record the odometer reading.

Step 2 The next time that you buy gas, fill the tank again. Record the number of gallons of gas that you bought and the odometer reading.

Step 3 Subtract the two odometer readings to find the number of miles driven.

Step 4 Divide this answer by the number of gallons of gas that you just bought. Round to the nearest whole number.

$$\begin{array}{rl} 36{,}982.8 & \text{Reading at second filling} \\ -\ 36{,}784.3 & \text{Reading at first filling} \\ \hline 198.5 & \end{array}$$

You buy 7.3 gallons of gas.

$$7.3\,\overline{)\,198.5} = 27.1 \approx 27 \text{ miles to the gallon}$$

Exercise A Compute the gas mileage each driver gets. Write your answers on a separate sheet of paper.

	Reading at First Filling	Gallons of Gas Bought	Reading at Second Filling	Gas Mileage
1)	43872.5	6.2	44075.2	______
2)	39989.6	9.2	40230.3	______
3)	56035.3	10.3	56398.5	______
4)	87392.7	8.4	87631.6	______
5)	21981.3	7.6	22160.1	______
6)	70384.3	9.3	70699.2	______
7)	06721.9	8.9	06997.9	______
8)	13297.2	7.2	13491.6	______
9)	00428.4	8.4	00779.6	______
10)	66879.2	8.1	67041.0	______

The display on a gas pump shows the amount of gas you purchased. You can use this information to calculate your gas mileage.

Lesson 3 Gasoline Expenses

The cost of an automobile trip can be found by multiplying the number of gallons of gasoline used times the cost per gallon. Round the cost to the nearest cent.

EXAMPLE Find the total cost of 12.3 gallons of gasoline used at $1.49 per gallon.

```
      1.4 9  Cost per gallon
×     1 2.3  Number of gallons
      4 4 7
    2 9 8
+ 14 9
$ 18.3 2 7 ≈ $18.33
```

$18.33 is the total cost.

Exercise A Find the total cost of gasoline. Round to the nearest cent.

1) 1.6 gallons at $1.05

2) 25.1 gallons at $1.25

3) 1.1 gallons at $1.24

4) 80 gallons at $1.04

5) 26.7 gallons at $1.35

6) 3.3 gallons at $1.25

7) 18.4 gallons at $1.35

8) 27.5 gallons at $1.28

9) 27.4 gallons at $1.11

10) 52.5 gallons at $1.19

11) 3.5 gallons at $1.32

12) 39 gallons at $1.07

13) 3.2 gallons at $1.28

14) 50 gallons at $1.25

15) 42.9 gallons at $1.35

16) 31.5 gallons at $1.28

17) 43.2 gallons at $1.06

18) 4.6 gallons at $1.26

19) 37.7 gallons at $1.33

20) 42.9 gallons at $1.24

21) 2.9 gallons at $1.16

22) 31.4 gallons at $1.05

23) 17.5 gallons at $1.17

24) 10.8 gallons at $1.28

25) 1.6 gallons at $1.29

26) 12.3 gallons at $1.22

Lesson 4 Car Rental Rates

Some travelers need to rent a car. Rental rates differ for different types of cars.

Type of Car	Per Day	Per Week	Plus per Mile
Subcompact	$13.50	$72.50	14¢
Compact	$18.95	$120.00	16¢
Midsized	$23.95	$151.00	18¢
Large	$35.95	$231.50	20¢
Van	$45.95	$295.00	22¢

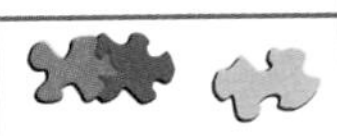

PROBLEM SOLVING

Exercise A Use the chart of car rental rates to help you answer these questions.

1) How much does renting a midsized car for one day cost if you drive it 127 miles?

2) Hilary rents a compact car for one week. She drives it 628 miles. What is the cost?

3) Audrey rents a van for four days. What is the charge if she drives the car 473 miles?

4) How much would Audrey pay if she rents a compact car instead of the van?

5) How much would Audrey save if she rents the compact car instead of the van?

6) What does Bob pay to rent a large car for two weeks if he drives 473 miles?

7) Kim rents a subcompact car for four days. She drives 608 miles. How much does Kim pay?

8) Juan drives the midsized car that he rents 462 miles. How much does Juan pay if he rents the car for three days?

Lesson 5 Using a Map

Using a map to compute distances traveled often requires the use of basic mathematical operations.

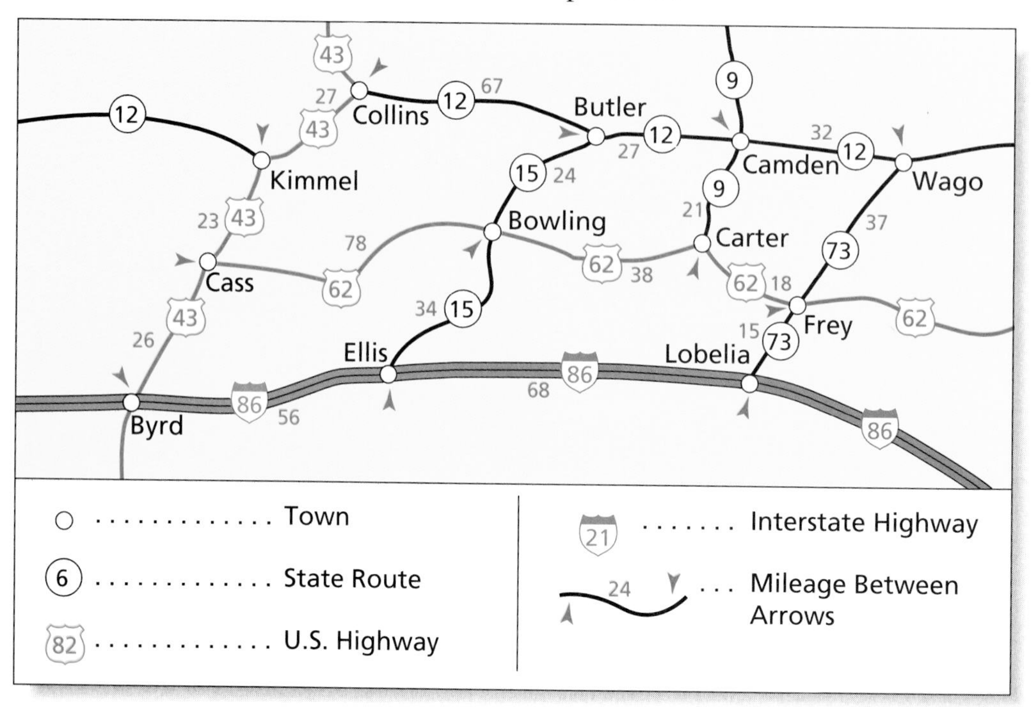

EXAMPLE If you drive from Camden to Bowling on (9) and (62), then you will travel 21 + 38, or 59 miles.

If you average 35 miles per hour, then what will your travel time be?

Divide by 35 and round to the nearest tenth.

$$\begin{array}{r} 1.68 \approx 1.7 \text{ hours} \\ 35\overline{)59.00} \\ -35 \\ \hline 24\,0 \\ -21\,0 \\ \hline 3\,00 \\ -2\,80 \\ \hline 20 \end{array}$$

PROBLEM SOLVING

Exercise A Use the road map to answer the questions. Round any remainders to one decimal place.

1) How far will you drive if you go from Butler to Cass along (15) and (62)?

2) If you average 42 miles per hour, then how long will this trip take?

3) You drive from Lobelia to Bowling along (86) and (15). How far will you travel?

4) If the trip from Lobelia to Bowling takes 2.3 hours, then what is the average rate of speed?

5) What is the distance from Byrd to Frey along (86) and (73)?

6) If you average 52 miles per hour, then how long will it take you to make this trip?

7) How far is it from Camden to Cass along (9) and (62)?

8) How far is it from Camden to Cass along (12) and (43)?

9) If you go from Camden to Cass along (9) and (62), then you can average 37 miles per hour. If you use (12) and (43), then you can average 42 miles per hour. Which route takes less time?

10) How far is it from Kimmel to Lobelia along (43) and (86)?

Lesson 6 Gas Consumption

Gas mileage is found by dividing the distance traveled by the gallons of gas used. If you know the number of miles that you get per gallon of gas, you can predict the amount of gas that you will use to drive a given distance. You divide the distance by the mile per gallon.

EXAMPLE Drove 206 miles and got 32 miles per gallon.

$$\begin{array}{r} 6.43 \\ 32\overline{)206.00} \\ -\underline{192} \\ 14\,0 \\ -\underline{12\,8} \\ 1\,20 \\ -\underline{96} \\ 24 \end{array} \approx 6.4 \text{ gallons of gas}$$

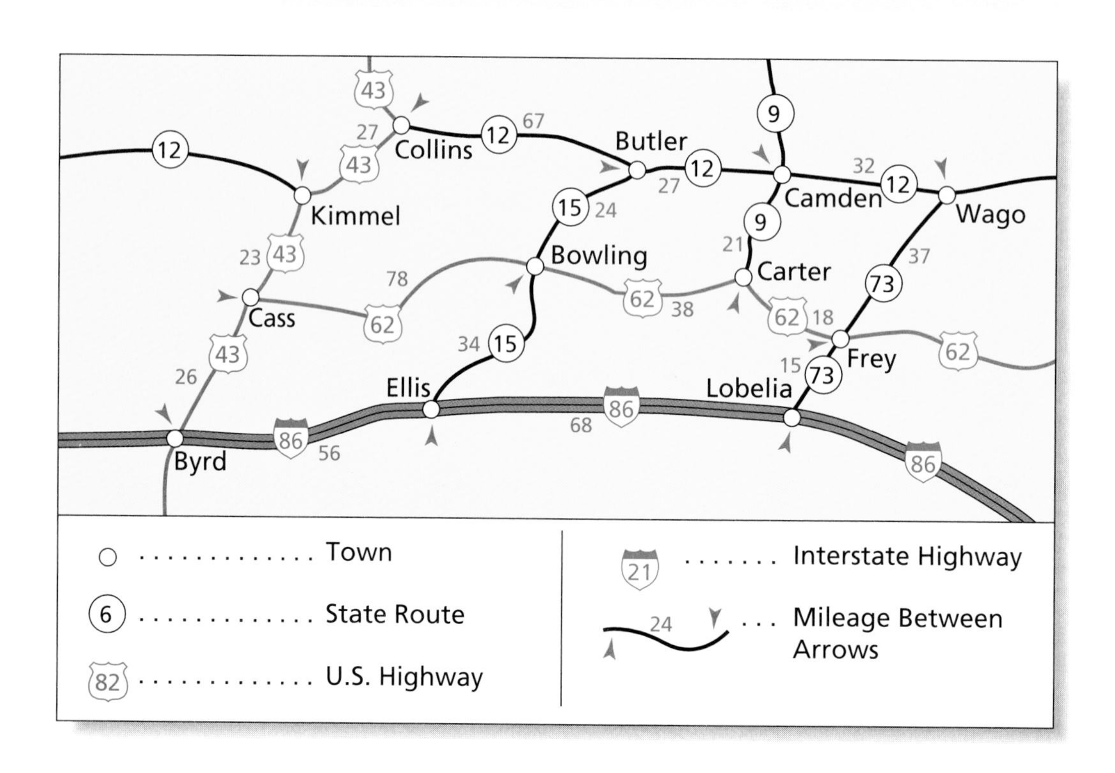

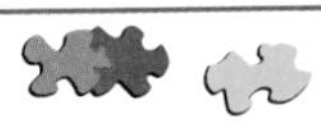

PROBLEM SOLVING

Exercise A Use the map to help you answer these questions about gasoline consumption. Round any remainders to one decimal place.

1) You use 3.2 gallons of gas to go from Collins to Carter along (12) and (9). What is your gas mileage?

2) You drive from Ellis to Wago along (86) and (73). If your car gets 31 miles to the gallon of gas, how many gallons do you use?

3) You drive from Cass to Lobelia and use 5.2 gallons of gas. What is your mileage? You drive along (62) and (73).

4) You use 3.9 gallons of gas to drive from Carter to Byrd along (62), (15), and (86). What is your mileage?

5) How many gallons of gas will you use to drive from Bowling to Collins along (15) and (12) if your car gets 34 miles per gallon?

6) You drive from Frey to Cass along (62). How many gallons of gas do you use if your car gets 28 miles per gallon?

7) You use 3.5 gallons of gas to drive from Camden to Ellis along (9), (62), and (15). What is your gas mileage?

8) Your car gets 36 miles per gallon. How many gallons of gas will you use to drive from Collins to Frey along (12), (15), and (62)?

Lesson 7 Hotel Rates

Hotel rates are given as the cost for each person.

Hotel Length of Stay	Room Type	Single	Extra Night	Double Cost for Each	Extra Night
Seaside Inn					
3 Nights	Standard	113.25	36.25	65.25	20.25
	Deluxe	137.25	44.25	77.25	24.25
7 Nights	Standard	257.25	36.25	145.25	20.25
	Deluxe	313.25	44.25	173.25	24.25
Bay Hotel					
3 Nights	Superior	80.30	25.30	51.80	15.80
7 Nights	Superior	180.30	25.30	113.80	15.80
Forest Lodge					
3 Nights	Standard	131.35	42.35	71.35	22.35
7 Nights	Standard	299.35	42.35	159.35	22.35

EXAMPLES

Mr. and Mrs. Mendez are spending three nights at the Seaside Inn in a deluxe double room.

The cost is 2 × \$77.25, or \$154.50.

Carl spends Friday, Saturday, Sunday, and Monday night in a superior single room at the Bay Hotel.

The cost is \$80.30 + \$25.30 = \$105.60.

Wong spends 7 nights in a standard single room at the Seaside Inn. Rachelle and Gary spend 8 nights at the Forest Lodge in a standard double room.

The cost is \$257.25 + (2 × \$159.35) + (2 × \$22.35) = \$620.65.

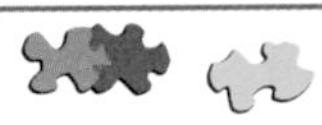

PROBLEM SOLVING

Exercise A Use the rate chart to answer these questions.

1) How much will Elise pay to spend seven nights at the Forest Lodge in a single room?

2) Yuneng and Miranda are going to spend seven nights in a standard room at the Seaside Inn. What will they pay if they share a double room?

3) How much will four nights cost in a single room at the Bay Hotel?

4) How much will Pat and Lee pay to stay for eight nights at the Bay Hotel?

5) A travel agent arranges for a group of 38 people to stay for three nights. They are all staying in double rooms. Twelve people are staying at the Seaside Inn in deluxe rooms; 16 at the Forest Lodge; and 10 at the Bay Hotel. What is the total bill?

Often the difference between a standard and a deluxe room at a seaside resort is a view of the ocean from your window.

Lesson 8 Currency Conversion

Currency

Money.

Conversion factor

A number you multiply a measurement by to obtain an equivalent measurement.

If you are traveling outside of our country, you will need to change from United States **currency** to another country's currency. To do this, multiply by the **conversion factor**. To change from another country's currency to United States currency, divide by the conversion factor.

EXAMPLE Change 40 U.S. dollars to Barbados currency.

$$\begin{array}{r} 1.96 \\ \times\ 40 \\ \hline 78.40 \end{array}$$

40 United States dollars equal 78.40 Barbados dollars.

Change 46 Barbados dollars to U.S. currency.

$$23.469 \approx 23.47$$

$$1.96.\overline{)46.00.000}$$

$$\begin{array}{r} -\ 39\ 2 \\ \hline 6\ 80 \\ -\ 5\ 88 \\ \hline 92\ 0 \\ -\ 78\ 4 \\ \hline 13\ 60 \\ -\ 11\ 76 \\ \hline 1\ 840 \\ -\ 1\ 764 \\ \hline 76 \end{array}$$

46 Barbados dollars equal $23.47 in United States currency.

Country	Currency	Conversion Factor 1 U.S. Dollar =
Barbados	Barbados dollar = 100 cents	1.96 BDD
Bermuda	Bermudan dollar = 100 cents	1.00 BED
Cayman Islands	Cayman Is. dollar = 100 cents	.85 CID
Haiti	Gourde = 100 centimes	5.00 GOU
Jamaica	Jamaican dollar = 100 cents	32.15 JAD
Trinidad	Trinidad dollar = 100 cents	4.72 TTD
West Indies	East Carib dollar = 100 cents	1.85 ECD

PROBLEM SOLVING

Exercise A Use the conversion chart to help you make these currency conversions. Round any remainders to two decimal places.

1) Change 43 United States dollars to Haitian currency.

2) Change 36 Cayman Islands dollars to United States currency.

3) Change 30 East Carib dollars to United States currency.

4) Change 85 United States dollars to Trinidad dollars.

5) Change 78 Jamaican dollars to United States currency.

6) Change 75 gourdes to United States currency.

7) Change $46.76 in Bermudan currency to United States currency.

8) Change $8.52 in Cayman Islands currency to United States currency.

9) Change $35.48 in United States currency to Barbados currency.

10) Change 14 gourdes and 75 centimes to United States currency.

11) Change $42.56 in United States currency to West Indies currency.

Jamaica's dollars are more colorful than U.S. dollars.

Lesson 9 Cruise Rates

You can purchase a package tour from a travel agent. This offers the air flight and the sea cruise for one basic price. The price that you pay depends on the city from which you fly and the deck your ship's room is on.

Decks	Cruise Only Rates per Person	Flight/Cruise Package Rates			
		New York	Washington	Detroit	St. Louis
Erato	975.59	1,160.02	1,170.48	1,210.62	1,240.32
Clio	1,005.48	1,189.91	1,200.37	1,240.51	1,270.21
Polymnia	1,160.56	1,344.99	1,355.45	1,395.59	1,425.29
Thalia	1,390.73	1,575.16	1,585.62	1,625.76	1,655.46
Child Under 12	250.45	434.88	445.34	485.48	515.18

Single Occupant Pays 1.5 Times the Cruise-Only Rate.
All rates are for one person and are for double occupancy.

Cruise ships sail to exotic locations throughout the world.

EXAMPLE If two people fly from Detroit and stay on the Clio deck, then they will pay 2 × $1,240.51, or $2,481.02.

PROBLEM SOLVING

Exercise A Use the chart to help you find the total cost.

1) Carlos and Juditha have a room on the Thalia deck. What is the cost of their trip if they fly from New York?

2) Christie and Alphonse are taking their eight-year-old grandson on a cruise. They are leaving from St. Louis and staying on the Erato deck. What is the total cost of their trip?

3) The plane fare is the difference between the cruise-only rate and the flight/cruise rate. What is the plane fare from Washington?

4) What is the plane fare from New York?

5) Greg wants to fly from Detroit and stay in a room by himself on the Polymnia deck. How much will this trip cost? Remember to include his plane fare.

6) Fred and Dottie are flying from Washington. How much will their trip cost if they stay on the Erato deck?

7) Beth and Hank are taking two-year-old Sally along. They are staying on the Thalia deck. What will it cost them if they leave from St. Louis?

8) Julio and Delores fly from New York and stay on the Clio deck. How much does their trip cost?

9) Inez and Irv are staying on the Erato deck. How much is their trip if they leave from Detroit?

10) Jim and Janice are traveling with Mary and Eli. They leave from St. Louis and stay on the Clio deck. What is the total cost of the four travelers' trip?

Chapter 10 Review

Find the answers.

1) 48.6 − 5.324

2) 4.023 × 0.93

3) 9.048 ÷ 2.6

4) 36.83 + 9.284 + 52

Answer these word problems.

5) Tom drives to the beach for the day. When he leaves the house, his odometer reads 0168325. When he arrives at the beach, it reads 0169094. How far is it to the beach?

6) While driving, Mike sees a sign that reads "Portland–187 miles." Mike looks at his odometer and sees that it reads 0370425. What does Mike's odometer read when he gets to Portland?

7) Find the total cost of 12.2 gallons of gasoline at $1.50 per gallon.

8) Will rents a midsized car for 4 days. He pays $16.95 per day plus 18¢ per mile. How much does Will pay if he drives the car 482 miles?

9) One U.S. dollar equals .85 Cayman Islands dollars. What is 40 U.S. dollars in Cayman Islands currency?

10) One U.S. dollar equals 32.15 Jamaican dollars. What is 62 Jamaican dollars in U.S. currency? Round to two decimal places.

11) How much will 11.5 gallons of gasoline cost at $1.75 per gallon?

12) Bob rents a compact car for $13.95 per day plus 16¢ per mile. Bob drove 382 miles in two days. How much does he pay?

Find the gas mileage.

	Reading at First Filling	Gallons of Gas Bought	Reading at Second Filling	Gas Mileage
13)	48537.2	9.3	48835.8	______
14)	10736.5	5.8	10872.8	______

Use this road map to help you answer the questions.

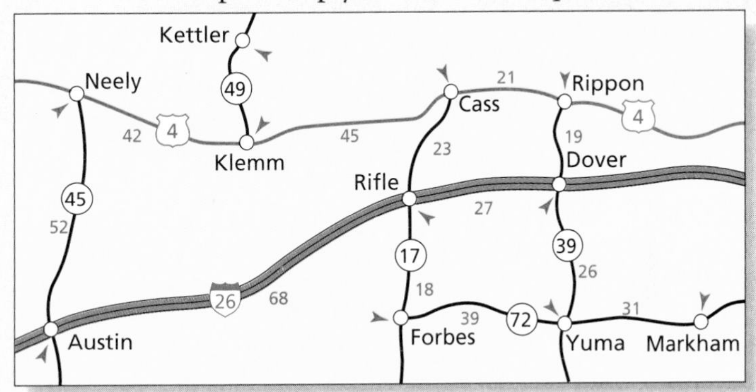

15) How far will you drive if you go from Dover to Klemm along (39) and [4]?

16) This trip takes 1.7 hours. What is your average rate of speed?

17) You drive from Austin to Cass along (45) and [4]. How far do you drive?

18) You use 5.2 gallons of gas to make this trip. What is your gas mileage rounded to one decimal place?

19) You drive from Yuma to Cass along (72) and (17). How far do you drive?

20) How much shorter would the trip be if you drive along (39) and [4]?

Test Taking Tip

When you read a mathematics problem, decide whether multiple steps are required to solve the problem.

Great Cities
Information

Chapter 11 Watching the Clock

Here's a riddle for you to solve—What has hands but cannot wave? If you guess a clock, you're right! Clocks come in many styles. Some have hands, some are digital, and others have Roman numerals. Some clocks even have no numbers at all. Knowing how to tell time and compute with hours and minutes helps us at work, at home, and in school. When we understand time, we can make better decisions and choices in scheduling our activities.

In Chapter 11, you will explore time, using clocks with faces and digital clocks. You will also discover ways to use time to help you predict arrivals and calculate parking fees.

Goals for Learning

- To tell time, using analog and digital clocks
- To find elapsed time
- To use time skills to interpret television programming schedules
- To compute fees for parking meters
- To use a schedule of times to calculate elapsed time

Lesson 1 Elapsed Time

Elapsed time

The difference between the starting time and the ending time.

Elapsed time is the amount of time that has passed from one time to another. Find the amount of elapsed time by subtracting the earlier time from the later time. The later time is written on the top of a subtraction problem. If you must rename, then remember that one hour is the same as sixty minutes.

Elapse

To slip by.

EXAMPLES How much time has **elapsed** from the time shown on Clock A to the time shown on Clock B?

1) Clock A

Clock B shows 7:52
Clock A shows 3:28

$$\begin{array}{r} 7:52 \\ -3:28 \\ \hline 4:24 \end{array}$$

Clock B

Four hours and twenty-four minutes have elapsed.

2) Clock A

Clock B shows 7:21
Clock A shows 2:42

7:21 ← Rename 1 hour to 60 minutes → 6:81

$$\begin{array}{r} 7:21 \\ -2:42 \\ \hline \end{array} \qquad \begin{array}{r} 6:81 \\ -2:42 \\ \hline 4:39 \end{array}$$

Clock B

Four hours and thirty-nine minutes have elapsed.

3) Clock A

Clock B shows 4:33
Clock A shows 11:26

4:33 ← Add 12 hours → 16:33

$$\begin{array}{r} 4:33 \\ -11:26 \\ \hline \end{array} \qquad \begin{array}{r} 16:33 \\ -11:26 \\ \hline 5:07 \end{array}$$

Clock B

Five hours and seven minutes have elapsed.

Exercise A Subtract to find how much time has elapsed from the time shown on Clock A to the time shown on Clock B.

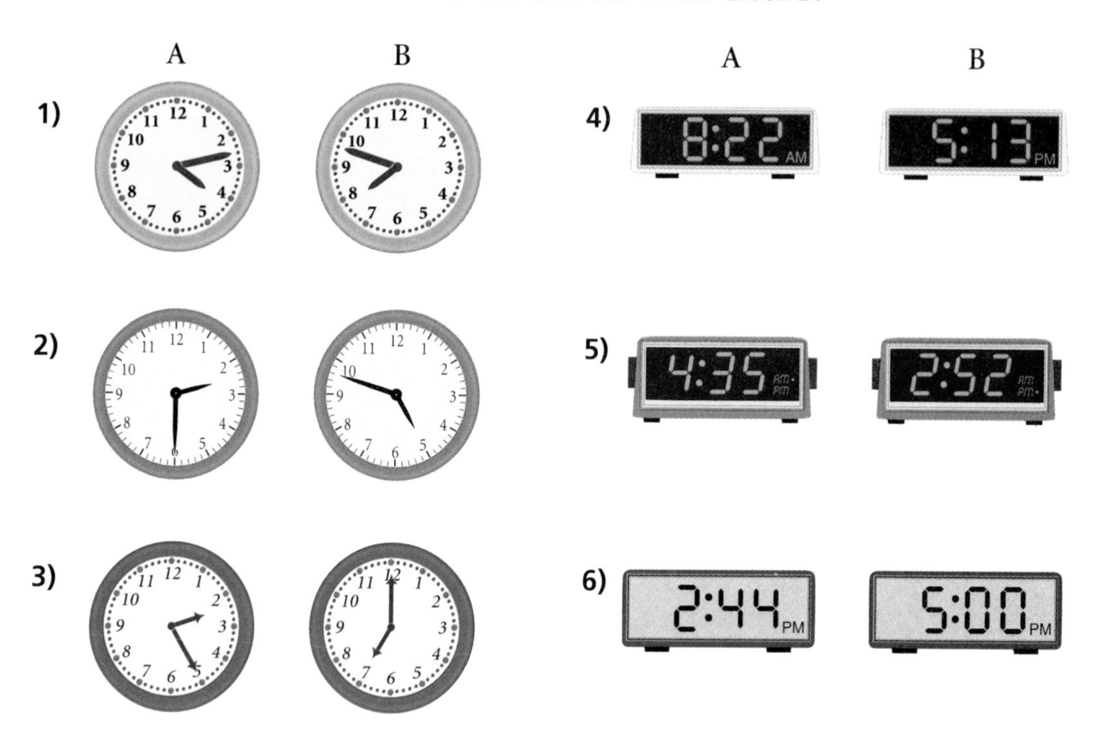

Exercise B Subtract to find the amount of time that has elapsed.

1) From 3:46 to 7:58

2) From 3:45 to 7:26

3) From 5:18 to 7:25

4) From 6:21 to 11:54

5) From 3:59 to 4:16

6) From 3:37 to 10:21

7) From 1:45 to 11:26

8) From 11:26 to 1:45

9) From 3:16 to 8:42

10) From 3:46 to 1:18

11) From 12:15 to 2:30

12) From 5:36 to 12:52

13) From 6:27 to 3:49

14) From 4:17 to 7:30

15) From 6:30 to 10:42

16) From 4:56 to 1:23

17) From 5:45 to 9:51

18) From 1:21 to 8:25

19) From 3:56 to 11:21

20) From 2:48 to 1:00

PROBLEM SOLVING

Exercise C Solve these word problems. Use the clock next to each problem to help you.

1) Jeff waits for a bus that is scheduled to arrive at 11:45. How long will Jeff wait?

2) Carlo's favorite TV program, *Albuquerque,* comes on at 9:00 P.M. How long must Carlo wait for his show?

3) Ginny went to sleep at 10:42 at night. When she wakes this morning, she looks at the clock by her bed. How long has she slept?

4) Barry arrives at the dentist's office at 12:15 P.M. for his appointment. He looks at his watch when his name is called. How long has Barry been waiting?

5) Maria leaves the house at 9:23 and drives to Dewey Beach. She arrives at the beach and looks at her dashboard clock. How long has Maria been driving?

6) The umpire stops the game because of rain at 7:23. When play is resumed, Georgia looks at her watch. How long has the game been delayed?

In some situations, you know the time now and you know how many hours and minutes until a future event begins. You may want to know what time it will be at the time of the event. To do a problem like this, you would add the hours and minutes to the current time.

EXAMPLE Tell what time it will be when the given amount of time elapses from the time shown on the clock.

1)

$$\begin{array}{r} 5{:}14 \\ +3{:}28 \\ \hline 8{:}42 \end{array}$$

3 hours, 28 min.
The new time
will be 8:42.

2)

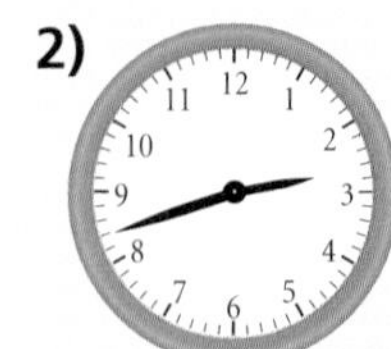

$$\begin{array}{r} 2{:}42 \\ +2{:}35 \\ \hline 4{:}77 \end{array}$$

or 5:17

2 hours, 35 min. (60 of the
minutes make 1 hour.)
The new time will be 5:17.

3)

$$\begin{array}{r} 11{:}22 \\ +3{:}18 \\ \hline 14{:}40 \end{array}$$

or 2:40

3 hours, 18 min.
The new time
will be 2:40.

Exercise D

Add to find the time after the given amount of time has elapsed.

1)

3 hours, 18 min.

2)

1 hour, 13 min.

3)

5 hours, 38 min.

4)

2 hours, 19 min.

5)

1 hour, 35 min.

6)

3 hours, 29 min.

7)

4 hours, 18 min.

8)

1 hour, 12 min.

9)

3 hours, 19 min.

10)

6 hours, 9 min.

11)

5 hours, 43 min.

12)

2 hours, 18 min.

Lesson 2 Television Schedules

To use a TV schedule, it is helpful if you are able to calculate time.

Morning

Time	Channel	Program
5:20	4	Exercises
5:35	4	Aerobics
5:50	45	News
5:55	20	Bob's Place
6:00	2	News
	7	ABC News
	8	Early Today
	13	Morning Stretch
	20	Pat's Recipe
	45	Stock Quotes
6:05	4	Bob Turk
6:15	7	News
6:30	2 4	Early Today
6:30	7 47	ABC News
	8	Country Music Videos
	9	Kids' Corner
	11	Learning to Do
	13	News
	45	Pat's Recipe
6:45	7	News
	22 67	A.M. Weather
7:00	2 4 8	Today
	5	Stock Quotes
	7 13 47	Morning News
	9 20	Bugs Bunny and Friends
	11 16	Morning America
7:00	22 67	Three Stooges
	45	American Story
7:30	5	Little Rascals
	20	Sesame Street
	22 67	Great Space Coaster
	45	Woody Woodpecker
8:00	5	The Flintstones
	20	Porky Pig
	45	Mighty Mouse
8:30	20	Great Space Coaster
	22 67	Mister Rogers
	26	Casper
	45	MacNeil-Lehrer Hour

PROBLEM SOLVING

Exercise A Answer the questions about this TV program schedule.

1) At what time does *American Story* come on?

2) On what channel can you watch *Country Music Videos?*

3) How long is *Exercises?*

4) How long does the 6:45 news last?

5) What time does *Bugs Bunny and Friends* come on? What stations carry this program?

6) How long is *Bob Turk* on?

7) What times does *Stock Quotes* come on?

8) How long does *Bob's Place* last?

9) Sharina turns on her TV at 6:43. How much of *Learning to Do* has she missed?

10) At what times does channel 7 broadcast news come on?

11) Willie wakes up at 8:17. How many more minutes is the *Mighty Mouse* show on?

12) Jim turns on the TV at 6:42. How long does he wait for the *Casper* show to come on?

Lesson 3 Parking Meters

Metered parking space

A space where you must put money in a parking meter.

When you park your car, you may use a **metered parking space**. You will look at your watch, decide how long you need to run your errands, and then decide what time you must return to avoid getting a parking ticket. Once you know how much time you will be away from your car, you can put the required amount of money into the meter.

PARKING RATES

$1\frac{1}{2}$ Hour for 25¢

$\frac{1}{2}$ Hour for 10¢

$\frac{1}{4}$ Hour for 5¢

EXAMPLE Yun Lee put 35¢ in the parking meter at 2:43. By what time must he return?

35¢ for $1\frac{1}{2} + \frac{1}{2}$ hour = 2 hours

$$\begin{array}{r} 2:43 \\ +2:00 \\ \hline 4:43 \end{array}$$

Yun must return by 4:43.

PROBLEM SOLVING

Exercise A Answer these questions about parking meters. Use the parking rates above. Use the most quarters that you can when solving each problem.

1) Lynn puts 40¢ in the meter at 2:32. By what time must she return?

2) At 3:52 George puts 15¢ in the meter. By what time must he return?

3) Donna puts 45¢ in the meter at 11:42. By when must she return?

4) Ellie puts 15¢ in the meter at 1:17. When must she return to her car?

5) Sam puts 30¢ in the meter at 12:23. By what time must he return?

6) Anne parks her car at 10:48. She puts 50¢ in the meter. By what time must Anne return to avoid being ticketed?

7) Maggie needs twenty minutes to complete her errands. How much money should she put in the meter?

Lesson 4 Bus Schedules

Bus schedules indicate the leaving and arriving times for commercial buses. A better understanding of how these schedules work requires an understanding of elapsed time. Elapsed time is the amount of time it takes to complete a trip.

BUFFALO - ELMIRA - WILLIAMSPORT - SUNBURY

HARRISBURG - BALTIMORE - WASHINGTON

DOWN		7144	UP	
	EW 195		WE 196	
11:15	----	Lv *BUFFALO, N.Y.* .... **GL** .. Ar	----	8:35
11:35	----	Lv *Buffalo Int'l Airport* .... Ar	----	8:15
f	----	Lv *Clarence* .... Ar	----	f
12:35	----	Lv *Batavia* .... Ar	----	7:20
f	----	Lv *Pavilion* .... Ar	----	f
1:15	----	Lv *Mt. Morris* .... Ar	----	6:40
1:35	----	Lv *Dansville* ..... *(257)* .... Ar	----	6:20
2:05	----	Lv *Hornell* .... Ar	----	5:50
2:45	----	Lv *Bath* .... Ar	----	5:10
f	----	Lv *Painted Post* .... Ar	----	f
3:15	----	Ar *Corning* Lv	----	4:40
3:30	----	Lv *Corning* .... Ar	----	4:25
3:55	----	Ar *ELMIRA, N.Y.* .... **GL** .. Lv	----	4:00
	2:25	Lv *Binghamton, N.Y.* ...... **CPB** . Ar	5:05	
	3:55	Ar *Elmira, N.Y.* ...*(7143)*........ Lv	3:30	
	4:30	Lv ▲**ELMIRA, N.Y.** .... **CPB** . Ar	3:30	
----	f	Millerton, Pa.	f	----
----	hs	Tioga	hs	----
----	5:25	**Mansfield, Pa.**	2:30	----
----	f	Covington	f	----
----	5:35	▲Blossburg	2:15	----
----	f	Liberty	f	----
	f	Trout Run	f	
	6:40	Ar▲**Williamsport, Pa.** ...... **CPB** .. Lv	1:20	
9:00		Lv *Williamsport, Pa.* .... **TWI** . Ar		1:20
9:35		Ar *Lock Haven, Pa.* .*(7866)*........ Lv		12:35
10:25		Ar *State College, Pa.* Lv		11:35
----	6:55	Lv ▲**Williamsport, Pa.** ...... **CPB** . Ar	12:55	----
----	f	Allenwood	f	----
----	7:35	▲**Lewisburg**	12:15	----
----	7:55	Ar▲**SUNBURY, PA.** .... **CPB** .. Lv	11:55	----
----	8:00	Lv *SUNBURY, PA.* .... **GL** .. Ar	11:50	----
----	9:20	Ar *Harrisburg, Pa.* Lv	10:30	----
----	10:15	Ar *York, Pa.* ..... *(265)* Lv	9:10	----
----	11:25	Ar *Baltimore, Md.* Lv	8:00	----
----	12:20	Ar *WASHINGTON, D.C.* ..... **GL** .. Lv	6:50	----

Bus schedules are really two schedules in one. The first is on the left, reading down. Bus 195 leaves Elmira at 4:30 and arrives in Williamsport at 6:40.

The second schedule is on the right, reading up. Bus 196 leaves Williamsport at 1:20 and arrives in Elmira at 3:30.

Here are some symbols that are used on this bus schedule:

Lv	=	leaves
Ar	=	arrives
f	=	flag stop
hs	=	highway stop

EXAMPLE How long does the bus ride take from Mansfield, PA, to Lewisburg, PA? Mansfield is above Lewisburg, so use the left schedule reading down.

$$\begin{array}{r} 7:35 \\ -5:25 \\ \hline 2:10 \end{array}$$

The bus ride takes 2 hours and 10 minutes.

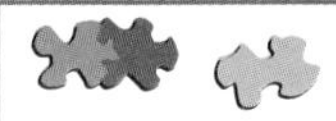

PROBLEM SOLVING

Exercise A Answer these questions. Use the bus schedule to help you.

1) It is now 12:45. How long will it be before the bus for Elmira leaves Dansville, NY?

2) It is now 5:23. How long will it be before the bus for Buffalo leaves Washington, D.C.?

3) John is riding the bus from Trout Run, PA, to Batavia, NY. How long will the bus ride last?

4) Frank lives in Lewisburg. Frank needs 20 minutes to walk to the bus station. What time must he leave his house if he is to catch the bus to York?

5) How long is the bus ride from:

a) Bath to Blossburg?

b) York to Elmira?

c) Corning to Batavia?

d) Hornell to Williamsport?

e) Elmira to Mt. Morris?

f) Baltimore to Mansfield?

Lesson 5 Parking Lot Rates

Many airports have different parking lots. The lot you park in determines how much you pay.

AIRPORT PARKING RATES

Short-Term Lot

Up to 1/2 hour	$1.50
31 min. to 1 hr. and 5 min.	$2.00
1 hr. and 6 min. to 1 1/2 hours	$2.50
1 1/2 hours to 2 hours	$3.00
2 hours to 3 hours	$4.00
3 hours to 4 hours	$5.00
4 hours to 5 hours	$6.00
5 hours to 24 hours	$10.00

General Lot

Up to 1 hour	$1.00
1 hour to 3 hours	$2.00
3 hours to 8 hours	$3.50
8 hours to 24 hours	$7.50

Valet Lot

1 day	$10.00
2 days	$15.00
3 days	$18.00
Each additional day	$5.00

EXAMPLE Gwen parks her car at 2:47 P.M. She is meeting some friends at the airport. She leaves the lot at 4:26 P.M. How much does Gwen pay for parking?

$$\begin{array}{r} 4{:}26 \\ -2{:}47 \\ \hline 1{:}39 \end{array} = 1 \text{ hour } 39 \text{ minutes}$$

The price Gwen pays for parking:

. . . if she is on the short-term lot............$3.00

. . . if she is on the general lot.................$2.00

. . . if she is on the valet lot $10.00

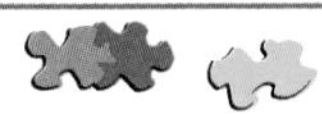

PROBLEM SOLVING

Exercise A Answer these questions about parking at the airport. Use the rates to help you.

1) Greg parks in the general lot from 12:48 P.M. to 1:19 P.M. How much does he pay?

2) Diane is making a short business trip. She parks her car at 7:23. She plans to return at 4:50. Which lot should she use to pay the least amount of parking fees?

3) How much will Diane pay?

4) Cindy and Jerry are going to Seattle for 6 days. How much will they pay for parking in the valet lot while they are gone?

5) How much would you pay for parking:

   a) from 8:52 P.M. to 10:03 P.M. on the short-term lot?

   b) from 12:34 P.M. to 1:17 P.M. on the general lot?

   c) from 9:23 A.M. to 12:31 P.M. on the general lot?

Calculator Practice

Calculator Exercise Convert the following units of time. Use your calculator and the time chart.

1) 5 years = _____ days

2) 13 days = ___ hours

3) 6 hours = ___ minutes

4) 23 hours = _____ minutes

5) 42 days = _____ hours

6) 17 minutes = _____ seconds

Time Chart

1 year	=	365 days
1 day	=	24 hours
1 hour	=	60 minutes
1 minute	=	60 seconds

Chapter 11 Review

Answer these questions.

1) What time is on this clock?

2) How much time has elapsed from Clock A to Clock B?

3) The baseball game begins at 12:15 P.M. It is now 12:08 P.M. How long will it be until the game starts?

4) How much time elapses from 11:23 A.M. to 2:45 P.M.?

5) What will the time be when it is 3 hours and 25 minutes later than the time shown on this clock?

6) The sign on the parking meter says, "Half-hour for 10¢." You put 30¢ in the meter at 11:42 A.M. By what time must you return?

7) How long is Channel 45's news program?

Time	Channel	Program
5:20	4	Exercises
5:35	4	Aerobics
5:50	45	News
5:55	20	Bob's Place
6:00	2	News
	5	Panorama
	7	ABC News
	8	Early Today
	13	Morning Stretch
	45	Stock Quotes

8) Oswald's Parking Lot charges $1.25 for the first hour and 50¢ for each half-hour after that. How much will you pay at Oswald's from 7:52 A.M. to 12:15 P.M.?

9) How long is the bus ride from Sunbury, PA, to Washington, D.C.?

10) How long is the bus ride from Corning, NY, to Batavia, NY?

Test Taking Tip Decide which questions you will do first and last. Limit your time on each question accordingly.

Chapter 12

Baseball Statistics

Besides being called America's favorite game, baseball has been described as an ocean of statistics. Pitchers talk about their ERAs, managers argue about batting averages, and teams boast their standings in a league. Player statistics can be found on baseball cards and in newspapers. The numbers you find there have a mathematical meaning that helps you tell how well players are doing. Baseball statistics are a fun way to become familiar with the branch of mathematics called data and statistics.

In Chapter 12, you will use real data to find the statistics of baseball players that may be found on your hometown team.

Goals for Learning

- To rename fractions as decimals and percents
- To determine slugging percentages and baserunning averages
- To find a player's fielding percentage
- To compute the ERA of a pitcher
- To find and use the won-lost percentage to determine league standings

Lesson 1 Batting Averages

Batting average
A ratio of hits to at bats.

Statistics
Facts collected and arranged so as to show certain information.

Sacrifice outs
Outs made to advance base runners.

A baseball player's **batting average** is a **statistic** that measures how well the player hits. The higher the batting average, the better the player hits. A batting average is written as a decimal rounded to three places. A player's batting average is found by dividing the number of hits by the number of times at bat the player has had. Walks and **sacrifice outs** do not count as official times at bat.

EXAMPLE If a player has 24 hits for 62 at bats, then what is the batting average?

$$\text{Batting average} = \frac{\text{Number of hits}}{\text{Number of times at bat}} = \frac{24}{62}$$

$$\begin{array}{r} .3870 \approx .387 \\ 62\,\overline{)\,24.0000} \\ -\,18\,6 \\ \hline 5\,40 \\ -\,4\,96 \\ \hline 440 \\ -\,434 \\ \hline 60 \end{array}$$

Exercise A Find the batting average for each player.

1) Ymato Ma
45 at bats
18 hits

2) Gail Wills
32 at bats
12 hits

3) Mike Speer
90 at bats
26 hits

4) Sol Lausch
51 at bats
15 hits

5) Gil French
43 at bats
25 hits

6) Walt Jones
73 at bats
37 hits

7) Gwen Smith
28 at bats
9 hits

8) Ben Cardin
63 at bats
35 hits

9) Vic Salski
29 at bats
15 hits

10) Jake Shane
51 at bats
20 hits

11) Tom Foster
28 at bats
10 hits

12) Robin Jay
22 at bats
6 hits

Lesson 2 Slugging Percentages

Slugging percentage

Ratio of total bases to at bats.

Two baseball players may have the same batting average, but the first player may hit the ball farther, resulting in getting to more bases—either a double, triple, or home run. The player who hits the ball a shorter distance may only make it to first base—a single. A baseball statistic that fans use to measure how well a player bats is the **slugging percentage**, given as a decimal rounded to three places.

EXAMPLE What is this player's slugging percentage? Remember, walks and sacrifice outs do not count when finding a player's official at bats.

$$\text{Slugging Percentage} = \frac{\text{Total Bases}}{\text{Official at Bats}}$$

Home runs count as four bases, triples count as three bases, as so on.

3 home runs	→	12	→	3
2 triples	→	6	→	2
10 doubles	→	20	→	10
15 singles	→	+ 15	→	15
9 walks		53 Bases		+ 32
32 outs				62 At Bats
7 sacrifices				

```
      .8548 ≈ .855
62 ) 53.0000
   − 49 6
      3 40
    − 3 10
       300
     − 248
       520
     − 496
        24
```

Exercise A Find each player's slugging percentage. Remember that walks and sacrifice outs do not count as official at bats.

1) Bill Light
1 home run
4 triples
6 doubles
16 singles
5 walks
21 outs
7 sacrifices

2) Skip Carr
4 home runs
12 triples
6 doubles
11 singles
8 walks
12 outs
15 sacrifices

3) George Gill
0 home runs
1 triple
4 doubles
15 singles
3 walks
21 outs
3 sacrifices

4) Riva Lewis
5 home runs
1 triple
11 doubles
21 singles
4 walks
20 outs
9 sacrifices

5) Iona Williams
2 home runs
6 triples
5 doubles
13 singles
18 walks
32 outs
6 sacrifices

6) Joe Leake
3 home runs
0 triples
2 doubles
8 singles
10 walks
18 outs
8 sacrifices

Baseball players work hard to improve their slugging percentages.

Lesson 3 Fractions as Percents

A fraction may be written as a percent by following these steps:

Step 1 Divide the denominator into the numerator.

Step 2 Divide to four decimal places.

Step 3 Round to three decimal places.

Step 4 Multiply your rounded quotient by 100.

One way to perform the last step is to move the decimal point two places to the right.

EXAMPLES Rewrite $\frac{8}{11}$ as a decimal. Then, convert the decimal to a percent.

$$11\overline{)8.0000} = .7272 \approx .727 = 72.7\%$$

$$\begin{array}{r} 8.0000 \\ -7\,7 \\ \hline 30 \\ -22 \\ \hline 80 \\ -77 \\ \hline 30 \end{array}$$

Rewrite $\frac{7}{8}$ as a decimal. Then, convert the decimal to a percent.

$$8\overline{)7.000} = .875 = 87.5\%$$

$$\begin{array}{r} 7.000 \\ -6\,4 \\ \hline 60 \\ -56 \\ \hline 40 \\ -40 \\ \hline 0 \end{array}$$

Some quotients will not go to four decimal places.

Exercise A Rewrite these fractions as percents. If the division does not divide evenly, then round to three decimal places.

1) $\frac{4}{7}$

2) $\frac{7}{12}$

3) $\frac{3}{8}$

4) $\frac{8}{9}$

5) $\frac{4}{11}$

6) $\frac{3}{4}$

7) $\frac{5}{6}$

8) $\frac{2}{3}$

9) $\frac{4}{5}$

10) $\frac{5}{7}$

11) $\frac{6}{13}$

12) $\frac{1}{8}$

13) $\frac{7}{15}$

14) $\frac{5}{9}$

15) $\frac{2}{9}$

16) $\frac{5}{8}$

17) $\frac{6}{23}$

18) $\frac{12}{15}$

19) $\frac{4}{27}$

20) $\frac{9}{18}$

Lesson 4 Baserunning Averages

Baserunning average

Ratio of stolen bases to attempted steals.

Percent

Number per hundred.

Putout

A play in which the batter or runner is retired.

After getting on base, a player may try to steal the next base. This adds to the excitement of the game and advances the base runner to scoring position. How successful a base runner is at stealing bases is measured by the **baserunning average**. The baserunning average is found by dividing the number of bases stolen by the number of attempts. It is given as a **percent**. The percent is found by multiplying the decimal by 100.

EXAMPLES

Bella Kemp has 15 steals and 27 **putouts** while attempting to steal. What is Bella's baserunning average?

$$\text{Baserunning Average} = \frac{\text{Bases Stolen}}{\text{Attempted Steals}}$$

$$\text{Baserunning Average} = \frac{15}{42} \quad (15 + 27 = 42)$$

$$.3571 \approx .357 = 35.7\% \leftarrow \text{Baserunning Average}$$

$$\begin{array}{r} .3571 \\ 42\overline{)15.0000} \\ -12\,6 \\ \hline 2\,40 \\ -2\,10 \\ \hline 300 \\ -294 \\ \hline 60 \\ -42 \\ \hline 8 \end{array}$$

Bernie Mason has 29 steals and 33 putouts while attempting to steal. What is Bernie's baserunning average?

$$\text{Baserunning Average} = \frac{29}{62}$$

$$.4677 \approx .468 = 46.8\% \leftarrow \text{Baserunning Average}$$

$$\begin{array}{r} .4677 \\ 62\overline{)29.0000} \\ -24\,8 \\ \hline 4\,20 \\ -3\,72 \\ \hline 480 \\ -434 \\ \hline 460 \\ -434 \\ \hline 26 \end{array}$$

Exercise A Find the baserunning average for each record.

1) 16 steals
8 putouts

2) 24 steals
30 putouts

3) 45 steals
18 putouts

4) 21 steals
12 putouts

5) 36 steals
14 putouts

6) 18 steals
7 putouts

7) 30 steals
16 putouts

8) 19 steals
7 putouts

9) 41 steals
28 putouts

10) 16 steals
6 putouts

11) 14 steals
18 putouts

12) 38 steals
16 putouts

13) 30 steals
7 putouts

14) 51 steals
21 putouts

Stealing a base often means the player slides to avoid being called out.

Lesson 5 Fielding Percentage

Fielding percentage
Ratio of assists and putouts to total chances.

The ability of a fielder is measured with the **fielding percentage**. It is found by dividing the total number of chances that the fielder has to make a play into the number of **assists** plus the number of putouts. A player's fielding percentage is given as a decimal rounded to three places. The total chances are: assists + putouts + **errors**.

Assist
A defensive play by a fielder that helps to make a putout.

Error
Misplay in fielding a ball that allows a player to advance.

EXAMPLE During one game, Mario Martinez makes 16 assists and 8 putouts while committing 2 errors. What is Mario's fielding percentage?

$$\text{Fielding Percentage} = \frac{\text{Assists} + \text{Putouts}}{\text{Total Chances}}$$

$$\text{Fielding Percentage} = \frac{16 + 8}{16 + 8 + 2} = \frac{24}{26}$$

$$26\overline{)24.0000} = .9230 \approx .923 \text{ Fielding Percentage}$$

$$\begin{array}{r} 24.0000 \\ -23\,4 \\ \hline 60 \\ -52 \\ \hline 80 \\ -78 \\ \hline 20 \end{array}$$

Exercise A Express each player's fielding percentage as a decimal rounded to three places.

1) J. J. John — 8 assists, 7 putouts, 2 errors

2) Chris Sneed — 8 assists, 13 putouts, 1 error

3) Elva Ellis — 8 assists, 15 putouts, 0 errors

4) John Gaines — 16 assists, 23 putouts, 3 errors

5) Beth Wells — 5 assists, 2 putouts, 1 error

6) Trang Young — 11 assists, 0 putouts, 3 errors

Lesson 6 Earned Run Average

Earned run average
A statistic that describes how many runs a pitcher allows.

A pitcher's most important statistic is probably the **earned run average** (ERA). The ERA is a measure of how many runs a pitcher allows in a game. It is found by multiplying the number of runs that the pitcher has allowed by 9 and then dividing by the number of innings that the pitcher has pitched. Any parts of an inning pitched are rounded off to the nearest whole number. $21\frac{1}{3}$ innings becomes 21 innings. $21\frac{2}{3}$ innings becomes 22 innings. The ERA is expressed as a decimal number rounded to two places.

$$\text{Earned Run Average} = \frac{\text{Earned Runs} \times 9}{\text{Innings Pitched}}$$

EXAMPLE Cara Yamamoto allows 6 runs in 23 innings. What is her earned run average?

$$\text{Earned Run Average} = \frac{6 \times 9}{23} = \frac{54}{23}$$

$$\begin{array}{r} 2.347 \\ 23\overline{)54.000} \\ -46 \\ \hline 8\,0 \\ -6\,9 \\ \hline 1\,10 \\ -92 \\ \hline 180 \\ -161 \\ \hline 19 \end{array}$$

$2.347 \approx 2.35$ ← Earned run average

Exercise A Find each pitcher's earned run average in these eight problems. Express the ERA as a decimal rounded to two places.

1) Lee Gonzalez
16 innings
3 earned runs

2) Gina Statham
24 innings
2 earned runs

3) Larry McCoy
18 innings
2 earned runs

4) Bob Gold
$17\frac{2}{3}$ innings
6 earned runs

5) Cranston Cross
$23\frac{1}{3}$ innings
5 earned runs

6) Peter Li
$21\frac{1}{3}$ innings
4 earned runs

7) Tomas Provo
14 innings
5 earned runs

8) Harrison Kirk
8 innings
3 earned runs

Pitchers practice for hours to keep their ERAs as low as possible.

Lesson 7 Won-Lost Percentage

Won-lost percentage

Ratio of wins to games played.

One of the most important statistics for a team is its **won-lost percentage**. The team with the largest won-lost percentage is in first place. The won-lost percentage is written as a decimal rounded to three places. It is found by dividing the number of team wins by the number of games that team has played.

$$\text{Won-Lost Percentage} = \frac{\text{Number of Wins}}{\text{Games Played}}$$

EXAMPLE The Metros win 14 games and lose 18 games. What is their won-lost percentage?

$$\text{Won-Lost Percentage} = \frac{14}{14 + 18} = \frac{14}{32}$$

$$\begin{array}{r} .4375 \approx .438 \leftarrow \text{Won-lost percentage} \\ 32 \overline{)14.0000} \\ -12\,8 \\ \hline 1\,20 \\ -96 \\ \hline 240 \\ -224 \\ \hline 160 \\ -160 \\ \hline \end{array}$$

Exercise A Find each team's won-lost percentage for the American and National leagues. Then, list the teams in order of their standing. The team with the largest won-lost percentage in each division is in first place. The other teams follow in the order of their won-lost percentages.

1) American League

East Division

Team	*Won*	*Lost*
Detroit	37	48
Boston	46	39
New York	45	39
Toronto	39	46
Baltimore	41	44

American League *(continued)*

Central Division

Team	*Won*	*Lost*
Milwaukee	42	42
Kansas City	41	42
Chicago	38	43
Minnesota	35	51
Cleveland	52	32

West Division

Team	*Won*	*Lost*
Texas	44	42
Oakland	43	44
California	52	34
Seattle	42	43

2) National League

East Division

Team	*Won*	*Lost*
Florida	42	40
Philadelphia	41	45
Atlanta	50	35
New York	39	47
Montreal	44	42

Central Division

Team	*Won*	*Lost*
Chicago	40	45
St. Louis	38	48
Cincinnati	48	35
Houston	48	38
Pittsburgh	37	47

West Division

Team	*Won*	*Lost*
Colorado	42	41
San Diego	41	45
Los Angeles	46	42
San Francisco	40	46

Calculator Practice

You may use a calculator to help you convert fractions to decimals and then to percents.

EXAMPLE Express $\frac{7}{12}$ as a percent.

Step 1 Divide the numerator by the denominator.
7 [÷] 12 [=] .5833333

Step 2 Round the answer to the nearest thousandth.
$.5833333 \approx .583$

Step 3 Move the decimal point two places to the right. Write the answer as a percent.
$.583 = 58.3\%$

Calculator Exercise Express these fractions as decimals, then as percents. Use a calculator to help you.

1) $\frac{7}{8}$

2) $\frac{5}{6}$

3) $\frac{4}{12}$

4) $\frac{9}{11}$

5) $\frac{9}{10}$

6) $\frac{4}{5}$

7) $\frac{1}{7}$

8) $\frac{2}{7}$

9) $\frac{12}{13}$

10) $\frac{5}{8}$

11) $\frac{2}{3}$

12) $\frac{9}{13}$

13) $\frac{3}{17}$

14) $\frac{5}{19}$

15) $\frac{2}{21}$

16) $\frac{1}{6}$

17) $\frac{11}{16}$

18) $\frac{2}{5}$

19) $\frac{4}{9}$

20) $\frac{3}{4}$

Lesson 8 Games Back

Games back

Difference in wins and losses between a team and the first place team.

A statistic given with the won-lost percentage is the number of games that each team is back from first place. The number of **games back** from first place is found by comparing the wins and losses of each team with those of the first-place team.

$$\text{Games Back} = \frac{\text{Difference of Each Team's Wins} + \text{Difference of Each Team's Losses}}{2}$$

EXAMPLE

Team	*Won*	*Lost*	*Pct.*	*GB*
California	23	14	.622	–
Texas	19	18	.514	■
Oakland	17	19	.472	■

$$\text{Texas–Games Back} = \frac{(23 - 19) + (18 - 14)}{2}$$

$$\frac{(4 + 4)}{2} = 4$$

$$\text{Oakland–Games Back} = \frac{(23 - 17) + (19 - 14)}{2}$$

$$\frac{6 + 5}{2} = 5\frac{1}{2}$$

Exercise A For each baseball league, compute the teams' won-lost percentage and the number of games back.

American League

Team	*Won*	*Lost*
Boston	32	20
Milwaukee	29	21
New York	30	22
Texas	28	24
Kansas City	27	24
Baltimore	27	24
Chicago	25	28
Seattle	24	28
Oakland	18	33

National League

Team	*Won*	*Lost*
Atlanta	36	20
Montreal	34	23
Philadelphia	34	24
Houston	29	28
Chicago	28	30
Colorado	27	30
San Diego	22	36
Pittsburgh	21	36
San Francisco	18	38

Chapter 12 Review

Rename each fraction as a decimal rounded to three places.

1) $\frac{7}{8}$ **2)** $\frac{5}{13}$

Rename each fraction as a percent. Round to one decimal place.

3) $\frac{3}{7}$ **4)** $\frac{7}{12}$

Give the batting average for each player as a three-place decimal number.

5) Patty Chan/8 hits for 21 at bats

6) Jo Cox/15 hits for 38 at bats

Give the slugging percentage for each player as a three-place decimal number.

7) Henry Wolpert
1 home run
2 triples
4 doubles
8 singles
3 walks
10 outs
8 sacrifices

8) Juan Cortez
0 home runs
1 triple
3 doubles
12 singles
6 walks
9 outs
2 sacrifices

Give each baserunning average as a percent rounded to one decimal place.

9) Juanita Sanchez steals 18 bases and is put out 13 times while attempting to steal.

10) Sam Foxtree steals 9 bases and is put out 14 times while attempting to steal.

Give each player's fielding percentage as a decimal number rounded to three places.

11) Joe Shaw has 8 assists and 4 putouts. He makes 2 errors.

12) Morris Corona has 7 assists and 9 putouts. He makes 1 error.

Give each pitcher's ERA as a two-place decimal number.

13) Don Coleman pitches 14 innings and allows 8 earned runs.

14) Marian Finney pitches 24 innings and allows 8 earned runs.

For each team, find the won-lost percentage and the number of games that the team trails the first-place team.

15)

Team	*Won*	*Lost*
Texas	33	15
Kansas City	29	18
California	27	21

Test Taking Tip

Look for specifics in each question that tell you in what form your answer is to be. For example, some questions ask for a paragraph, and others may require only one sentence.

Clearance
30% OFF
Price tickets are not
on selected items.
The price will be
scanned at checkout
Brushes & Sponges
Gloves
Housekeeping

Chapter 13

Using Percent

As you find ways to spend or try to budget your hard-earned money, you are sure to discover that you need to understand percent. Sales tax, discounts, and credit cards are some of the areas that calculate amounts of money by using a percent. Even if you save your money and never spend it, you will do better if you know more about percent. Certainly, if you wish to be a wise consumer, then you will be glad to know more about the mathematics of percent.

In Chapter 13 you will explore ways that percent helps you to find the best buy and make the best investment.

Goals for Learning

- To compute the discount, given the original price
- To compute the sales tax and the price plus sales tax
- To find the percent of spending
- To make a circle graph to display budgets

Lesson 1 Sales Tax

Sales tax

A tax on sales or services, added to the price.

A state **sales tax** is collected for most sales. Although not all states have a sales tax, the majority do. The state uses this money for such things as education, police protection, and keeping the highways in good condition. To compute a sales tax is to find a **percentage.**

Percentage

A given part or amount in every hundred; the part in a percent.

Rate

Percent.

EXAMPLE Bill buys a school notebook for $5.85. The sales tax is 5%. What is the price of the notebook with tax?

Step 1 Multiply the price by the **rate** of the tax.

$ 5.85 Original price
× .05 Rate of tax
$ .29 25 Tax
$ .29 25 ≈ .30 (State sales tax is always rounded up)

Step 2 Add the tax to the original price.

$5.85 Original price
+ .30 Tax
$6.15 Total price including tax

Exercise A Find the sales tax and the total price including tax.

1) CD $12.95 with a 5% sales tax

2) Calculator $9.65 with a 5% sales tax

3) Breath mints $2.20 with a 6% sales tax

4) Shirt $22.99 with a 5% sales tax

5) Shoes $55 with a 4% sales tax

6) Dictionary $9 with a 5% sales tax

7) Granola bar $.49 with a 5% sales tax

8) Computer cable $8.50 with a 7% sales tax

9) Bookshelf $39.95 with a 5% sales tax

10) Blanket $32.00 with a 6% sales tax

11) Picture frame $16 with a 4% sales tax

12) Car $7,285.92 with a 5% sales tax

Lesson 2 Discount

Discount

The amount taken off the usual price.

Sales are often advertised in the form of **discounts,** such as "10% off." Knowing the exact amount of the discount is important for wise shopping. To calculate a discount is to find a percentage.

EXAMPLES Jenny wants a bike that originally cost $90. If she gets a 25% discount, how much will the bike cost?

Step 1 Multiply the original price by the rate of discount.

$ 90.00	Original price
× .25	Rate of discount
4 50 00	
+18 00 0	
$ 22.50 ~~00~~	Discount

Step 2 Subtract the discount from the original price.

$ 90.00	Original price
− 22.50	Discount
$ 67.50	Sale price

With a 25% discount, the bike costs $67.50.

Kristina picks out a winter coat with a price tag of $89.50. The coat is on sale at 15% off the marked price. How much of a discount does she get? What is the **sale price?**

Sale price

Reduced price of an item.

Step 1 Multiply.

$ 89.50	Original price
× .15	Rate of discount
4 47 50	
+8 95 0	
$13.42 50	≈ $13.43 Discount

Step 2 Subtract.

$ 89.50	Original price
− 13.43	Discount
$ 76.07	Sale price

Exercise A Find the discount and the new sale price for each.

1) Radio $169.00 with a discount rate of 20%

2) Calculator $14.20 with a discount rate of 10%

3) Shirt $17.00 with a discount rate of 15%

4) Shoes $32.50 with a discount rate of 20%

5) Blouse $16.75 with a discount rate of 25%

6) Handbag $10 with a discount rate of 10%

7) Flashlight $3.95 with a discount rate of 10%

8) Baseball $4.50 with a discount rate of 25%

9) Television $289 with a discount rate of 30%

10) Rug $175.92 with a discount rate of 10%

11) Chair $109.68 with a discount rate of 15%

12) Shovel $10.99 with a discount rate of 25%

13) Notebook $6.25 with a discount rate of 20%

14) Computer $349 with a discount rate of 15%

15) Scarf $2.75 with a discount rate of 50%

16) Bike $110.25 with a discount rate of 10%

17) Skates $52.98 with a discount rate of 40%

18) Cassette deck $48.95 with a discount rate of 12%

19) Computer game $200 with a discount rate of 20%

20) Keyboard $159 with a discount rate of 25%

21) Lawn mower $289 with a discount rate of 15%

22) Hammer $18.60 with a discount rate of 10%

Lesson 3 Personal Spending

Budget

A plan for managing money.

Income

Money earned.

One step in **budget** planning is to find what percent of **income**, or earnings, is usually spent on certain items. You can find the percent, or rate, by dividing.

EXAMPLE Sandee earns $222 per week and spends $50 per week for food. What percent of her salary does she spend on food per week?

Rate × Base	=	Percentage
___% of $222	=	$50
___%	=	$50 ÷ $222

$$\begin{array}{r} .225 \\ 222\overline{)50.000} \\ -\underline{44\,4} \\ 5\,60 \\ -\underline{4\,44} \\ 1\,160 \\ -\underline{1\,110} \\ 50 \end{array}$$

← Insert enough zeros to allow 3 decimal places

To express a decimal as a percent, move the decimal point two places to the right.

.225 = 22.5%

Sandee spends 22.5% of her salary for food.

Comparing prices on different brands and sizes is one way to save money on food.

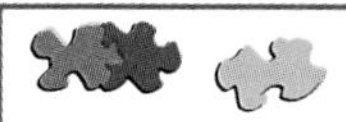

PROBLEM SOLVING

Exercise A Find the rate of earnings spent.

1) Lee spends $50 of his income on apartment rent. If he earns $170 per week, what percent does he spend on rent?

2) Yoko earns $65 per week and spends $18 on bus fare. What percent does she spend on bus fare?

3) Laurie needs $7 each week for lunch. If she earns $18 per week, what percent is spent for lunch?

4) Marnie earns $170 during the week and spends $40 for food. What percent is spent for food?

5) Nicholas earns $56 during the week and spends $45 for food. What percent is spent for food?

6) Cara earns $18 during the week and spends $15 on bus fare. What percent is spent on bus fare?

7) José earns $52 during the week and spends $25 on clothes. What percent is spent on clothes?

8) Ben earns $28 during the week. He spends $5 on bus fare and $5 on lunches. What percent is spent on bus fare? What percent is spent on lunches?

9) Rita earns $85 during the week. She spends $10 for bus fare and $8 on lunches. What percent is spent on bus fare? What percent is spent on lunches?

10) Malcolm earns $262 during the week. He spends $16 during the week for bus fare and $50 for a car payment. What percent is spent on bus fare? What percent is spent on the car payment?

11) Jesse earns $350 during the week. He spends $15 on clothes and $75 for rent. What percent is spent on clothes? What percent is spent on the rent?

12) Luis earns $170 during the week. He spends $25 on books and $35 on his gas bill. What percent is spent on books? What percent is spent on the gas bill?

13) Erica earns $275. She spends $55 on her phone bill and $51 on a birthday gift for a friend. What percent is spent on her phone bill? What percent is spent on the birthday gift?

Lesson 4 Personal Savings

If you know the rate of earnings saved and the percentage of earnings saved, then you can find the total earnings by dividing.

Base

An amount that a percent is taken of.

EXAMPLES Donnell is saving 20% of his earnings for college. If he saves $17 per week, then how much does he earn per week?

Rate × **Base** = Percentage

20% × Base = $17

Base = $17 ÷ .20 Because 20% is .20.

$$\begin{array}{r} \$\quad 85. \\ .20\overline{)\$17.00} \\ -16\,0 \\ \hline 1\,00 \\ -1\,00 \\ \hline \end{array}$$

Base = $85. Donnell earns $85 per week.

Lionel saves 15% of his weekly wages. If he saves $13.80 per week, then what are his weekly wages?

Rate × Base = Percentage

15% × Base = $13.80

Base = $13.80 ÷ .15

$$\begin{array}{r} \$\quad 92. \\ .15\overline{)\$13.80} \\ -13\,5 \\ \hline 30 \\ -30 \\ \hline \end{array}$$

Base = $92. Lionel earns $92 per week.

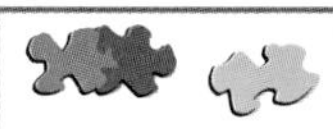

PROBLEM SOLVING

Exercise A Find the earnings.

1) Abbott is saving 30% of his weekly salary for a car. If he saves $24.60 per week, how much does he earn per week?

2) Manuel deposits 25% of his weekly earnings in a savings account. If he deposits $19.50 weekly, then how much does he earn?

3) Rachel saves $32.90 per week from her part-time baby-sitting job. If she saves 35% of her earnings, then how much does she earn?

4) Bo wants to save 25% of his weekly income for school. How much will he have to make to save $11.75 per week?

Exercise B Find the weekly earnings.

1) 20% saved
Saved $80
Earned ____

2) 25% saved
Saved $22.50
Earned ____

3) 20% saved
Saved $13
Earned ____

4) 30% saved
Saved $16.20
Earned ____

5) 35% saved
Saved $13.30
Earned ____

6) 22% saved
Saved $12.10
Earned ____

7) 15% saved
Saved $12.15
Earned ____

8) 40% saved
Saved $42
Earned ____

9) 10% saved
Saved $2.60
Earned ____

10) 12% saved
Saved $18
Earned ____

Lesson 5 Using Circle Graphs

Circle graph
Way to show comparisons by using segments of a circle.

Degree
1/360th of a circle.

Protractor
An instrument used for plotting and measuring angles.

Radius
A line from the center to the edge of a circle.

Budgets are often shown with a **circle graph**. Each section of the graph represents a different kind of expense. You can clearly see what rate of total earnings is spent for each purpose.

EXAMPLE Make a circle graph to show Jiang's budget.

Jiang's Budget

Rent	25%
Car	10%
Savings	30%
Other	35%

Follow these steps:

Step 1 Draw a circle. Mark the center.

Step 2 There are 360° in a circle. Find the number of **degrees** needed for each item by multiplying the percent by 360°.

.25	×	360°	=	90°	Rent
.10	×	360°	=	36°	Car
.30	×	360°	=	108°	Savings
.35	×	360°	=	126°	Other

Step 3 Draw a **radius** and use a **protractor** to measure and help draw each segment.

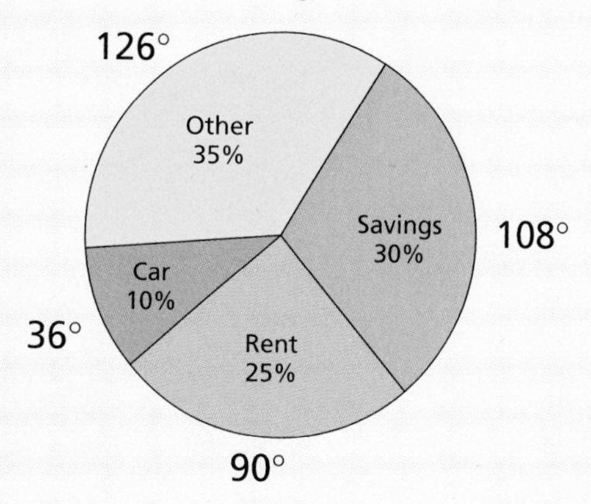

Exercise A Make a circle graph for each budget. Round degrees to the nearest whole number.

1) Rent 25%
Food 15%
Car 15%
Other 45%

2) Rent 30%
Food 25%
Car 10%
Other 35%

3) Rent 20%
Clothing 15%
Savings 5%
Other 60%

4) Entertainment 14%
Housing 26%
Savings 10%
Other 50%

5) Transportation 15%
Savings 20%
Food 35%
Housing 20%
Clothing 10%

6) Entertainment 5%
Housing 20%
Food 30%
Clothing 15%
Other 30%

7) Rent 25%
Food 22%
Clothing 18%
Other 35%

8) Savings 15%
Food 17%
Clothing 13%
Other 55%

Calculator Practice

You can use a calculator to help you find discounts.

EXAMPLE Find the discount of 20% on $55.88.

Step 1 Multiply the price by the discount rate.

55.88 [×] .20 [=] 11.176

Step 2 Round your answer to the nearest cent.

$11.167 = $11.18

Calculator Exercise Use your calculator to help you find the discounts.

1) $25 at 25%

2) $13.50 at 22%

3) $125.52 at 32%

4) $18.95 at 10%

5) $120 at 35%

6) $1.95 at 20%

7) $32.89 at 15%

8) $103.75 at 60%

9) $1,069.45 at 16%

10) $753.79 at 23%

11) $176.40 at 49%

12) $16.02 at 18%

13) $62,673.58 at 52%

14) $93 at 33%

15) $444.44 at 44%

16) $62 at 56%

Chapter 13 Review

Compute the discount and the new sale price for each.

1) A shirt priced at $23 with a 20% discount

2) A blouse priced at $26.95 with a 10% discount

Compute the sales tax and the price plus sales tax.

3) Radio $19.75 with a 5% sales tax

4) Computer $239.16 with a 6% sales tax

Find the percent.

5) Karen spends $29.75 of her savings for a coat. Find the percent spent if her savings is $85.

6) Patrice earns $36 one week tutoring. She spends $3.96 for school supplies. What percent does Patrice spend on school supplies?

Find the earnings.

7) Kirk saves 15% of his part-time earnings for clothes. If he saves $8.25 for clothes, then how much does he earn?

8) Luke saves 30% of his weekly earnings for college. If he saves $13.50 weekly, then how much does he earn per week?

Make a circle graph for each budget. Use a protractor to help you.

9) Housing 25%

Transportation 10%

Other 65%

10) Housing 30%

Food 20%

Entertainment 20%

Other 30%

Test Taking Tip

Before taking a test, find out what tools, such as a calculator or protractor, you need to bring with you.

For Sale
SOLD
Properties
826-188
MEDIUM-3.0 CU. FT.

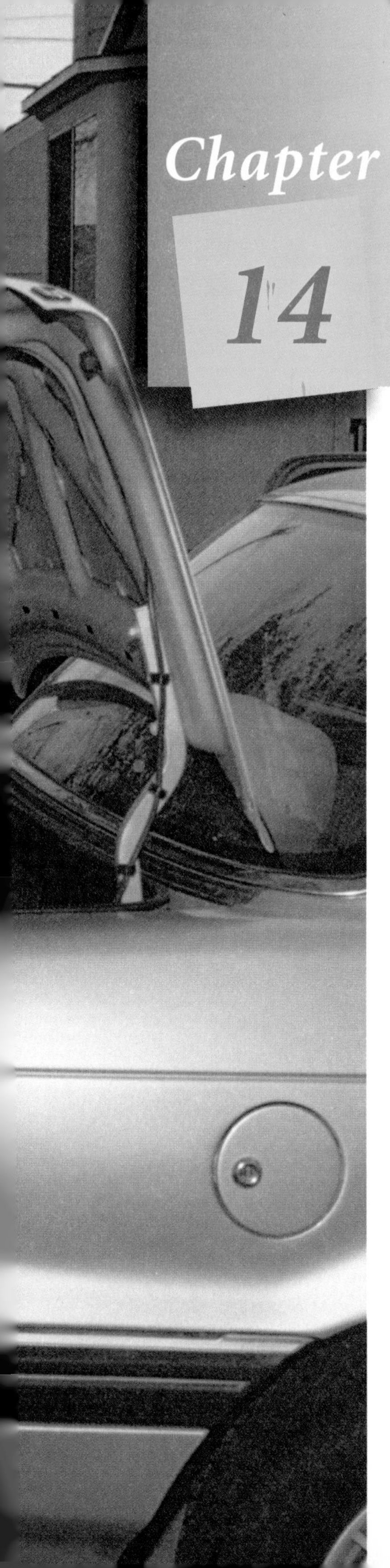

Chapter 14

Working With Interest

Banks, finance companies, and sometimes even friends charge interest for the money that you borrow from them. A loan may be in the form of a bank loan, such as a home mortgage. Or, interest may be in the form of charges on a credit card. Whatever the reason, you are sure to encounter interest charges throughout your life. Understanding interest and how it is calculated is another way that you can use mathematics to help you solve problems in your everyday life.

In Chapter 14, you will apply the skills necessary to compute interest and to help you make informed money decisions.

Goals for Learning

- To compute simple and compound interest
- To use a table to compute payments
- To use the addition and subtraction methods to compute loan payments

Lesson 1 Simple Interest

Interest
Amount paid for the use of money.

Interest rate
Percent paid or charged for the use of money.

Loan
Money given to a borrower that is to be returned with interest.

Principal
Amount of a loan or a deposit.

Rate
Percent.

Simple interest
Interest computed on principal only.

Time
Duration of a loan or deposit.

Calculate **interest** by multiplying the **principal** times the **rate** of interest times the **time.** The principal is the amount of the **loan** or the amount in your savings account. The rate is a percent paid for each time period. The time is how long you have the loan or the time the money is in the account.

EXAMPLE Felipe's car costs $2,478.93. His uncle agrees to loan Felipe the money at a simple **interest rate** of $18\frac{1}{2}$% per year for $2\frac{1}{4}$ years. How much **simple interest** will Felipe have to pay?

Compute the simple interest on $2,478.93 at $18\frac{1}{2}$% per year for $2\frac{1}{4}$ years. Convert the rate and time to decimals: $18\frac{1}{2}\% = .185$; $2\frac{1}{4} = 2.25$

Interest = Principal × Rate × Time in Years
Interest = $2,478.93 × .185 × 2.25

Step 1

$ 2,478.93	Principal
× .185	Interest rate
$458.60205	
$458.60	Rounded interest for 1 year

Step 2

$ 458.60	Interest
× 2.25	Time in years
$1,031.85	Total interest

Remember to convert months to a decimal.
3 years, 7 months = 3.58 years using the chart.

Converting Months to Years

Months	Fractional Part of Year	Rounded Decimals	Months	Fractional Part of Year	Rounded Decimals
1	$\frac{1}{12}$	.08	7	$\frac{7}{12}$	.58
2	$\frac{2}{12}$	.17	8	$\frac{8}{12}$	.67
3	$\frac{3}{12}$	.25	9	$\frac{9}{12}$	.75
4	$\frac{4}{12}$	.33	10	$\frac{10}{12}$	.83
5	$\frac{5}{12}$	.42	11	$\frac{11}{12}$	.92
6	$\frac{6}{12}$	.5			

Exercise A Find the product.

1) \$60 × 4% × 2 years

2) \$120 × 6% × 1 year

3) \$250 × 6% × 4 years

4) \$96 × 3% × 5 years

5) \$320 × 7% × 4 years

6) \$136 × 3% × 3 years

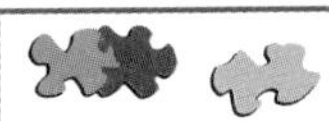

PROBLEM SOLVING

Exercise B Find the simple interest. Annual interest rates are given.

1) Huilde has a principal of \$165 with a rate of interest of 6% for 4 years. How much is the interest?

2) Elise borrows \$235 from her sister with a rate of interest of 7% for 3 years. How much will she pay in interest?

3) Eduardo borrows \$1,095 from his mother for 6 months at 9% interest. What is the amount Eduardo pays in interest?

4) Preeti needs \$49.92 more to buy a new CD player. Her brother agrees to loan her the money, if Preeti will pay back her brother at the rate of 5% over 4 months. How much will Preeti need to pay in interest if she accepts her brother's offer?

5) Sigfredo borrows \$2,065 from an uncle to buy a motorcycle. He agrees to pay 6% for 2 years. How much interest does Sigfredo pay to his uncle?

6) John has a loan from the garden shop for \$38. He agrees to pay it back in 6 months at 6% interest. How much interest will John pay?

7) Ung borrows \$92 from his neighbor for a new drill. If Ung agrees to pay his loan in 8 months at 9% interest, then how much interest does Ung pay?

8) Latrice borrows \$102.26 from her grandmother for 2 years at 7% interest. How much interest does Latrice pay?

9) Tamara's bank agrees to lend her \$1,000 at 7% for 10 years. How much will Tamara pay in interest?

10) Maggie agrees to lend Glen \$23.40 for a calculator. However, Glen must pay the money back in 6 months at 5% interest. How much will Glen pay Maggie in interest?

The rate of interest my contain a fraction. To compute the interest, you can change the fraction to its decimal equivalent. Then, multiply.

EXAMPLE Compute the simple interest on a principal of \$200 at $6\frac{1}{2}$% per year for 2 years.

Interest = Principal × Rate × Time

$6\frac{1}{2}\% = .065$

\$ 200	Principal
× .065	Rate of interest
1.000	
12.000	
\$13.000	Interest for 1 year
\$ 13.00	Interest for 1 year
× 2	Interest for 2 years
\$ 26.00	

$\frac{1}{4} = .25$

$\frac{1}{2} = .5$

$\frac{3}{4} = .75$

Exercise C Find the simple interest. Annual interest rates are given.

1) \$400 at $8\frac{1}{2}$% for 2 years

2) \$175 at $6\frac{1}{4}$% for 2 years

3) \$200 at $6\frac{3}{4}$% for 3 years

4) \$75 at $6\frac{1}{2}$% for 6 months

5) \$62 at $7\frac{3}{4}$% for 9 years

6) \$380 at $6\frac{3}{4}$% for 5 years

7) \$1,800 at $9\frac{3}{4}$% for 1 year

8) \$350 at $7\frac{1}{4}$% for 3 years

9) \$395 at $7\frac{3}{4}$% for 2 years

10) \$80 at $8\frac{1}{2}$% for 6 months

11) \$267 at $9\frac{3}{4}$% for 3 years

12) \$132 at $5\frac{1}{4}$% for 5 years

13) \$17 at $9\frac{1}{4}$% for 2 years

14) \$500 at $6\frac{1}{4}$% for 4 years

Lesson 2 Compound Interest

Compound interest

Interest computed on principal plus interest.

Quarterly

Happening at regular intervals four times a year.

Balance

The amount due.

You earn **compound interest** when the bank pays interest on the principal *and* on the interest already earned on money in a savings account.

EXAMPLE Janna deposits $150 in her savings account and receives 6% interest compounded **quarterly**. What is her **balance** at the end of one year?

Interest = Principal × Rate × Time

First Quarter

a) $ 150 Principal
× .015 (6% divided by 4)
$2.250 Interest

b) $150.00 Principal
+ 2.25 Interest
$152.25 New principal

Second Quarter

c) $ 15 2.25 Principal
× .0 15 Rate
$2.28 3 75 Interest

d) $152.25 Principal
+ 2.28 Interest
$154.53 New principal

Third Quarter

e) $ 15 4.53 Principal
× .0 15 Rate
$2.31 7 95 Interest

f) $154.53 Principal
+ 2.32 Interest
$156.85 New principal

Fourth Quarter

g) $ 156.85 Principal
× .015 Rate
$2.35275 Interest

h) $156.85 Principal
+ 2.35 Interest
$159.20 New principal

The balance at the end of one year is $159.20.

Exercise A Find the interest compounded quarterly and the new balance at the end of one year.

1) \$200 at 8%

2) \$500 at 6%

3) \$250 at 10%

4) \$300 at 10%

5) \$450 at 8%

6) \$1,000 at 9%

7) \$850 at 12%

8) \$960 at 12%

9) \$2,000 at 7%

10) \$1,500 at 9%

11) \$1,600 at 8%

12) \$145 at 10%

Your money begins earning compound interest as soon as you make a deposit at the bank.

Lesson 3 Borrowing Money

Lend
To loan.

The Subtraction Method Some lenders of money subtract the interest due from the total amount that they **lend**. The borrower does not receive the full amount but does pay back the full amount.

EXAMPLE Hideo wants to borrow $1,000 at 12% annual interest for 18 months, making 18 monthly payments. How much is each payment?

Step 1

$ 1,0 00	Loan
× .12	Interest rate
$120.00	Interest for one year

$1,000 is the amount Hideo will pay back.

Step 2

$12 0	Interest for one year
× 1.5	Number of years
$18 0	Total interest

Step 3

$ 1,000	Loan
− 180	Interest
$ 820	Loan minus interest

$820 is the amount Hideo will receive.

Step 4 (Months)

$1,000 ÷ 18 = $55.555 Round the payment up

= $55.56 Monthly payment for 17 months

Step 5

Notice that $55.56 × 18 = $1,000.08.

The last payment, then, is $55.56 − $.08, or $55.48.

Exercise A Find the monthly payment. Write the amount of the last payment if it differs from the first payment. Use the subtraction method.

1) $600 at 10% for 12 months

2) $700 at 12% for 12 months

3) $950 at 12% for 18 months

4) $550 at 10% for 12 months

5) $12,000 at 14% for 6 months

6) $1,000 at 10% for 18 months

7) $1,500 at 10% for 12 months

8) $1,100 at 12% for 18 months

9) $1,200 at 12% for 12 months

10) $1,600 at 14% for 10 months

11) $450 at 16% for 12 months

12) $900 at 10% for 12 months

The Addition Method Some lenders add the interest to the amount of the loan. The borrower pays back the full amount of the loan plus interest.

Lanita wants to borrow $1,000 at 12% annual interest for 18 months, making 18 monthly payments. How much is each payment?

Step 1

$ 1,0 00	Loan
× .12	Interest rate
$120.00	Interest for one year

$1,000 is the amount Lanita will receive.

Step 2

$12 0	Interest for one year
× 1.5	Number of years
$18 0	Total interest

Step 3

$1,000	Loan
+ 180	Interest
$1,180	Loan plus interest

$1,180 is the amount Lanita will pay back.

Step 4

$1,180 ÷ 18 = $65.555 Round the payment up

= $65.56 Monthly payment for 17 months

Step 5

Notice that $65.56 × 18 = $1,180.08.

The last payment, then, is $65.56 − $.08, or $65.48.

Exercise B Find the monthly payment. Write the amount of the last payment if it differs from the first payment. Use the addition method.

1) $600 at 10% for 12 months

2) $800 at 12% for 18 months

3) $1,200 at 8% for 6 months

4) $950 at 9% for 12 months

5) $75 at 10% for 12 months

6) $200 at 20% for 12 months

7) $500 at 12% for 6 months

8) $150 at 8% for 9 months

9) $1,000 at 7% for 9 months

10) $1,500 at 14% for 9 months

11) $2,500 at 15% for 12 months

12) $230 at 8% for 24 months

Exercise C Find the monthly payment. Write the amount of the last payment if it differs from the first payment. Use the subtraction method.

1) \$500 at 12% for 12 months

2) \$750 at 10% for 12 months

3) \$650 at 12% for 12 months

4) \$850 at 9% for 12 months

5) \$780 at 10% for 9 months

6) \$900 at 10% for 12 months

7) \$900 at 9% for 18 months

8) \$800 at 14% for 18 months

9) \$500 at 8% for 12 months

10) \$1,200 at 6% for 10 months

11) \$1,000 at 10% for 18 months

12) \$1,100 at 10% for 12 months

13) \$1,300 at 9% for 10 months

14) \$1,250 at 15% for 9 months

Exercise D Find the monthly payment. Write the amount of the last payment if it differs from the first payment. Use the addition method.

1) \$2,000 at 8% for 18 months

2) \$1,900 at 10% for 18 months

3) \$1,850 at 14% for 12 months

4) \$2,000 at 12% for 6 months

5) \$1,700 at 16% for 9 months

6) \$1,700 at 10% for 12 months

7) \$1,600 at 12% for 12 months

8) \$400 at 12% for 12 months

9) \$350 at 9% for 12 months

10) \$450 at 14% for 18 months

11) \$960 at 10% for 12 months

12) \$825 at 10% for 6 months

13) \$1,350 at 14% for 6 months

14) \$1,735 at 16% for 9 months

Lesson 4 Credit

Credit

The right to buy now and to pay later.

Finance charge

Money paid for the use of money.

Buying with **credit** is like borrowing money. Credit allows you to buy an item now and pay for it later. When you pay later, you pay a percent of interest for the use of the money. This interest is charged to your account each month. The first month is usually interest free.

EXAMPLE Mariah purchases a lawn mower on sale for $205 on the condition that she makes monthly payments of $30 per month with a **finance charge** of $1\frac{1}{2}$% on any unpaid balance. She will make her first payment on the first day of January.

Step 1	$205	Balance
	− 30	January payment
	$175	New balance for February
Step 2	$ 175	Previous balance
	× .015	Finance rate
	$2.625	Finance charge
	$2.63	Rounded to $2.63
Step 3	$175.00	Previous balance
	+ 2.63	Finance charge
	$177.63	Before payment
Step 4	$177.63	Before payment
	− 30.00	Payment
	$147.63	New balance for March

Exercise A Complete the information for this chart for the lawn mower.

Month	Previous Balance	Finance Charge	Before Payment	Monthly Payment	New Balance
Jan.	$205.00	$—	$205.00	$30	$175.00
Feb.	$175.00	$2.63	$177.63	$30	$147.63
March	$147.63	$2.21	$149.84	$30	$119.84
April	$119.84				
May					
June					
July					

When you use a credit card to make a purchase, you will receive a monthly statement. It shows the balance due and any finance charges that you owe.

PROBLEM SOLVING

Exercise B Complete the information for these charts.

1) Rolf purchases his school clothes for a total of \$111. He agrees to make \$15 monthly payments with first month interest free. His finance charge is $1\frac{1}{2}\%$ on any unpaid balance.

Month	Previous Balance	Finance Charge	Before Payment	Monthly Payment	New Balance
Aug.	\$111.00	\$—	\$111.00	\$15	\$96.00
Sept.	\$ 96.00	\$1.44	\$ 97.44	\$15	\$82.44
Oct.	\$ 82.44				
Nov.					
Dec.					
Jan.					
Feb.					
March					
April					

2) Nicole purchases a birthday gift for \$143. She agrees to make payments of \$20 per month with a finance charge of 2% on any unpaid balance. Her first month will be interest free.

Month	Previous Balance	Finance Charge	Before Payment	Monthly Payment	New Balance
Feb.	\$143.00	\$—	\$143.00	\$20	\$123.00
March	\$123.00	\$2.46	\$125.46	\$20	\$105.46
April	\$105.46				
May					
June					
July					
Aug.					
Sept.					
Oct.					

Calculator Practice

Budgeting often requires you to find a percentage of earnings. Use a calculator to help you find the percentages for the budgets below. Round your answers to the nearest cent.

Megan's Budget With $200 per Week		Amount
Entertainment	5%	
Food	20%	
Car	25%	
Rent	19%	
Savings	15%	
Miscellaneous	16%	

Eduardo's Budget With $175 per Week		Amount
Rent	25%	
Car	20%	
Savings	10%	
Food	15%	
Clothes	5%	
Miscellaneous	25%	

Chapter 14 Review

Compute the simple interest.

1) \$125 at 10% for 3 years

2) \$110 at 7% for 6 months

3) \$290 at $6\frac{1}{2}$% for 5 years

4) \$206 at $7\frac{1}{4}$% for 2 years

Compute the compound interest quarterly.

5) \$300 at 8% for 1 year

6) \$275 at 10% for 1 year

Complete the information in the table on credit buying.

7) A purchase of \$175 with monthly payments of \$50 and a finance charge of $1\frac{1}{2}$% on the unpaid balance. The first month will be interest free.

Month	Previous Balance	Finance Charge	Before Payment	Monthly Payment	New Balance
Jan.	\$175.00	\$—	\$175.00	\$50.00	\$125.00
Feb.	\$125.00	\$1.88		\$50.00	
March				\$50.00	
April					\$000.00

Find the payments.

8) Use the addition method to compute the first and last payments on a loan of $175 at 10% for 12 months.

9) Use the subtraction method to compute the first and last payments on a loan of $200 at 15% for 10 months.

10) Use the addition method to compute the first and last payments on a loan of $100 at 8% for 6 months.

Test Taking Tip

If you have time, compute problems a second time, then check your original answer.

Chapter 15

Insurance

People buy insurance as a way to protect themselves financially. Home insurance protects a person's home and belongings. Life insurance provides money for the survivors when death occurs. Automobile insurance ensures a car owner that in the event of an accident, damages are covered. Insurance is available for many other catastrophes, including poor health. As people invest their income in cars and homes, it is wise for them also to invest in insurance, which protects that investment.

In Chapter 15, you will explore the ways to compute the cost of insurance before you make an investment.

Goals for Learning

- To use a chart to determine cost of health insurance
- To identify the types of life insurance
- To use replacement cost and location multiplier to find the cost of homeowners insurance
- To use a rate chart to determine premium
- To compute automobile insurance costs with the aid of a table

Lesson 1 Health Insurance

Coverage
Insurance for a loss.

Insurance
Coverage by a contract in which one party guarantees another against loss.

Premium
Amount paid for insurance.

Premium chart
List of amounts to be paid for insurance.

Families buy health **insurance** so that they have less worry about how they will pay their doctors' and hospital bills if they have an accident or become ill. Most health care companies offer a variety of health insurance plans. Better **coverage** costs more money. The amount of money that you pay for the health insurance is called the **premium**. You can determine premium by reading an insurance **premium chart**.

EXAMPLE Jorge is 42 years old. His wife, Susan, is 39 years old. They and their two children are enrolled in Plan B of the health care program. They do not have maternity benefits. How much is their monthly premium? Use the chart to help you.

$$\begin{array}{r} \$104.54 \\ \$93.03 \\ +\$137.56 \\ \hline \$335.13 \end{array}$$ Monthly premium

Exercise A Find the monthly premium for each coverage described below.

1) Single adult 43 years old, Plan A
2) Single adult 51 years old, Plan C
3) Husband 28 years old, wife 27 years old, Plan B
4) Husband 41 years old, wife 38 years old, three children, Plan B
5) Husband 54 years old, wife 52 years old, Plan A
6) Husband 32 years old, wife 29 years old, Plan C
7) Single adult 56 years old, Plan B
8) Husband 63 years old, wife 65 years old, Plan A
9) Husband 27 years old, wife 27 years old, one child, Plan B
10) Husband 36 years old, wife 33 years old, two children, Plan A

Health Care Insurance

PLAN A

Pays 100% benefit from the first day of covered accidents or illnesses.

Age at Enrollment	Monthly Premium per Adult
3 mo.-18 yr.	$69.99
19-29	$80.13
30-34	$87.35
35-39	$94.67
40-44	$106.39
45-49	$129.83
50-54	$168.71
55-59	$219.32
60-64	$240.62
65+	$240.62

Additional Costs:
Children up to age 19
(or 25 if full-time student)

1 child	$69.99
2 children	$139.98
3 or more	$209.97

PLAN B

Pays 80% benefit from the first day of covered accidents or illnesses.

Age at Enrollment	Monthly Premium per Adult
3 mo.-18 yr.	$68.78
19-29	$78.74
30-34	$85.83
35-39	$93.03
40-44	$104.54
45-49	$127.57
50-54	$165.78
55-59	$215.50
60-64	$236.44
65+	$236.44

Additional Costs:
Children up to age 19
(or 25 if full-time student)

1 child	$68.78
2 children	$137.56
3 or more	$206.34

PLAN C

Pays 60% benefit from the first day of covered accidents or illnesses.

Age at Enrollment	Monthly Premium per Adult
3 mo.-18 yr.	$64.01
19-29	$73.29
30-34	$79.88
35-39	$86.58
40-44	$97.30
45-49	$118.74
50-54	$154.30
55-59	$200.58
60-64	$220.06
65+	$220.06

Additional Costs:
Children up to age 19
(or 25 if full-time student)

1 child	$64.01
2 children	$128.02
3 or more	$192.03

Major Medical Insurance Many health care plans place limits on covered expenses. Because of these limits, many companies provide their employees with **major medical insurance** coverage. Payroll deductions for part of the total premium can be made weekly, **semimonthly**, or monthly from your paycheck.

Major medical insurance
Insurance to cover larger medical expenses.

Semimonthly
Twice per month.

Rest Easy Major Medical Program Semimonthly Payroll Deductions	
Employee	$12.22
Employee and spouse	$14.98
Employee and family	$23.67

EXAMPLE Morgan and her husband are enrolled in the Rest Easy Major Medical Program. What is their annual premium?

$$\begin{array}{r} \$14.98 \\ \times \quad 24 \\ \hline 59\ 92 \\ +299\ 6 \\ \hline \$359.52 \end{array}$$ Annual premium

PROBLEM SOLVING

Exercise B Find the annual premium for each family described below. The person named is the employee.

1) Joe Kassa is married and has a two-year-old boy. How much is Joe's annual premium?

2) Bertha Guthrie has three children. How much is Bertha's annual premium for herself and her children?

3) Gus Harrington is single. How much is his annual premium?

4) Louis Kohn provides coverage for himself and his three young children. How much is Louis's annual premium?

5) Henry Jones is married with six children living at home. How much is his annual premium if he purchases insurance for himself and his family?

Lesson 2 Home Insurance

Unit count

A way to determine a house's size for insurance purposes.

Most families insure their homes against possible loss by buying insurance. If the house should catch fire, then the insurance company pays for the damages up to the amount of the insurance coverage. Most homeowners insure their homes for the full value of the house plus its contents. The first step in determining how much a house is worth is to do a **unit count** for the house.

Home insurance usually covers the structure of your home and all of its contents. It includes your furniture, pictures, and personal belongings.

Count 1 for Each Unit Below:	Count $\frac{1}{2}$ for Each Unit Below:
Kitchen Dining Room Living Room Bedroom Bathroom (3 or more **fixtures**) Den or Study Family Room Utility Room Finished Attic Finished Basement Two-Car Garage Central Air Conditioning	Half Bathroom (1 or 2 fixtures) One-Car Garage Dinette Breakfast Nook Unfinished Basement Unfinished Attic Enclosed Porch Fireplace

Fixtures

Toilet, sink, bathtub, or shower.

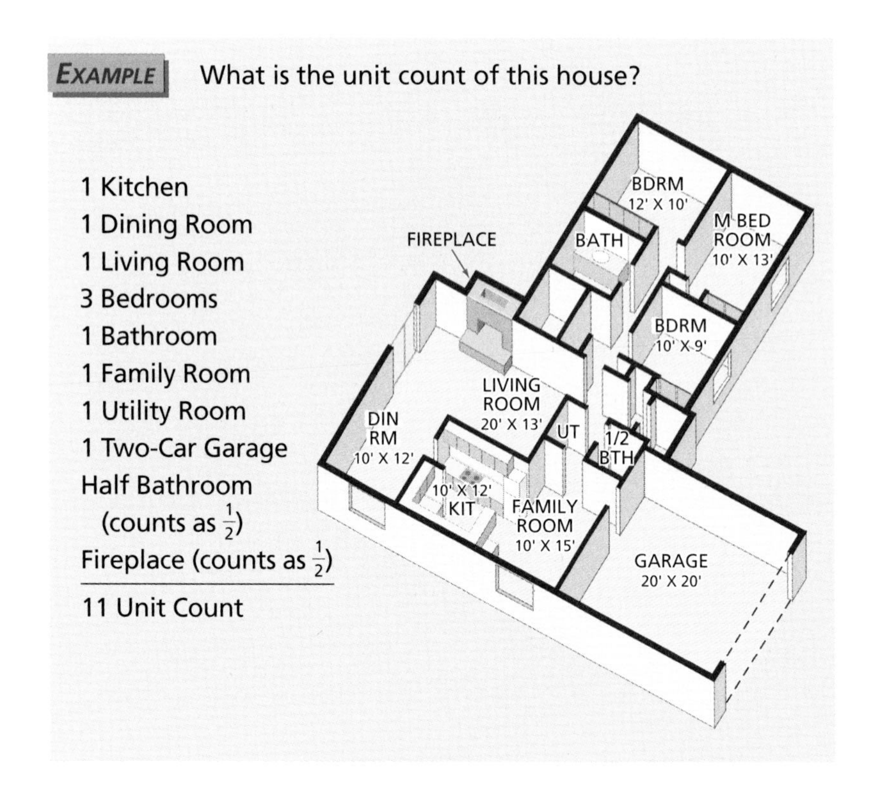

PROBLEM SOLVING

Exercise A Determine the unit count for each house below.

1)

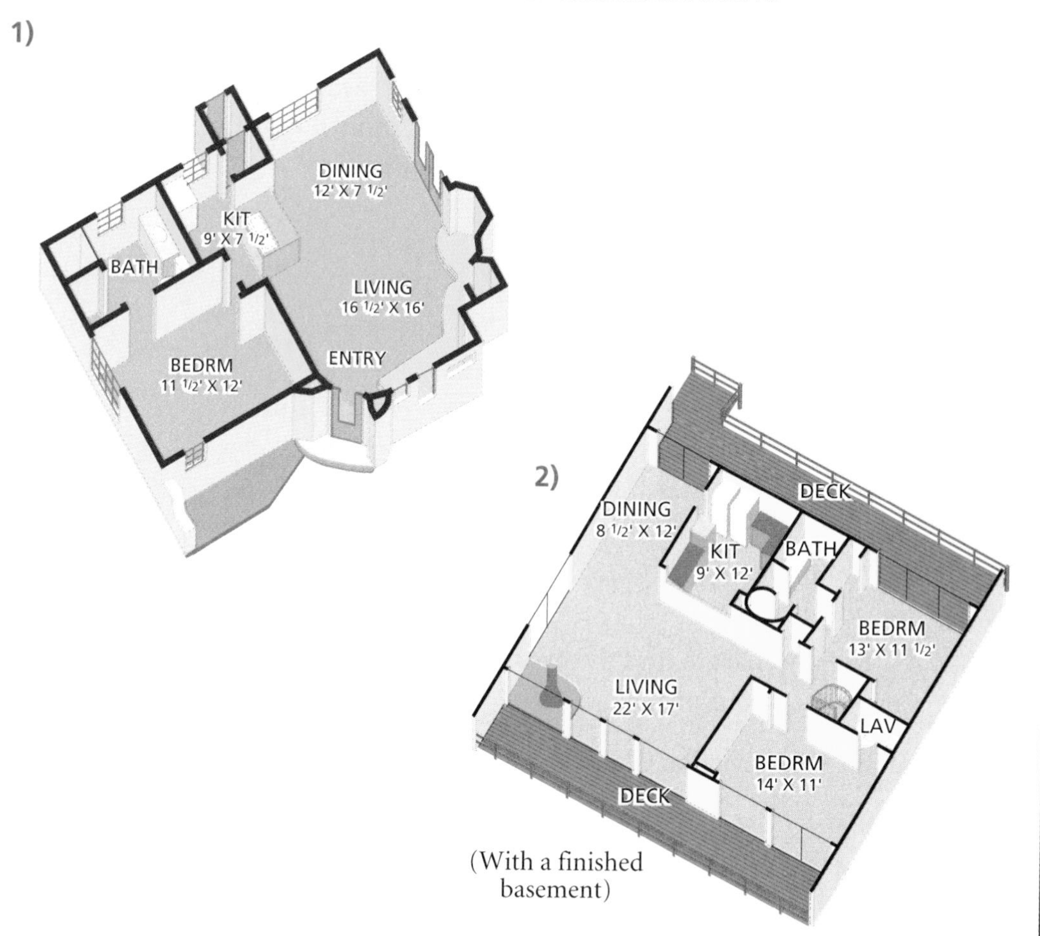

(With a finished basement)

3) A two-story house with 3 bedrooms, 2 full bathrooms, living room, dining room, kitchen, den, unfinished basement, central air conditioning, finished attic, and one-car garage.

Construction Class After you have determined the size of the house by doing a unit count, you must decide what type of house you have. Insurance companies have divided houses into four **construction classes**. When you know the unit count and the construction class, you find the house's base cost from a chart.

> ***Construction class***
>
> *Type of house.*

Class I
Plain design
Stock-type house
Tract-type house
Low cost
Just meets building codes
Dining area part of living room or kitchen
No special-purpose rooms

Class II
Simple design
Standard plans
Some ornamentation
Average quality
Meets or exceeds building codes
Dining room
Den or family room

Class III
Individual design
Modified plans
Built for a specific buyer
Average to above-average work
Meets or exceeds building codes
Den or family room
Foyer common

Class IV
One-of-a-kind design
Architect's plans
Above-average work
Exceeds building codes
Unique floor plan
Large rooms and foyer
Many special rooms

Exercise B Use the chart to find the base cost of each house. Write your answers on your paper.

	Unit Count	Construction Class	Base Cost
1)	$10\frac{1}{2}$	III	_______
2)	12	II	_______
3)	7	I	_______
4)	13	IV	_______
5)	$14\frac{1}{2}$	IV	_______
6)	$6\frac{1}{2}$	II	_______
7)	11	III	_______
8)	8	II	_______

Unit Count	Construction Class			
	I	II	III	IV
6	$20,900	$26,300	$33,400	$40,100
$6\frac{1}{2}$	$22,900	$29,000	$36,000	$44,000
7	$24,100	$30,600	$39,300	$45,700
$7\frac{1}{2}$	$26,200	$33,200	$42,500	$46,900
8	$27,800	$35,100	$44,900	$50,700
$8\frac{1}{2}$	$29,900	$37,700	$48,100	$57,400
9	$31,400	$39,700	$50,500	$60,300
$9\frac{1}{2}$	$33,400	$42,300	$53,700	$64,200
10	$35,500	$45,000	$56,200	$67,000
$10\frac{1}{2}$	$37,700	$47,600	$59,500	$70,800
11	$40,100	$49,500	$61,800	$73,700
$11\frac{1}{2}$	$40,800	$51,600	$64,500	$76,900
12	–	$54,500	$67,400	$80,400
$12\frac{1}{2}$	–	$57,100	$70,700	$84,300
13	–	$59,600	$73,000	$93,700
$13\frac{1}{2}$	–	$62,300	$76,400	$97,700
14	–	$65,000	$78,800	$98,600
$14\frac{1}{2}$	–	$67,600	$82,100	$99,700

Replacement Cost Once you know the base cost of a home, you can find the house's **replacement cost** by using a **location multiplier**. A location multiplier is used because the same house can be built for different prices in different areas. The cost of labor and materials varies from location to location. Insurance companies have researched these differences in building costs and organized their findings by ZIP codes.

Replacement cost

The cost to replace insured property.

Location multiplier

A chart that helps determine a house's replacement cost, based on its ZIP code location.

EXAMPLE A house of construction class III has a unit count of $10\frac{1}{2}$. The ZIP code is 40412. What is its replacement cost?

From the chart: Unit count is $10\frac{1}{2}$

Class III

Base cost = \$59,500

ZIP code is 40412

Location multiplier = 1.02

$$\begin{array}{r} \$\quad 59{,}5\,00 \\ \times\quad 1.02 \\ \hline 1\;19\,0\;00 \\ +59\;50\;0\;00 \\ \hline \$60{,}69\;0.00 \end{array}$$

The replacement cost is \$60,690.

Location by First 3 Digits of ZIP Code					
State and Zip Code	Location Multiplier	State and Zip Code	Location Multiplier	State and Zip Code	Location Multiplier
Kentucky		**Ohio**		**Indiana**	
400-402	1.02	430-433	1.06	460-462	1.06
403-405	1.02	434, 436	1.16	463-464	1.09
406-410	1.01	435	1.12	465-466	1.04
411-422	.99	437-439	1.04	467-468	1.01
423-424	1.01	440-443	1.10	469, 478-479	.96
425-427	.97	444-450	1.08	470-475	1.05
		451-455, 458	1.07	476-477	1.03
		456-457	1.14		

Exercise C Use the ZIP code chart and the construction class chart to help you find the replacement cost of each home. Write your answers on your paper.

	Unit Count	Class	ZIP Code	Replacement Cost
1)	12	II	42416	_______
2)	$13\frac{1}{2}$	III	46307	_______
3)	10	I	44321	_______
4)	$7\frac{1}{2}$	I	43516	_______
5)	$12\frac{1}{2}$	IV	45624	_______
6)	12	II	46602	_______
7)	$12\frac{1}{2}$	III	47933	_______
8)	9	II	42620	_______
9)	$13\frac{1}{2}$	IV	43414	_______
10)	6	I	41607	_______
11)	$8\frac{1}{2}$	IV	46401	_______
12)	$11\frac{1}{2}$	III	47221	_______

Calculator Practice

Insurance premiums are often given as an annual rate. You may have to budget your earnings to make your annual payment.

Calculator Exercise Use a calculator to help you divide the annual payments by 52 paychecks. Round the payments to the nearest cent.

1) $385

2) $272

3) $776.80

4) $105

5) $125

6) $603

7) $201.34

8) $89.90

9) $149.50

10) $200

11) $136.75

12) $492.50

Lesson 3 Fire Insurance

Face value

The worth printed or written on a policy.

After you find the replacement cost of your home, you can then determine how much insurance to buy. Many people insure their homes for replacement cost plus the value of the items in the home. Insurance is also available for people who live in apartments. The yearly charge for the insurance is called the premium. The amount of insurance protection is called the **face value** of the policy. The premium is found by multiplying the rate per $100 times the number of 100s in the face value of the policy. The rate per $100 varies according to the type of policy.

EXAMPLE

Face value: $23,500
Rate per $100 $.68
There are 235 hundreds in $23,500.

```
    235
×  $.68
$159.80   The yearly premium is $159.80.
```

House fires are tragic. You can protect your house and belongings with fire insurance.

Exercise A Find the yearly premium for each fire insurance policy. Write your answers on your paper.

	Face Value	Rate per $100	Yearly Premium
1)	$52,300	$.96	______
2)	$20,700	$.73	______
3)	$38,000	$.84	______
4)	$71,450	$.88	______
5)	$46,700	$.92	______
6)	$56,700	$.80	______
7)	$48,800	$.92	______
8)	$67,500	$.93	______
9)	$46,730	$.87	______
10)	$79,400	$.96	______
11)	$71,120	$.78	______
12)	$86,200	$.99	______
13)	$120,300	$.88	______
14)	$55,890	$.80	______
15)	$47,000	$1.04	______
16)	$200,000	$.82	______
17)	$77,340	$.70	______
18)	$99,940	$.95	______
19)	$80,000	$.91	______
20)	$104,000	$.89	______

Lesson 4 Auto Insurance

Liability

Insurance that protects the owner against claims resulting from an accident.

Auto liability insurance protects the owner of a car against claims arising from his or her car being involved in an accident. **Liability** insurance can cover both bodily injury and property damage. The premium that you pay for this protection, or coverage, is determined by the amount of protection and the region in which you live.

Coverage for a 50/100/25 Policy

Maximum of $50,000 for claim per injured person → 50/100/25 ← Maximum of $25,000 for property damage

↑

Maximum of $100,000 for claim per accident

Liability Insurance Rates							
	Bodily Injury				Property Damage		
Region	10/20	20/40	25/50	50/100	5,000	10,000	25,000
1	$101	$139	$152	$182	$68	$71	$73
2	$59	$81	$89	$106	$52	$55	$56
3	$50	$69	$75	$90	$56	$59	$60
4	$40	$55	$60	$72	$48	$50	$52
5	$53	$73	$80	$95	$47	$49	$51

EXAMPLE Mr. Tanaka lives in Region 3. His coverage is 50/100/25. Using the chart, his premium is $90 plus $60, or $150.

Exercise A Determine the amount of the basic premium for each liability insurance policy. Write your answers on your paper.

	Coverage	Region	Premium
1)	20/40/5	4	______
2)	20/40/25	1	______
3)	20/40/10	3	______
4)	25/50/10	2	______
5)	10/20/10	5	______
6)	20/40/25	3	______
7)	50/100/25	3	______
8)	20/40/5	2	______
9)	50/100/10	1	______
10)	10/20/10	3	______
11)	10/20/25	4	______
12)	25/50/25	2	______
13)	10/20/5	4	______
14)	20/40/5	3	______
15)	50/100/25	1	______
16)	20/40/25	5	______
17)	50/100/5	2	______
18)	10/20/10	4	______
19)	20/40/10	2	______
20)	25/50/5	1	______

Once the auto insurance agent has determined the basic premium for auto liability insurance coverage, the agent consults a **rate factor** table. Women pay less than men for the same insurance coverage. People pay less for insurance if they drive the car for pleasure or farm use than if they drive the car to work each day. Owners pay more if they use their car for business.

Rate factor

An amount by which the basic premium is multiplied.

Rate Factor Table

Age of Driver	Gender	Pleasure Use	Drives Less Than 10 mi. to Work	Drives 10 mi. or More to Work	Car Used for Work	Farm Use
17	M	1.80	1.90	2.20	2.30	1.55
	F	1.55	1.65	1.95	2.05	1.30
18	M	1.70	1.80	2.10	2.20	1.45
	F	1.40	1.50	1.80	1.90	1.15
19	M	1.60	1.70	2.00	2.10	1.35
	F	1.25	1.35	1.65	1.75	1.00
20	M	1.50	1.60	1.90	2.00	1.25
	F	1.10	1.20	1.50	1.60	.85

If you have a car accident, liability insurance pays for car repairs. It also lowers your medical costs if you are injured.

EXAMPLE Sara and Lito both have a basic insurance premium of \$131. Each is 19 years old and drives 7 miles to work. Sara's premium is \$176.85 (\$131 × 1.35). Lito's premium is \$222.70 (\$131 × 1.70).

PROBLEM SOLVING

Exercise B Find each person's insurance premium by multiplying the basic premium by the appropriate factor from the table.

1) Heidi is 17 years old. She drives 6 miles to work. Her basic premium is \$135.
2) Michael's basic premium is \$128. He uses the car only on the farm. He is 17 years old.
3) Gene is 18 years old. His basic premium is \$208. He uses the car only for pleasure.
4) Basamih is 20 years old. Her basic premium is \$147. She drives 16 miles to work.
5) Rudy drives 8 miles to work. He is 19 years old. His basic premium is \$183.
6) Ricardo is 20 years old. He uses the car in his work. His basic premium is \$236.
7) Angela is 18 years old. She drives 10 miles to work. Her basic premium is \$188.
8) Ronny drives 9 miles to work. He is 20 years old. His basic premium is \$306.
9) Ming is 17 years old. He uses his car for pleasure. His basic premium is \$294.
10) Sheila is 19 years old. She drives 14 miles to work. Her basic premium is \$289.

Lesson 5 Life Insurance

Beneficiary
A person who receives the face value of an insurance policy.

Endowment insurance
Insurance where premium is paid and face value is paid to the insured.

Limited-payment life insurance
Insurance that covers the policyholder until death.

Ordinary life insurance
Insurance where payments are made as long as the insured is alive.

Term insurance
Insurance where payments and insurance last for a fixed amount of time.

People buy life insurance to protect the dependents of the insured person. If the insured person dies, the person's **beneficiary** is paid the face value of the life insurance policy. A person can buy different kinds of life insurance. The four basic kinds of life insurance are:

1. **Term Insurance.** Premiums are paid only for a certain time. The policyholder is insured only during the stated time. Benefits are paid only if the policyholder dies during the term of insurance.

2. **Ordinary Life.** Premiums are paid until the policyholder dies. When the policyholder dies, the beneficiary is paid the face value of the policy.

3. **Limited-Payment Life Insurance.** The policyholder is insured until death. Premiums are paid for a limited period of time (20 or 30 years, usually). This is also called 20-payment or 30-payment life insurance.

4. **Endowment.** The policyholder pays premiums for a limited period of time (20 or 30 years, usually). At the end of this period of time, the policyholder is paid the face value of the policy. If the policyholder dies during the payment period, then the beneficiary is paid the face value of the policy.

The premiums are the lowest for term insurance. Ordinary life insurance costs more. Limited-payment insurance is more expensive. The most expensive insurance is endowment insurance.

Many families think about their life insurance needs after a baby is born. They want to make sure the child's needs will be met.

Annual premiums are based not only on the kind of insurance people buy. The face value of the policy raises or lowers the cost. People's age, health, or the work they do may change the premiums. They may pay more or less if they are married or single.

Tables are one tool to help insurance companies decide how much premiums will be. The premium tables on the next page show costs based on a policyholder's age. They show that the type of insurance changes how much a person pays.

Here are some premium tables for the four types of life insurance described:

Annual Premium Per $1,000 of Term Insurance					
Age		5-Year Term Policy		10-Year Term Policy	
Male	Female	$5,000-$9,999	$10,000-$19,999	$5,000-$9,999	$10,000-$19,999
20	23	$6.44	$5.69	$6.51	$5.76
25	28	$6.59	$5.84	$6.72	$5.97
30	33	$6.88	$6.13	$7.19	$6.44
35	38	$7.56	$6.81	$8.27	$7.52
40	43	$9.11	$8.36	$10.24	$9.49
45	48	$11.60	$10.85	$13.43	$12.68
50	53	$15.66	$14.91	$18.47	$17.72
55	58	$21.95	$21.20	$26.28	$25.53
60	63	$31.80	$31.05	$38.40	$37.65

Annual Life Insurance Premium Rates per $1,000							
		Ordinary Life		20-Payment Life		20-Year Endowment	
Age		$5,000-	$10,000-	$5,000-	$10,000-	$5,000-	$10,000
Male	Female	$9,999	$19,999	$9,999	$19,999	$9,999	$19,999
20	23	$15.07	$14.32	$22.90	$22.15	$46.70	$45.95
25	28	$17.08	$16.33	$25.43	$24.68	$46.93	$46.18
30	33	$19.63	$18.88	$28.42	$27.67	$47.36	$46.61
35	38	$22.94	$22.19	$32.02	$31.27	$48.19	$47.44
40	43	$27.25	$26.50	$36.40	$35.65	$49.66	$48.91
45	48	$32.85	$32.10	$41.72	$40.97	$52.01	$51.26
50	53	$40.23	$39.48	$48.33	$47.58	$55.76	$55.01
55	58	$49.93	$49.18	$56.64	$55.89	$61.64	$60.89
60	63	$62.47	$61.72	$67.70	$66.85	$70.59	$69.84

EXAMPLE What is the annual premium for a 38-year-old woman if she buys $15,000 of 20-payment life insurance?

From the chart: Rate per $1,000 = $31.27
Number of 1,000s in $15,000 = 15

$$\begin{array}{r} \$\ 31.27 \\ \times \quad 15 \\ \hline \$469.05 \end{array}$$ Annual premium

You can see from the premium tables that gender affects the cost of insurance. Also, the older you are when you buy insurance, the more you pay.

To determine the annual premium, find the type of insurance in the charts, find the correct age and gender, and read the rate per $1,000 of face value. You multiply this rate by the number of 1,000s in the face value of the policy.

Exercise A Find the annual premium for each life insurance policy below. Use the table to help you.

1) 45-year-old man, $10,000 5-year term policy

2) 48-year-old woman, $14,000 20-payment life policy

3) 40-year-old man, $6,000 ordinary life policy $

4) 58-year-old woman, $14,000 10-year term policy

5) 33-year-old woman, $15,000 20-year endowment policy

6) 20-year-old man, $17,000 20-year endowment policy

7) 40-year-old man, $19,000 20-payment life policy

8) 50-year-old man, $16,000 10-year term policy

9) 50-year-old man, $13,000 ordinary life policy

10) 28-year-old woman, $17,000 20-year endowment policy

11) 38-year-old woman, $9,000 ordinary life policy

12) 30-year-old man, $8,900 10-year term policy

Chapter 15 Review

Use this chart of payroll deductions for major medical insurance to find the annual premium for each family described below. The person named is the employee.

Rest Easy Major Medical Program – Semimonthly Payroll Deductions	
Employee only	$12.22
Employee and spouse	$14.98
Employee and family	$23.67

1) Ung and his wife and two children

2) Linda and her husband

3) Max Bauer

Answer these questions about replacement cost.

4) The base cost of a house is $48,600 and the location multiplier is 1.08. What is the house's replacement cost?

5) The base cost of a house is $67,400 and the location multiplier is .97. What is the house's replacement cost?

Find the yearly premium for each fire insurance policy.

6) The policy's face value is $52,400. The rate per $100 is $.96.

7) The policy's face value is $67,000. The rate per $100 is $.80.

Use this rate chart to find the basic premium for each auto liability insurance policy described.

Liability Insurance Rates							
	Bodily Injury				Property Damage		
Region	10/20	20/40	25/50	50/100	5,000	10,000	25,000
1	$101	$139	$152	$182	$68	$71	$73
2	$59	$81	$89	$106	$52	$55	$56
3	$50	$69	$75	$90	$56	$59	$60
4	$40	$55	$60	$72	$48	$50	$52

8) 20/40/10 coverage; Region 3

9) 25/50/25 coverage; Region 2

Find each person's insurance premium by multiplying the basic premium by the appropriate factor from this table.

Age of Driver	Gender	Pleasure Use	Drives Less Than 10 mi. to Work	Drives 10 mi. or More to Work	Car Used for Work
17	M	1.80	1.90	2.20	2.30
	F	1.55	1.65	1.95	2.05
18	M	1.70	1.80	2.10	2.20
	F	1.40	1.50	1.80	1.90
19	M	1.60	1.70	2.00	2.10
	F	1.25	1.35	1.65	1.75

10) Tooky is 18 years old. She drives 12 miles to work. Her basic premium is $165.

11) Mike is 19 years old. He uses his car for pleasure. His basic premium is $147.

12) Denise is 17 years old. She drives 6 miles to work. Her basic premium is $184.

Tell if the life insurance described is *term life, ordinary life, limited-payment life,* or *endowment life* insurance.

13) The policyholder pays premiums for a limited period of time. At the end of this period of time, the policyholder is paid the face amount of the policy.

14) The policyholder pays premiums for a limited period of time. The policyholder is insured only during this period.

15) The policyholder pays premiums until death. At death the beneficiary is paid the face value of the policy.

Test Taking Tip

When studying for a test, review the topics in the chapter, then make up a practice test for yourself.

Chapter 16

Lawn Care

Have you ever thought about all the ways you use measurement to make your life run more smoothly? Besides finding your height and weight or adjusting recipes, you can use measurement to help you calculate measurements needed to keep your property attractive. Fertilizing lawns, fencing yards, and planting hedges all require measurement and mathematics. Even pouring cement for sidewalks and patios is made easier if you know how to use mathematics to help you.

In Chapter 16, you will find ways to use formulas to help you compute area, perimeter, and volume.

Goals for Learning

- To find perimeter and area
- To calculate cost for hedging and fencing
- To measure to the nearest sixteenth of an inch
- To use a ruler to interpret scale drawings
- To find volume of rectangular prisms
- To calculate cost, using volume and cubic yards

Enclosing Your Yard

Perimeter

The distance around all the sides of a polygon.

One way to enclose your yard is to plant a hedge around its **perimeter**. To find the cost of putting a hedge around the yard, you first add the length of the sides of the area to be enclosed. You then multiply the cost of the hedge per yard by this answer.

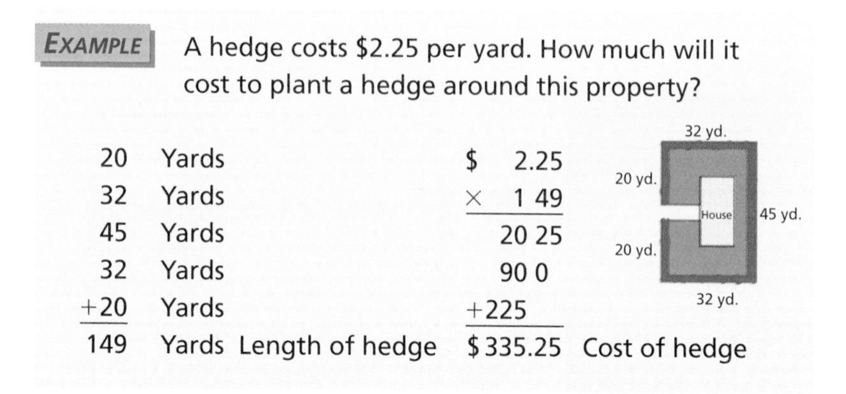
EXAMPLE A hedge costs $2.25 per yard. How much will it cost to plant a hedge around this property?

20	Yards		$ 2.25	
32	Yards		× 1 49	
45	Yards		20 25	
32	Yards		90 0	
+20	Yards		+225	
149	Yards	Length of hedge	$335.25	Cost of hedge

Exercise A Find the cost of planting a hedge along the dark lines for each property. Hedging costs $2.25 per yard. Round to the nearest cent.

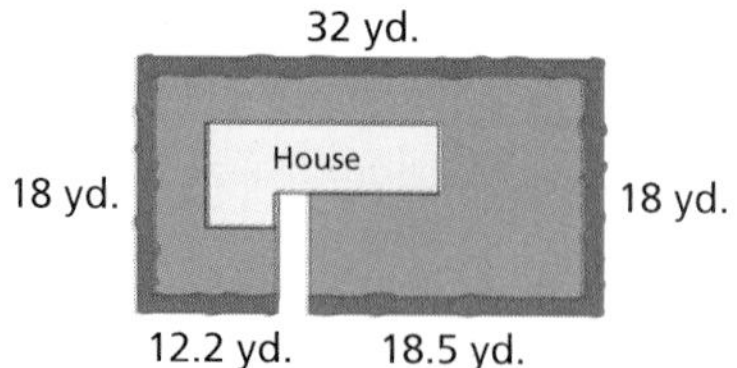

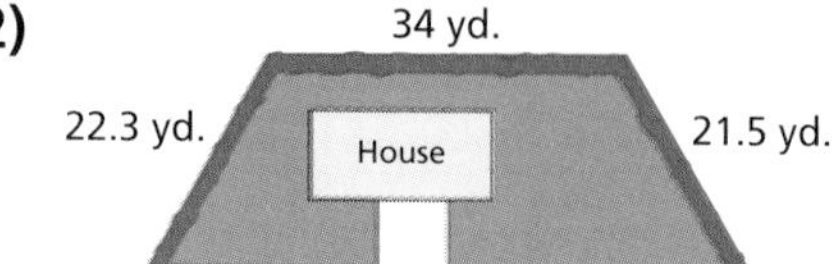

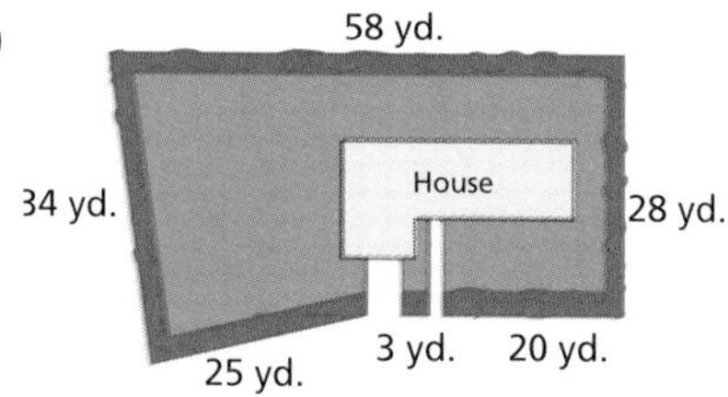

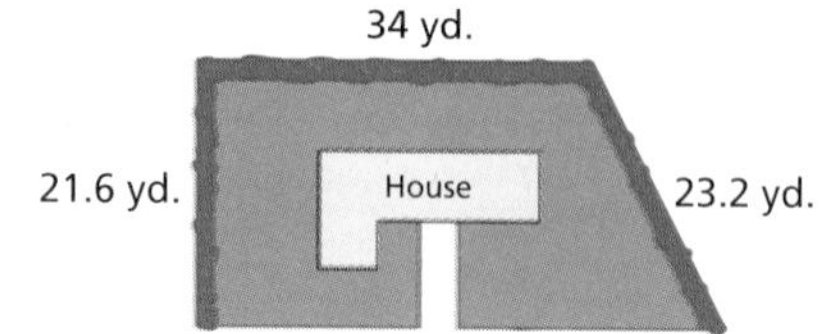

5)

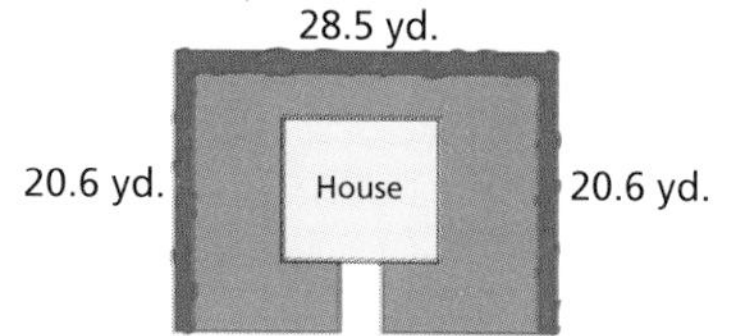

6)

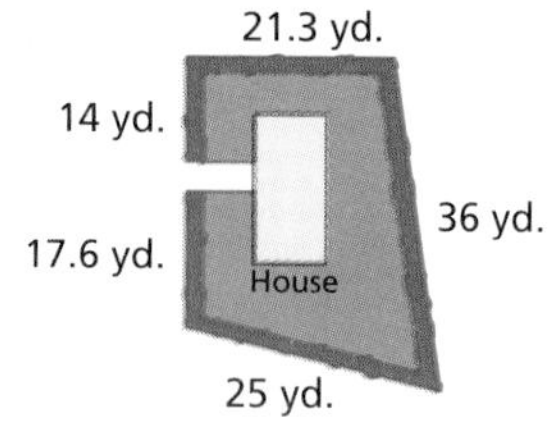

Another way to enclose your yard is with fencing.

EXAMPLE Find the cost of fencing in this yard. Chain-link fencing costs $6.50 per yard and fence posts cost $3.75 each. Gates cost $23.25 each.

Step 1 Find the length of fence needed.

18.3	Yards
26.4	Yards
30	Yards
26.4	Yards
+11	Yards
112.1	Yards

Step 2 Find the cost of fencing.

$$\begin{array}{r} 112.1 \\ \times\ \$6.50 \\ \hline 56050 \\ +6726 \\ \hline \$728.650 \end{array}$$

The total cost is $886.90.

Step 3 Find the cost of fence posts.

$ 3.75	Cost per fence post
× 36	Number of fence posts
22 50	
+112 5	
$135.00	

Step 4 Find the total cost.

$728.65	Fencing
$135.00	Fence posts
+$ 23.25	Gate
$886.90	

Exercise B Find the total cost of fencing in each yard. Use the prices from the example above.

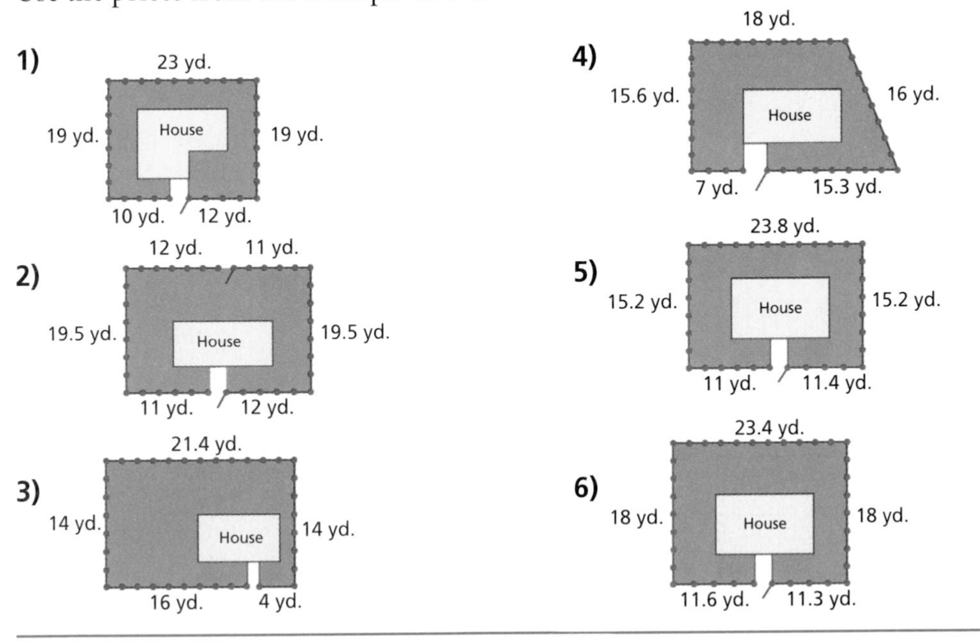

Lesson 2 Measuring in Inches

Line segment
A part of a line.

If you can measure with a ruler, then you will be better able to make plans for your work in the yard. A ruler is divided into inches and each inch can be divided into 16 parts as shown below.

EXAMPLE How long is each **line segment** to the nearest sixteenth of an inch?

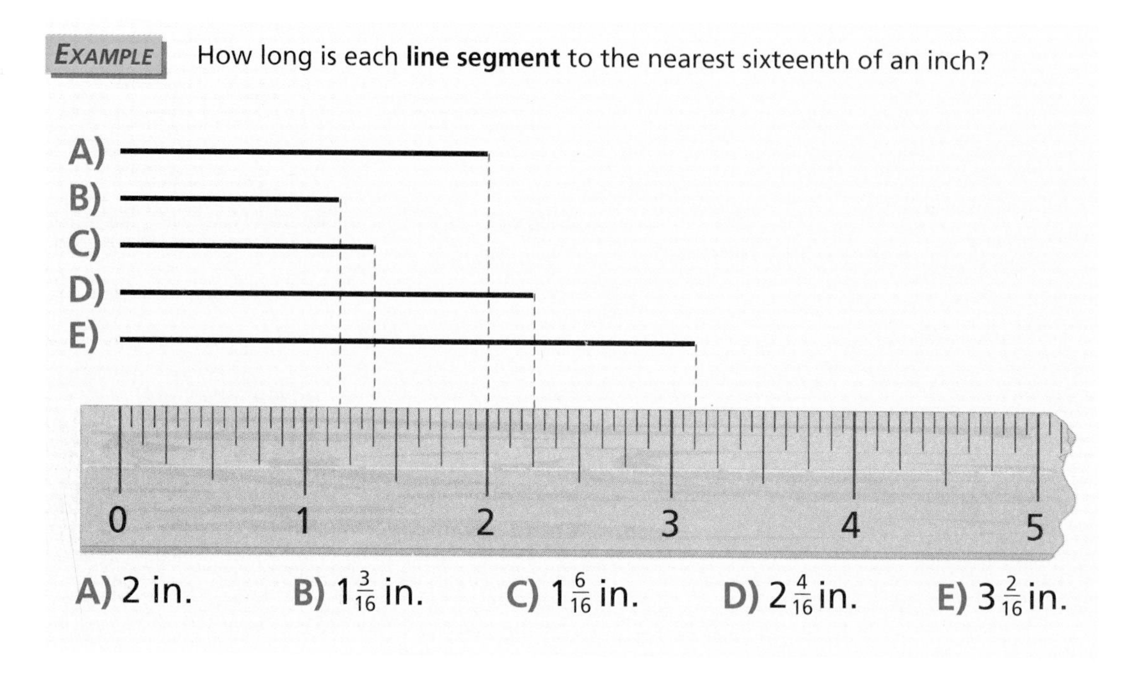

A) 2 in. B) $1\frac{3}{16}$ in. C) $1\frac{6}{16}$ in. D) $2\frac{4}{16}$ in. E) $3\frac{2}{16}$ in.

Exercise A Use a ruler to find the length of each line segment to the nearest sixteenth inch.

1) ______________________________
2) __________
3) __________
4) __________________________________
5) _
6) __
7) ____________________
8) ______________
9) ____________
10) __________________________
11) ________________________
12) ______________________________________

Lesson 3 Using a Scale Drawing

Scale drawing
A picture that shows relative sizes of real objects.

Scale
Ratio of the real size of an object or area to the map size.

When Denise plans her spring yard work, she makes this **scale drawing**. The **scale** at the bottom of the drawing means that $\frac{1}{16}$ inch equals 2 feet in the actual yard. Now Denise can make her plans without being outside in the yard.

EXAMPLE What is the actual length of the lot?
Use a ruler and measure 92 16ths.

$\frac{1}{2 \text{ feet}} = \frac{92}{N}$ ← Number of 16ths

$2 \times 92 = N$

$184 = N$

The lot is 184 feet long.

Exercise A Find these dimensions of the actual lot.

The length of the:		*The width of the:*	
1) house	_____	**7)** lot	_____
2) garage	_____	**8)** garden	_____
3) driveway	_____	**9)** driveway	_____
4) sidewalk	_____	**10)** patio	_____
5) patio	_____	**11)** house	_____
6) garden	_____	**12)** sidewalk	_____

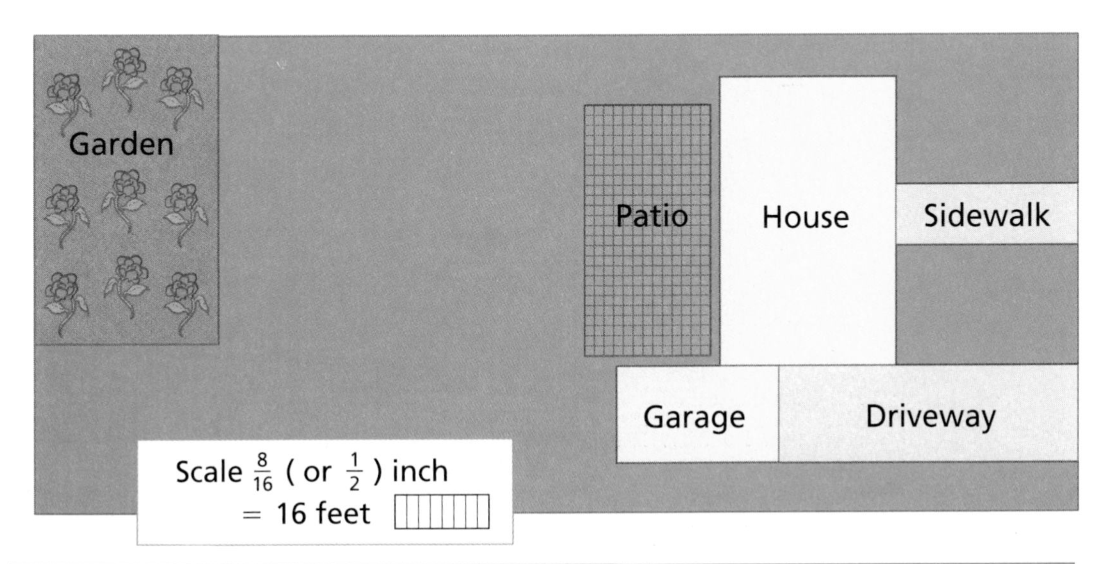

Lesson 4 Area

Some yard work requires knowing the area of the yard. To find the area of a rectangle, you can multiply the length by the width. Area is given in square units, like square inches (in.^{2}) or square yards (yd.^{2}).

EXAMPLE Find the area of these rectangles:

A)

$$\begin{array}{r} 13 \\ \times 7 \\ \hline 91 \end{array} \text{ in.}^2$$

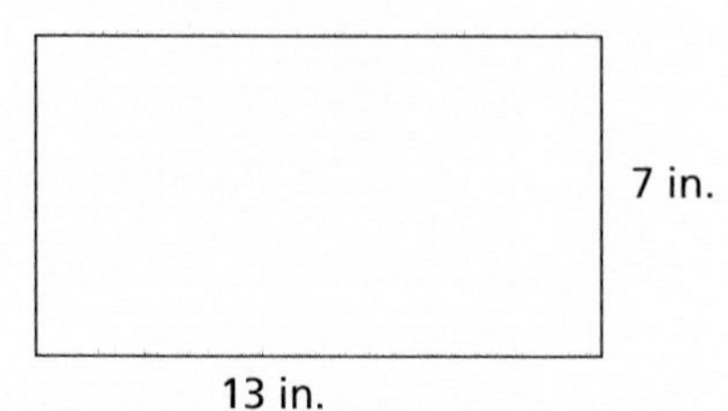

B)

$$\begin{array}{r} 16 \\ \times 8 \\ \hline 128 \end{array} \text{ ft.}^2$$

$$\begin{array}{r} 12 \\ \times 7 \\ \hline 84 \end{array} \text{ ft.}^2$$

$$\begin{array}{rl} 128 & \text{ft.}^2 \\ +84 & \text{ft.}^2 \\ \hline 212 & \text{ft.}^2 \end{array}$$

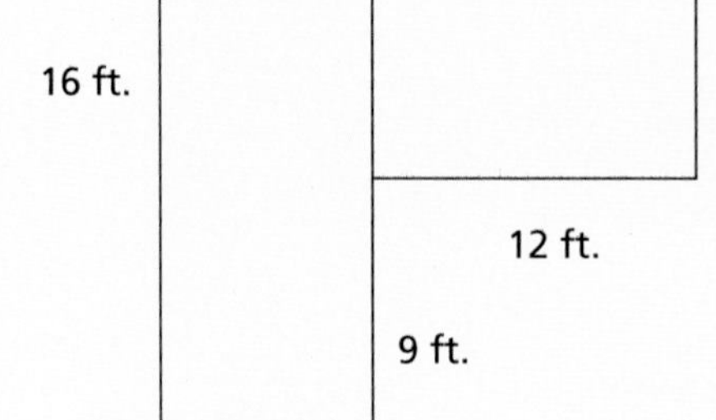

Exercise A Find the area of each shape.

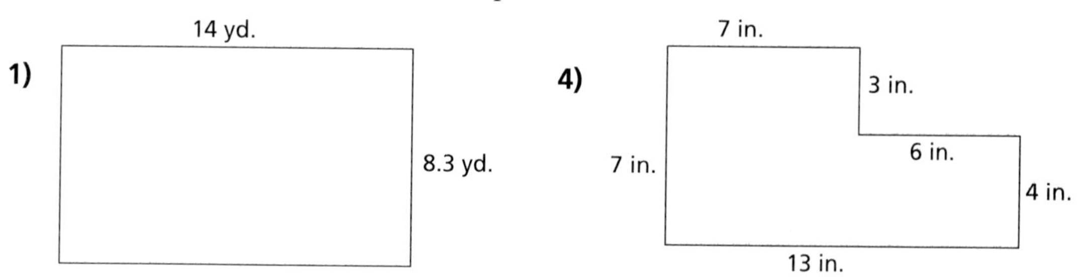

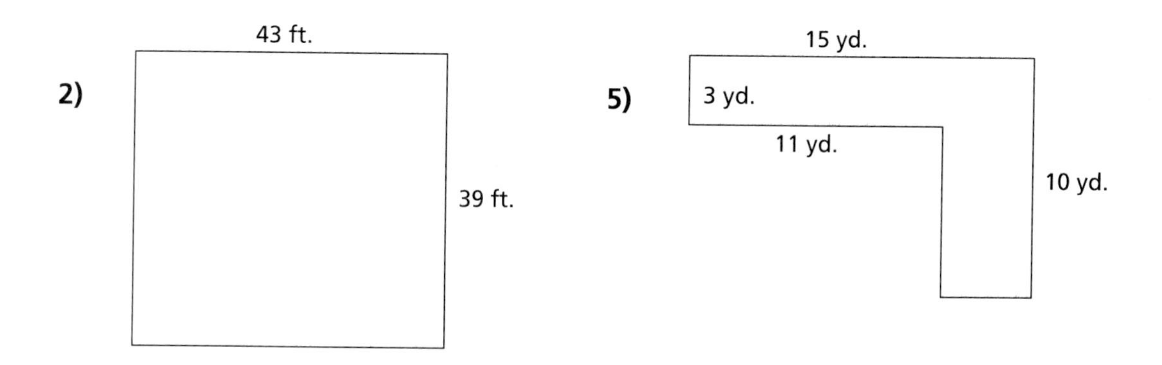

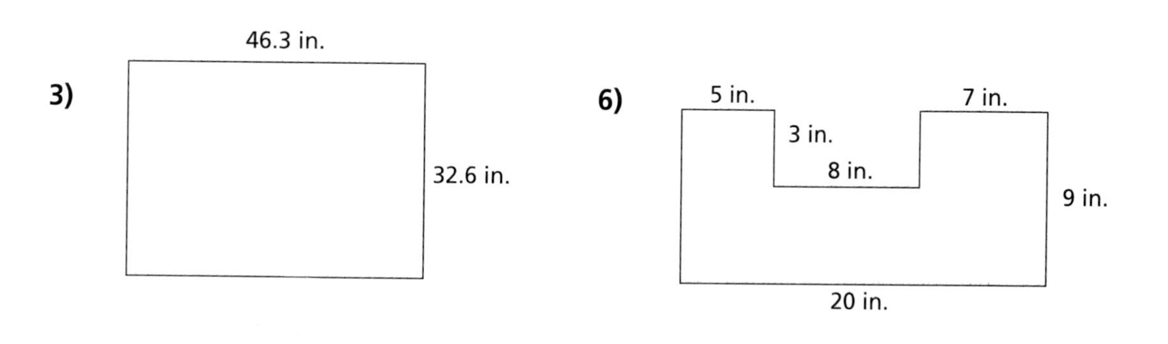

Lesson 5 Fertilizing Your Yard

Many people apply fertilizer to their lawn to make the grass healthier. If you apply too much, then it may kill the grass. For best results, you should use 5 lb. of fertilizer per 200 square feet of lawn. To find the number of square feet of lawn, follow these steps:

Step 1 Find the total area of the lot.

Step 2 Find the area of any places that are not to be fertilized.

Step 3 Subtract to find the area of the lawn.

Step 4 Divide by 200 to find the number of 5-lb. bags of fertilizer needed. Round to the nearest whole number.

EXAMPLE Find the amount of fertilizer needed for this lawn.

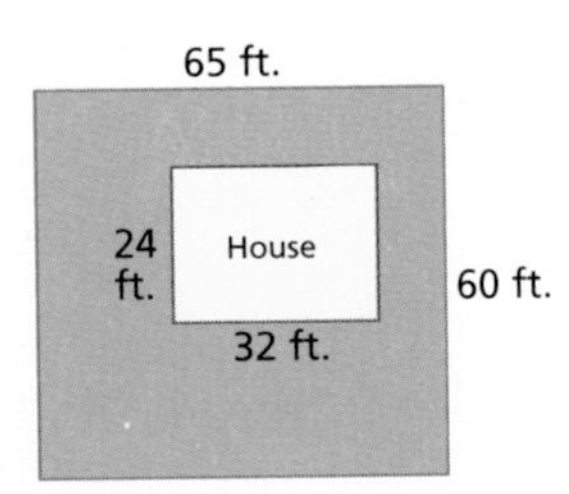

Step 1 Area of Lot

$$\begin{array}{rl} 65 & \text{feet} \\ \times\ 60 & \text{feet} \\ \hline 3{,}900 & \text{sq. feet} \end{array}$$

Step 2 Area of House

$$\begin{array}{rl} 32 & \\ \times\ 24 & \\ \hline 128 & \\ +64 & \\ \hline 768 & \text{sq. feet} \end{array}$$

Step 3 Area of Lawn

$$\begin{array}{rl} 3{,}900 & \\ -\ 768 & \\ \hline 3{,}132 & \text{sq. feet} \end{array}$$

Step 4 Amount of Fertilizer

$$\begin{array}{r} 15.6 \\ 200\,\overline{)\,3{,}132.0} \\ -2\ 00 \\ \hline 1\ 132 \\ -1\ 000 \\ \hline 132\ 0 \\ -120\ 0 \\ \hline 12\ 0 \end{array}$$

16 bags of fertilizer are needed for this lawn.

You should spread fertilizer evenly on your lawn for best results.

Exercise A Find the amount of fertilizer that you need to fertilize the shaded area of each lot.

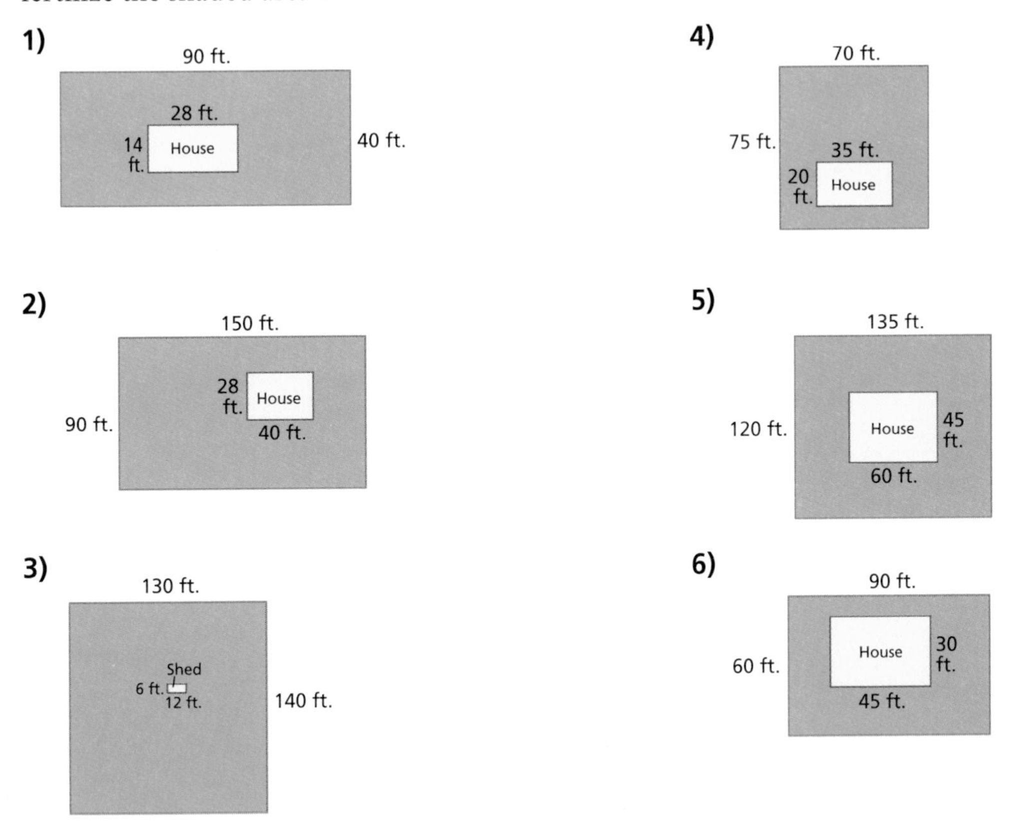

Lesson 6 Volume

Volume

The amount of space occupied in three dimensions.

Cubic

Measurement related to volume.

Rectangular prism

A solid figure with bases or ends that are parallel and sides that are rectangles.

For some jobs and tasks you need to know the **volume** of a container. Volume is given in **cubic** units, like cubic feet (ft.^{3}) or cubic yards (yd.^{3}). You can find the volume of a **rectangular prism** by multiplying the length times the width times the height, or depth.

EXAMPLE

Length = 4 yd.
Width = 2 yd.
Height = 3 yd.
Volume = $l \times w \times h$
= $4 \times 2 \times 3$
= 24 yd.^{3}

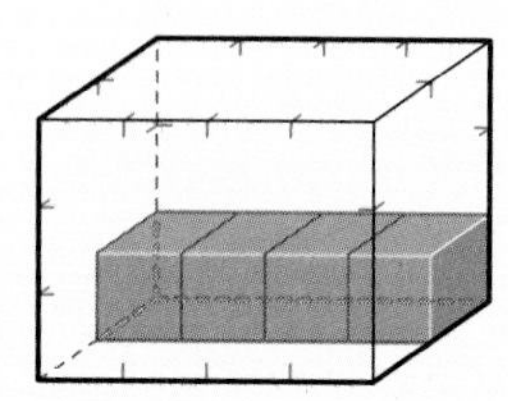

1 row of 4 yd.^{3} (4)

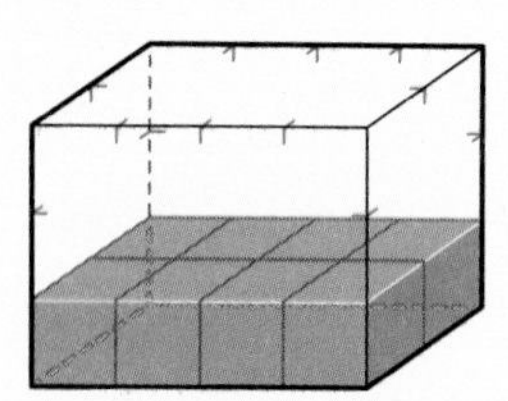

2 rows of 4 yd.^{3} (4×2)

3 layers of 8 yd.^{3} ($4 \times 2 \times 3$)

Exercise A Find the volume of each rectangular prism.

1)

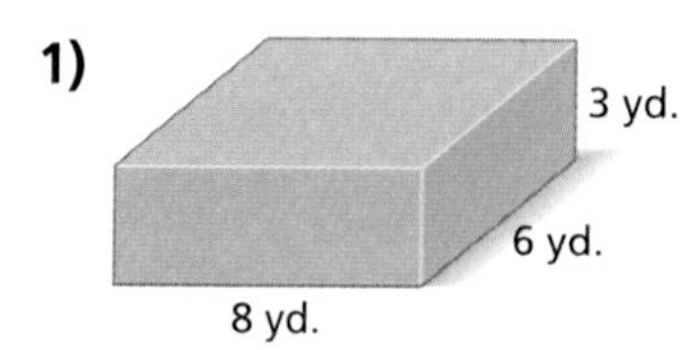

2)

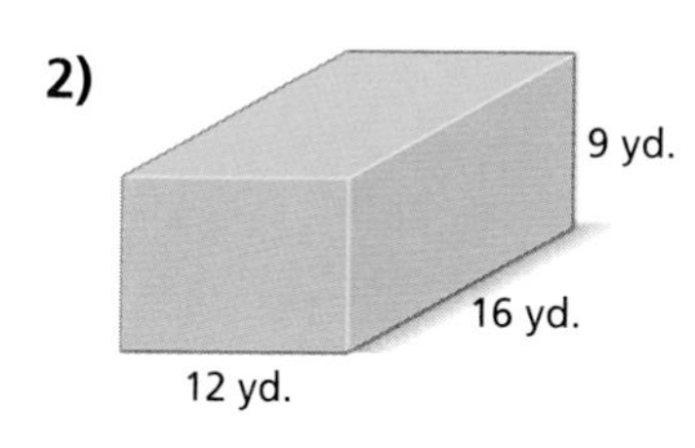

3)

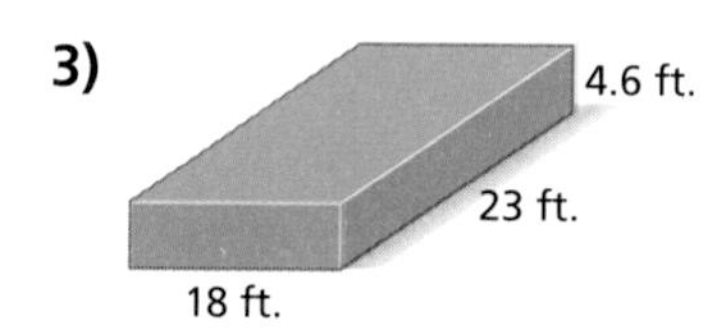

4)

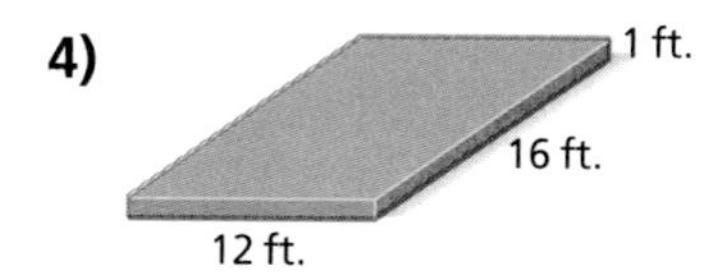

5)

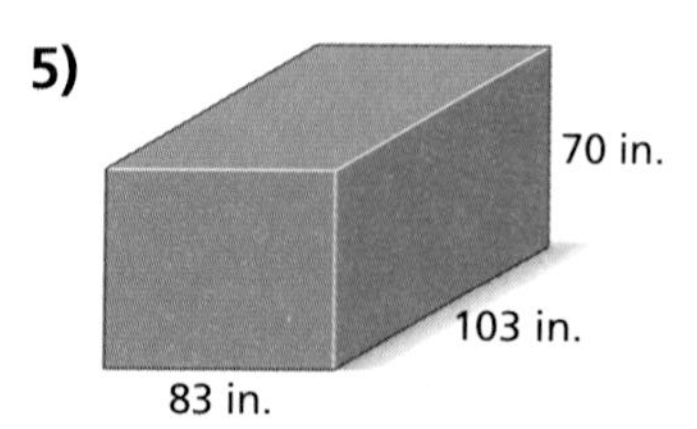

6)

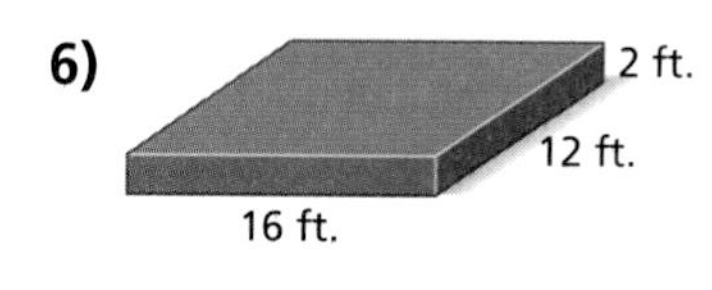

7)

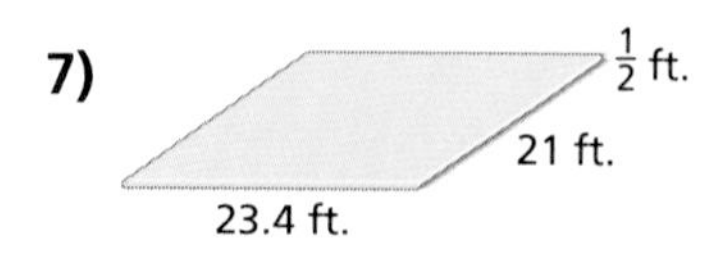

8)

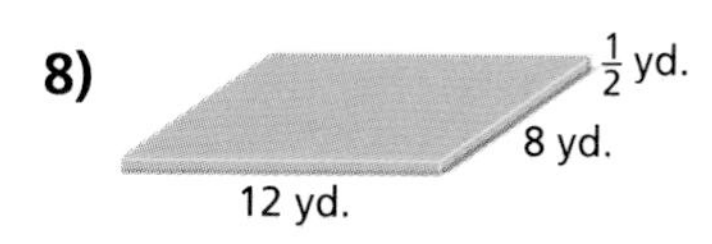

Lesson 7 Concrete

You might pour concrete in some yard projects, such as installing a patio or replacing a driveway or sidewalk. Concrete is ordered by the cubic yard. You can find the number of cubic yards of concrete that you will need by finding the volume of the space that the concrete will fill.

EXAMPLE How much concrete will you need to replace a sidewalk that is 18 yards long and 2 yards wide? The sidewalk is to be 4 inches thick. Round up to the next higher whole number. Express 4 inches as a yard.

$$\frac{\text{inches}}{\text{yard}} \quad \frac{4}{36} = \frac{1}{9}$$

$$V = l \times w \times h$$

$$V = 18 \times 2 \times \frac{1}{9}$$

$$V = 4$$

You need 4 cubic yards of concrete.

Exercise A Find the amount of concrete needed for each project. Assume that 4 inches is to be the thickness.

1)

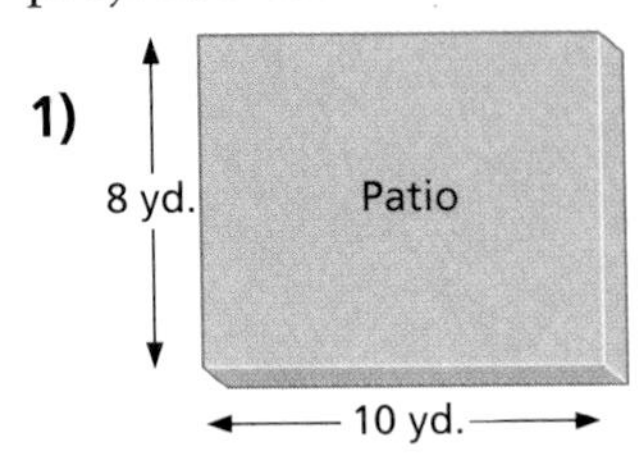

2) 2 yd. Sidewalk 36 yd.

3)

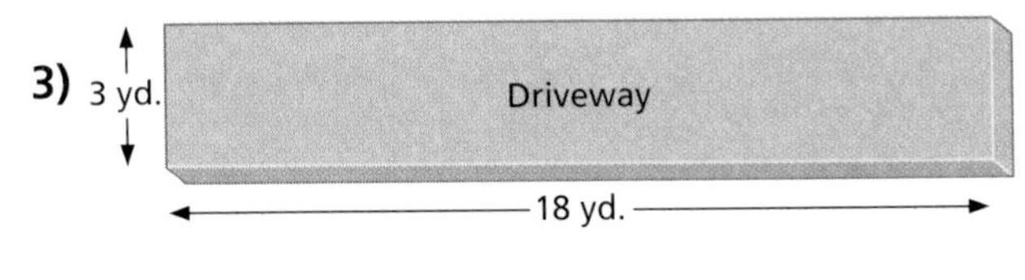

4)

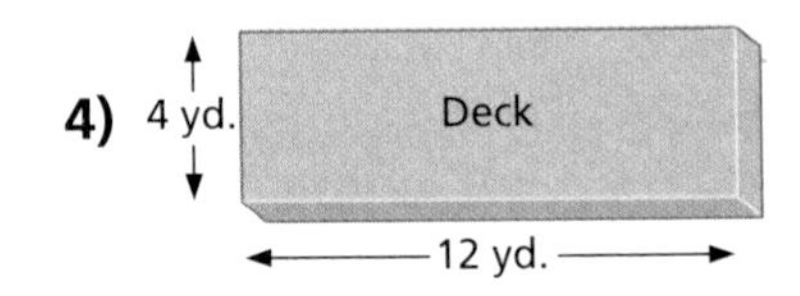

Exercise B Find the cost of the concrete needed for these projects if concrete costs $80 per cubic yard. Do not round your answers.

	Project	Dimensions	Amount of Concrete	Cost of Concrete
1)	Driveway	$3 \times 48 \times \frac{1}{6}$	______	______
2)	Patio	$4 \times 6 \times \frac{1}{6}$	______	______
3)	Sidewalk	$1 \times 12 \times .1$	______	______
4)	Wall	$14 \times 21 \times .2$	______	______
5)	Deck	$6 \times 5 \times \frac{1}{6}$	______	______

Calculator Practice You can use a calculator to help you solve proportion problems.

EXAMPLE

$$\frac{25}{■} = \frac{5}{11}$$

Step 1 Find the cross products.

Step 2 25 [×] 11 [=] 275. While 275 is still on the display, press [÷] 5.

275 [÷] 5 [=] 55

$$\frac{25}{N} \times \frac{5}{11}$$

$$N \times 5 = 25 \times 11$$

$$N = \frac{25 \times 11}{5}$$

$$N = 55$$

Calculator Exercise Use a calculator to help you solve these proportions.

1) $\frac{5}{16} = \frac{N}{256}$

2) $\frac{7}{28} = \frac{N}{308}$

3) $\frac{N}{16} = \frac{7}{56}$

4) $\frac{N}{576} = \frac{7}{18}$

Chapter 16 Review

Find the perimeter of each polygon.

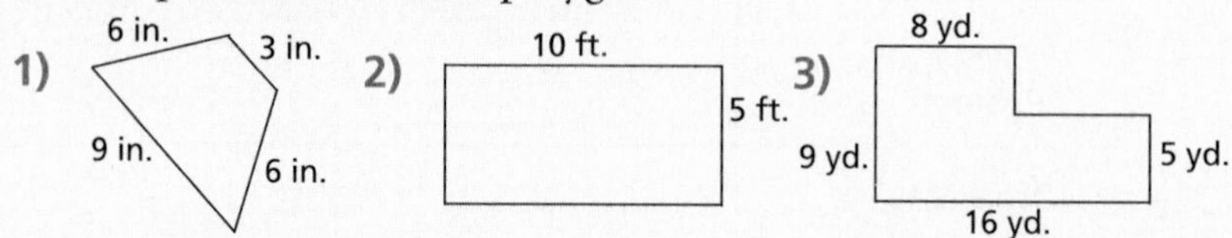

Find the cost of planting a hedge along the dark lines for each property. Hedging costs $2.38 per yard.

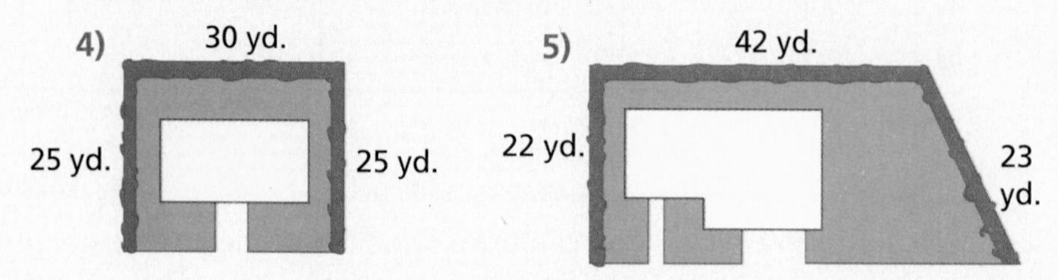

Measure each line segment to the nearest $\frac{1}{16}$ inch.

6) ______________________

7) ______________________

Use a ruler and this scale drawing of a yard to help you answer the following questions.

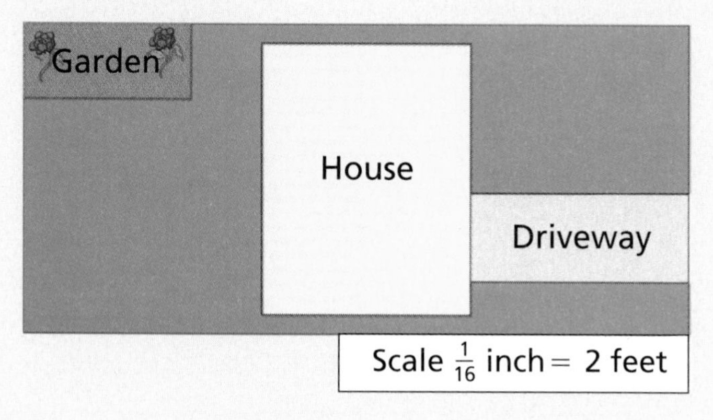

8) What is the width of the garden?

9) What is the length of the driveway?

10) What is the width of the house?

11) What is the length of the garden?

Find the area of each polygon.

12) **13)**

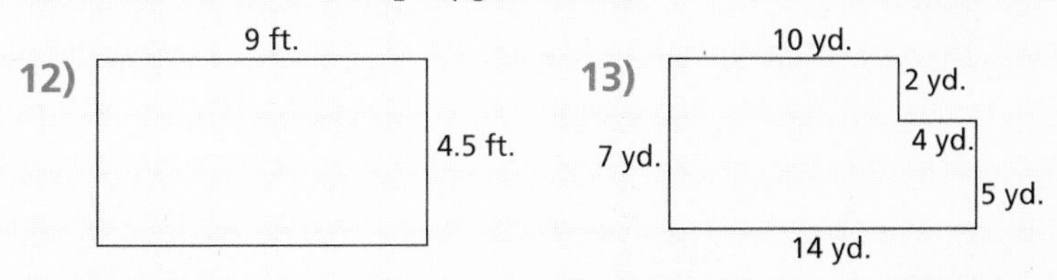

Find the number of bags of fertilizer needed to fertilize the shaded area of each lawn. You need a 5-lb. bag of fertilizer per 200 square feet.

14) **15)**

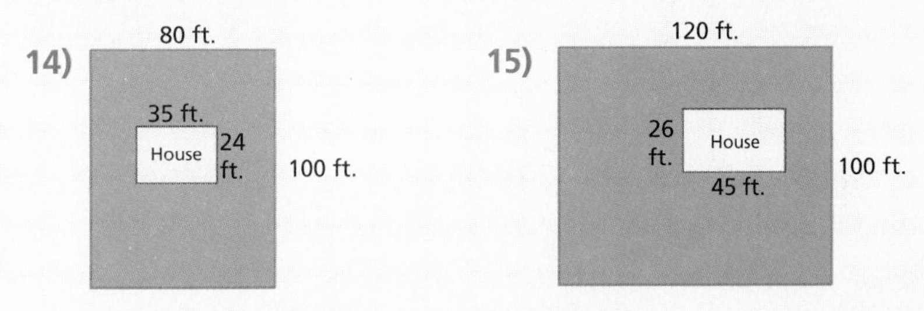

Find the volume of each rectangular prism.

16) **17)**

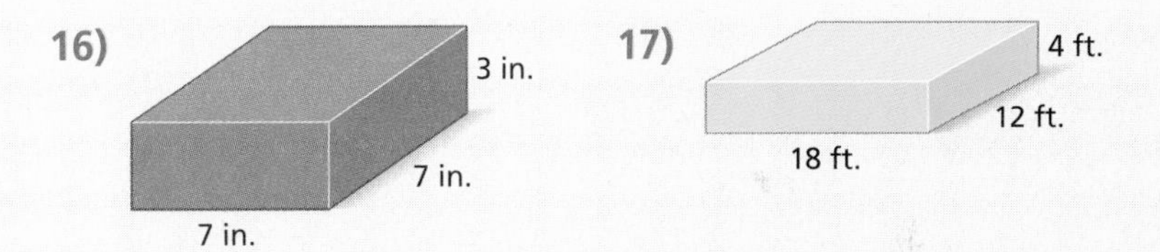

Find the cost of the concrete that you will need for these projects if concrete costs $80 per cubic yard.

18) Sidewalk 1 yd. by 10 yd. by .1 yd.

19) Driveway 4 yd. by 20 yd. by .16 yd.

20) Patio 5 yd. by 8 yd. by .1 yd.

Test Taking Tip When you read a question, notice what it is *not* asking for in your answer.

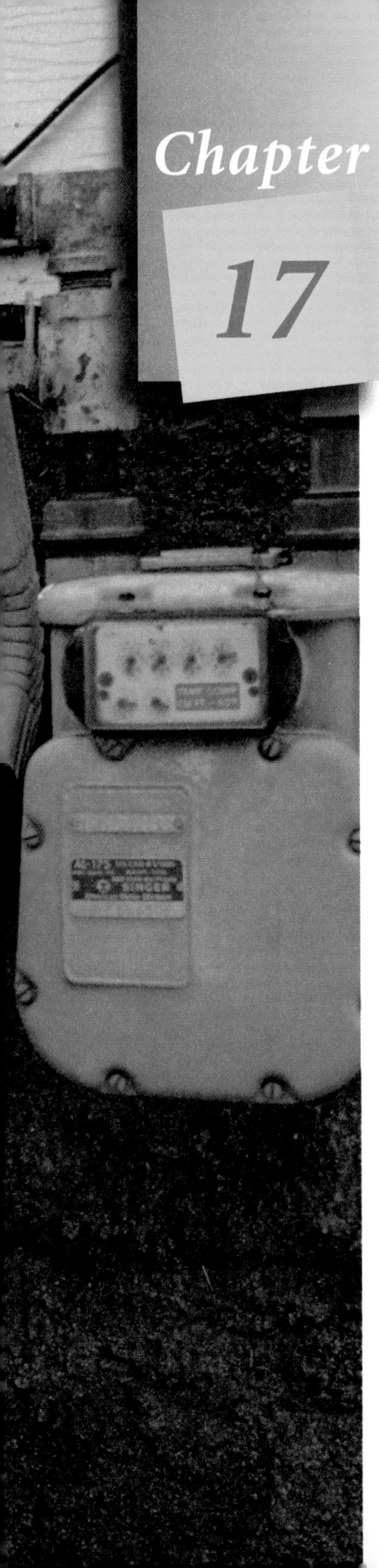

Chapter 17

Using Energy

Computers have changed the way many businesses operate. Businesses can use computers to help calculate costs, issue bills for customers, even allow customers to pay by phone. However, there is still at least one job that computers do not do. Take a guess what that job is. It is the job of a meter reader. These employees still drive and visit apartments, houses, and other buildings to read water, gas, or electric meters. The numbers the meter reader records tell the company how much of something a customer has used. Try to locate one of the meters where you live and read it as the meter reader would!

In Chapter 17, you will learn more about reading meters and calculating the costs of energy products such as gas.

Goals for Learning

- To read a meter dial
- To convert from hours of use to kilowatt-hours
- To find the amount of savings with different wattage bulbs
- To convert gas readings to hundreds of cubic feet
- To convert from Celsius to Fahrenheit, and from Fahrenheit to Celsius

Lesson 1 Kilowatt-Hours

Kilowatt
A unit of electrical power.

Watt
A unit of electrical power.

The amount of electricity a household uses is measured in **kilowatts.** However, light bulbs and electrical appliances in the home are labeled to show their power requirements in **watts.** You need to be able to convert watts to kilowatts to understand your electric bill. *Kilo* means "one thousand." A kilowatt is 1,000 watts.

EXAMPLE How many kilowatts do 3,000 watts equal?
To convert watts to kilowatts, divide the watts by 1,000.

$$\begin{array}{r} 3 \\ 1{,}000\,\overline{)\,3{,}000} \\ \underline{3{,}000} \\ 0 \end{array}$$

3,000 watts = 3 kilowatts

There is an easier way to convert watts to kilowatts. Just move the decimal point three places to the left.

EXAMPLES 3,450 watts = 3.450 kilowatts

28 watts = .028 kilowatts

Electricity travels to your house from large power plants.

Exercise A Convert these watts to kilowatts.

1) 2,000 watts
2) 1,500 watts
3) 3,500 watts
4) 4,000 watts
5) 2,300 watts
6) 1,600 watts
7) 3,800 watts
8) 92,000 watts
9) 5,305 watts
10) 60,000 watts
11) 28,000 watts
12) 32,100 watts
13) 39,400 watts
14) 358 watts
15) 805 watts
16) 105 watts
17) 100 watts
18) 200 watts
19) 39 watts
20) 58 watts
21) 80 watts
22) 29 watts
23) 64 watts
24) 913 watts
25) 51 watts
26) 12.3 watts
27) 2.63 watts
28) 75 watts
29) 120.3 watts
30) 40 watts
31) .34 watts
32) 1.2 watts
33) 5 watts
34) 2 watts
35) 4.6 watts
36) 1 watt

Electric companies bill their customers for the kilowatt-hours of electricity they use. You can estimate the watt-hours of electricity used.

EXAMPLE

A 100-watt bulb that burns for 2 hours uses 200 watt-hours of electricity (100 watts × 2 hours = 200 watt-hours).

Two 100-watt bulbs that burn for 1 hour use 200 watt-hours of electricity (200 watts × 1 hour = 200 watt-hours).

On the other hand, three 100-watt bulbs that burn for 8 hours use 2,400 watt-hours of electricity (300 watts × 8 hours = 2,400 watt-hours).

Number of Watts × Number of Hours = Watt-Hours

EXAMPLE Margo's family uses the following watts: three 100-watt lights for 8 hours, two 150-watt lights for 3 hours, and two 75-watt lights for 4 hours. Find the total kilowatt-hours they use.

Make a chart.

Number of Lamps	Watts	Hours Burned	Watt-Hours
3	100	8	2,400
2	150	3	900
2	75	4	600
		Total	3,900
		Kilowatt-hours	3.9

Explanation
$3 \times 100 \times 8 = 2{,}400$
$2 \times 150 \times 3 = 900$
$2 \times 75 \times 4 = 600$

Exercise B Complete the information for this chart. Convert the total watt-hours to kilowatt-hours. Write your answers on your paper.

	Number of Lamps	Watts	Hours Burned	Watt-Hours
1)	3	100	6	
2)	2	75	3	
3)	1	150	4	
4)	4	200	3	
5)	6	60	4	
6)	5	25	24	
7)	3	40	8	
8)			Total	
9)			Kilowatt-hours	

Reading Electric Meters You can read your electric **meter** to determine the number of kilowatt-hours used. Read the dials from right to left. Read the number the pointer has just passed. Take the lower number.

> ***Meter***
>
> *An instrument for measuring and recording rate of flow.*

EXAMPLE

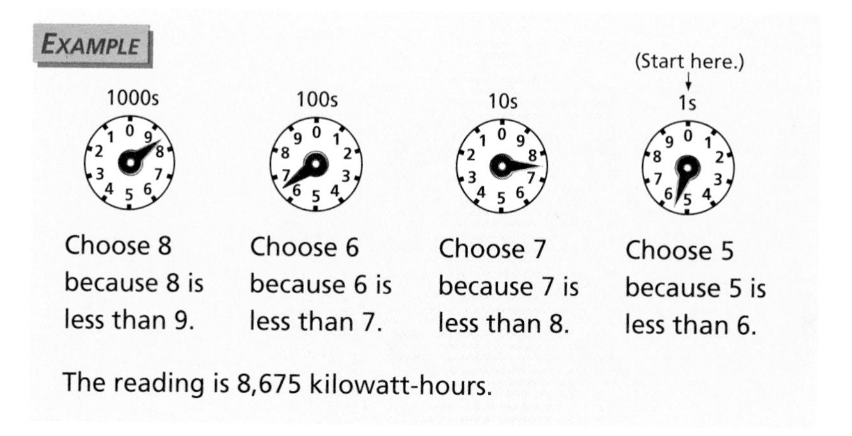

Choose 8 because 8 is less than 9.

Choose 6 because 6 is less than 7.

Choose 7 because 7 is less than 8.

Choose 5 because 5 is less than 6.

The reading is 8,675 kilowatt-hours.

Even though the pointer appears to be exactly on a number, read the next lower number—unless the pointer to its right has passed zero.

EXAMPLE

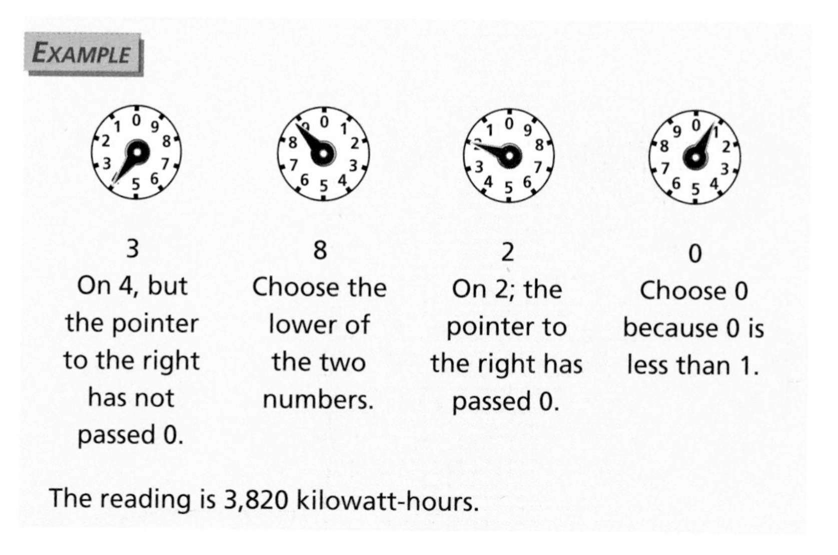

3
On 4, but the pointer to the right has not passed 0.

8
Choose the lower of the two numbers.

2
On 2; the pointer to the right has passed 0.

0
Choose 0 because 0 is less than 1.

The reading is 3,820 kilowatt-hours.

Some meters are digital. Look at these digital meters and read the numbers from left to right.

EXAMPLE

6528 5394 4816

Exercise C Read the following electric meters.

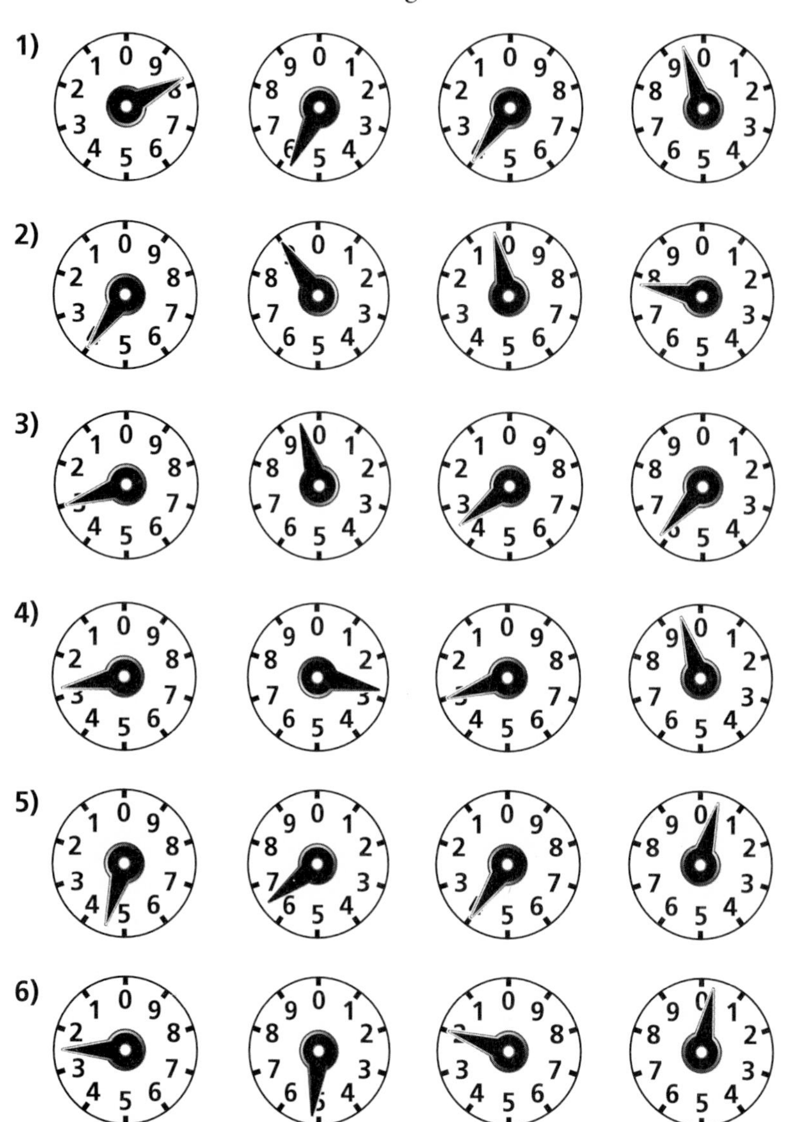

7) 9983

8) 0534

The Electric Bill The electric company bills its customers for the number of kilowatt-hours used during a billing period, which is usually one month. The cost per kilowatt-hour varies from one city or area to another.

EXAMPLE Olivia's family uses 1,263 kilowatt-hours for the month of April. Find the cost if the electric company charges 6¢ per kilowatt-hour.
A kilowatt-hour can be expressed as *kwh*.

1,263	Kilowatt-hours (kwh)
× .06	Price per kwh
$75.78	Cost for April

The electric company may add additional charges, such as fuel costs and customer service charges. The customer service charge covers the expense of reading the meter and keeping account records.

EXAMPLE Compute the electric bill for 1,520 kwh at 5¢ with a customer service charge of $2.89.

1,520	Kwh
× .05	Cost per kwh
$76.00	

$76.00	
+ 2.89	Customer service charge
$78.89	Total bill

Exercise D Compute each bill with a $2.89 customer service charge. Write your answers on your paper.

	Kwh Used	Rate per Kwh	Total
1)	2,150	6¢	______
2)	1,765	5¢	______
3)	5,020	7¢	______
4)	2,315	7¢	______
5)	983	6¢	______
6)	1,700	8¢	______
7)	671	5¢	______
8)	2,175	6¢	______
9)	1,008	9¢	______
10)	3,114	10¢	______
11)	5,102	7¢	______
12)	1,192	8¢	______
13)	1,983	6¢	______
14)	2,032	6¢	______
15)	4,452	7¢	______
16)	1,001	9¢	______

Calculator Practice

Use your calculator to determine the number of kilowatt-hours used.

Calculator Exercise Subtract the smaller reading from the larger.

1) 2,368 to 2,815

2) 5,872 to 6,023

3) 8,211 to 9,903

4) 4,020 to 5,107

5) 3,083 to 5,116

6) 4,135 to 6,102

7) 7,319 to 8,082

8) 6,129 to 7,815

9) 3,002 to 4,726

10) 8,362 to 9,108

11) 4,554 to 6,218

12) 2,315 to 4,063

13) 2,912 to 3,244

14) 6,691 to 8,354

15) 2,963 to 4,185

16) 8,615 to 9,031

17) 5,620 to 7,516

18) 8,001 to 9,532

19) 1,316 to 2,235

20) 2,273 to 3,442

21) 6,083 to 8,510

Lesson 2 Time-of-Use Rates

Peak hours
The time when usage is greatest.

Many electric companies encourage customers to avoid running appliances during **peak hours**. They do this by offering time-of-use (TOU) rates to consumers. The consumer pays a little more for a monthly charge but pays less for a kilowatt-hour during nonpeak hours. These charts help explain TOU rates.

Summer Rates
June Through September

	7AM–10AM	10AM–8PM	8PM–11PM	11PM–7AM
Monday				
Tuesday				
Wednesday	Mid	Peak Cost	Mid	Low Cost
Thursday	4.64¢	17.51¢	4.64¢	2.82¢
Friday				
Saturday	Low Cost			
Sunday	Low Cost			
All Days	Non-TOU Summer Rate 8.39¢			

Winter Rates
October Through May

	7AM–11AM	11AM–5PM	5PM–9PM	9PM–7AM
Monday				
Tuesday				
Wednesday	Peak	Mid Cost	Peak	Low Cost
Thursday	8.77¢	6.91¢	8.77¢	2.46¢
Friday				
Saturday	Low Cost			
Sunday	Low Cost			
All Days	Non-TOU Winter Rate 7.02¢			

Customer charge
Non-TOU = $4.50 / month TOU = $10.00 / month

EXAMPLE How much does it cost to burn a 60-watt bulb for 8 hours if you have TOU rates? How much will it cost if you have non-TOU rates?

$$\begin{array}{rl} 60 & \text{watts} \\ \times\ 8 & \text{hours} \\ \hline 480 & \text{watt-hours} = .48\text{ kwh} \end{array}$$

	Low	Mid	Peak	Non-TOU
TOU Summer	2.82¢	4.64¢	17.51¢	8.39¢
	× .48	× .48	× .48	× .48
	1.3536¢	2.2272¢	8.4048¢	4.0272¢
Winter	2.46¢	6.91¢	8.77¢	7.02¢
	× .48	× .48	× .48	× .48
	1.1808¢	3.3168¢	4.2096¢	3.3696¢

Exercise A Find the cost of burning a light bulb for TOU rates during low, mid, and peak hours and for non-TOU rates. Write your answers on your paper.

	TOU	Low	Mid	Peak	Non-TOU
1)	A 75-watt bulb for 6 hours during March.	______	______	______	______
2)	A 60-watt bulb for 15 hours during August.	______	______	______	______
3)	A 40-watt bulb for 8 hours during December.	______	______	______	______
4)	A 100-watt bulb for 6 hours during July.	______	______	______	______
5)	A 60-watt bulb for 4 hours during June.	______	______	______	______
6)	A 20-watt bulb for 8 hours during November.	______	______	______	______

Cutting Back You can save money by replacing a light bulb with a lower-watt bulb in areas where bright lights are not needed.

EXAMPLE The light in the hall closet burns twelve hours each month. Electricity costs 8.39¢ per kwh. How much will be saved each month if the 100-watt bulb is replaced by a 60-watt bulb?

Cost of 100-watt bulb

100	watts	8.39¢/kwh	
× 12	hours	× 1.2	kwh
1,200	wh = 1.2 kwh	10.068¢	

Cost of 60-watt bulb

60	watts	8.39¢/kwh	
×12	hours	× .72	kwh
720	wh = .72 kwh	6.0408¢	

Savings

10.068¢
− 6.0408¢
4.0272¢

About 4 cents per month will be saved.

The savings could also be found by subtracting 60 watts from 100 watts to find the savings in watts. Multiplying by hours and cost per kilowatt-hour would provide the savings.

Exercise B Find the savings per month. Write your answers on your paper.

	Old Bulb	New Bulb	Hours Used	Cost per Kwh	Savings
1)	100 watts	60 watts	32 hours	8.77¢	______
2)	75 watts	60 watts	25 hours	17.51¢	______
3)	100 watts	75 watts	16 hours	4.64¢	______
4)	75 watts	40 watts	36 hours	7.02¢	______
5)	100 watts	40 watts	35 hours	8.39¢	______
6)	75 watts	60 watts	80 hours	2.82¢	______
7)	100 watts	20 watts	70 hours	4.64¢	______
8)	75 watts	20 watts	40 hours	6.91¢	______
9)	75 watts	20 watts	18 hours	8.77¢	______
10)	100 watts	40 watts	50 hours	17.51¢	______

Lesson 3 Gas

The gas meter, like the electric meter, is read from right to left. A meter may have three or four dials, but all gas and electric meters are read the same way.

502 thousand cubic feet

Gas is measured in thousands of cubic feet. Gas customers, however, are billed for the hundreds of cubic feet they use. You can convert the reading to hundreds of cubic feet by multiplying the meter reading by 10.

EXAMPLE 502 thousand cubic feet = 5,020 hundred cubic feet because $502 \times 10 = 5{,}020$.

Exercise A Convert each gas reading to hundreds of cubic feet.

1) 236 thousand cu. ft.
2) 400 thousand cu. ft.
3) 356 thousand cu. ft.
4) 210 thousand cu. ft.
5) 109 thousand cu. ft.
6) 3,001 thousand cu. ft.
7) 291 thousand cu. ft.
8) 801 thousand cu. ft.
9) 407 thousand cu. ft.
10) 725 thousand cu. ft.
11) 4,063 thousand cu. ft.
12) 4,441 thousand cu. ft.
13) 268 thousand cu. ft.
14) 3,399 thousand cu. ft.
15) 2,912 thousand cu. ft.
16) 762 thousand cu. ft.
17) 1,000 thousand cu. ft.
18) 2,000 thousand cu. ft.
19) 3,022 thousand cu. ft.
20) 543 thousand cu. ft.
21) 304 thousand cu. ft.
22) 1,200 thousand cu. ft.
23) 206 thousand cu. ft.
24) 885 thousand cu. ft.
25) 2,934 thousand cu. ft.
26) 1,901 thousand cu. ft.
27) 415 thousand cu. ft.
28) 1,002 thousand cu. ft.

Exercise B Read each gas meter. Convert the reading to hundreds of cubic feet.

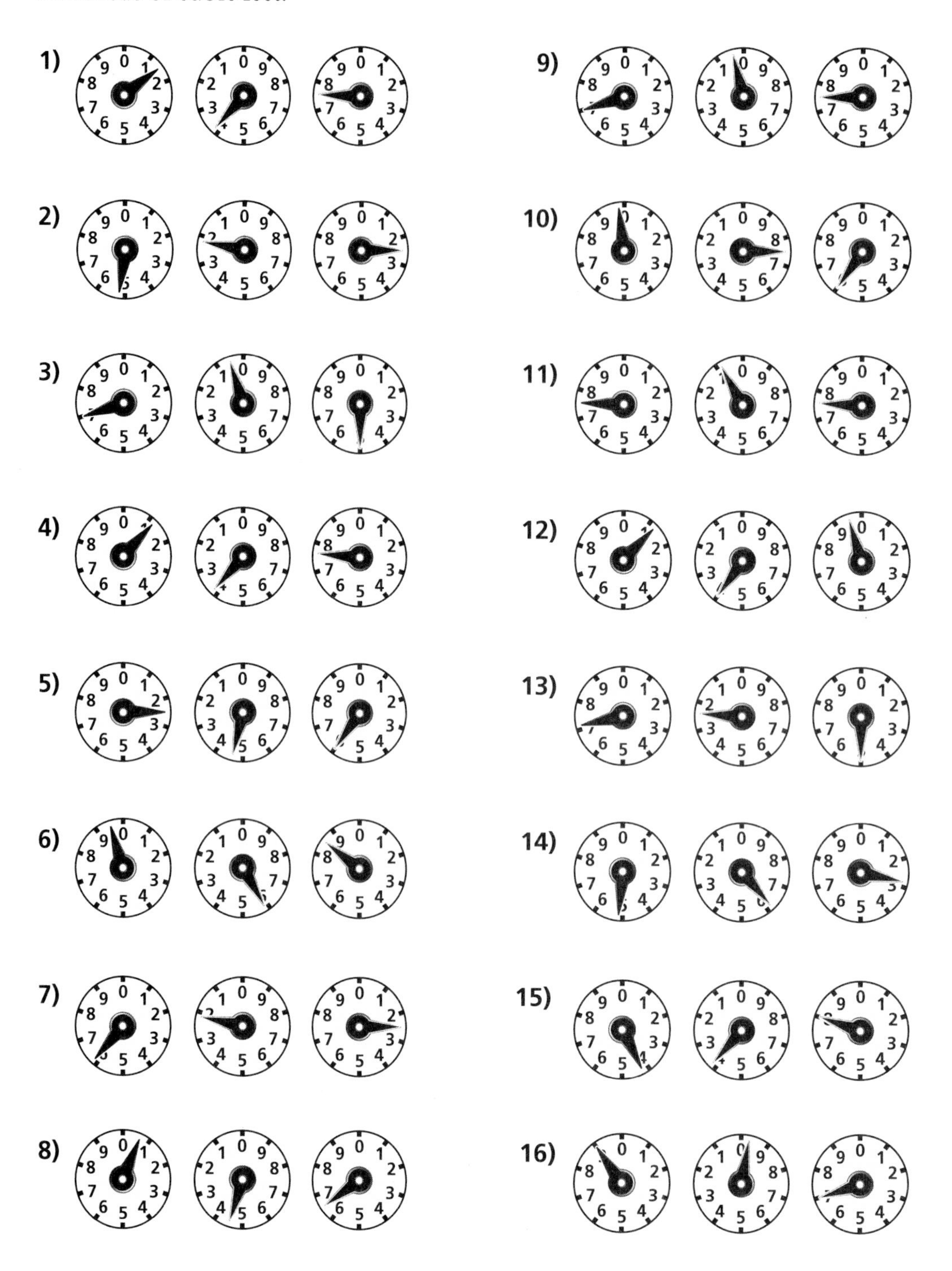

Lesson 4 Temperature

The amount of energy you use to heat or cool your home depends on weather conditions. Furnaces and water heaters work extra hard during freezing winter temperatures. Air conditioners and fans are used more during hot summer days.

Converting Celsius Readings to Fahrenheit

Temperatures may be reported in **Celsius** readings.

30°C is the same as 86°F.

To convert Celsius to **Fahrenheit,** use this formula:

$$F = \frac{9}{5} \times C + 32$$

F: Fahrenheit temperature

C: Celsius temperature

Celsius

A thermometer on which 0 degrees is the freezing point.

Fahrenheit

A thermometer on which 32 degrees is the freezing point.

EXAMPLES Convert 25° Celsius to Fahrenheit.

$$F = \frac{9}{5} \times C + 32$$

$$F = \frac{9}{5} \times 25 + 32$$

$$F = 45 + 32$$

$$F = 77^\circ$$

Convert 26° Celsius to Fahrenheit.

$$F = \frac{9}{5} \times C + 32$$

$$F = \frac{9}{5} \times 26 + 32$$

$$F = 46\frac{4}{5} + 32$$

$$F = 78\frac{4}{5}^\circ$$

Converting Fahrenheit Readings to Celsius To convert a Fahrenheit reading to Celsius, use this formula:

$$C = \frac{5}{9} \times (F - 32)$$

C = Celsius temperature; F = Fahrenheit temperature

EXAMPLES

Convert 75° Fahrenheit to Celsius.

$$C = \frac{5}{9} \times (F - 32)$$
$$C = \frac{5}{9} \times (75 - 32)$$
$$C = \frac{5}{9} \times 43$$
$$C = 23\frac{8}{9}^\circ$$

Convert 80° Fahrenheit to Celsius.

$$C = \frac{5}{9} \times (80 - 32)$$
$$C = \frac{5}{9} \times 48$$
$$C = 26\frac{2}{3}^\circ$$

Many gauges show both Fahrenheit and Celsius temperatures.

Exercise A Convert the following Celsius temperatures to Fahrenheit.

1) 25°

2) 30°

3) 60°

4) 15°

5) 55°

6) 36°

7) 42°

8) 45°

9) 20°

10) 53°

11) 18°

12) 23°

Exercise B Convert the following Fahrenheit temperatures to Celsius.

1) 68°

2) 50°

3) 122°

4) 104°

5) 32°

6) 80°

7) 62°

8) 35°

9) 44°

10) 98°

11) 72°

12) 85°

Chapter 17 Review

Convert to kilowatts.

1) 2,639 watts

2) 37 watts

Choose the correct answer.

3) 700 watts burning for 5 hours equals:

a) 35 kwh

b) .35 kwh

c) 3.5 kwh

d) 3,500 kwh

Read this electric meter.

4) 4 8 4 2

Answer these questions.

5) What are the charges for 2,367 kwh used at 7¢ per kwh?

6) What is the bill for 3,076 kwh used at 8¢ per kwh, with an added fuel cost of $15.16?

7) How many hundred cubic feet are equal to 28 thousand cubic feet?

8) What is 11°C converted to Fahrenheit?

9) What is 65°F converted to Celsius?

Read this gas meter.

10)   

11) A 100-watt light bulb in a hallway burns 8 hours per month. Electricity costs 8.39¢ per kwh. About how much is saved each month if the 100-watt bulb is replaced with a 60-watt bulb?

12) Explain why a customer saves money by using a 60-watt bulb instead of a 100-watt bulb in a lamp.

13) Draw four dials of an electric meter. Place the dials on the meters to show the amount of electricity used. Read your dials and record your reading.

14) Imagine you are a meter reader. Write a paragraph to explain your job to a friend.

15) If you are the supervisor at the electric company, would you recommend that the company increase the monthly charge, or change the time-of-use rates? Explain your thinking.

Test Taking Tip When answering multiple choice questions, first identify those you *know* are untrue.

Supplementary Problems

Review of Basic Skills 1

Identifying the Place Value of Whole Numbers

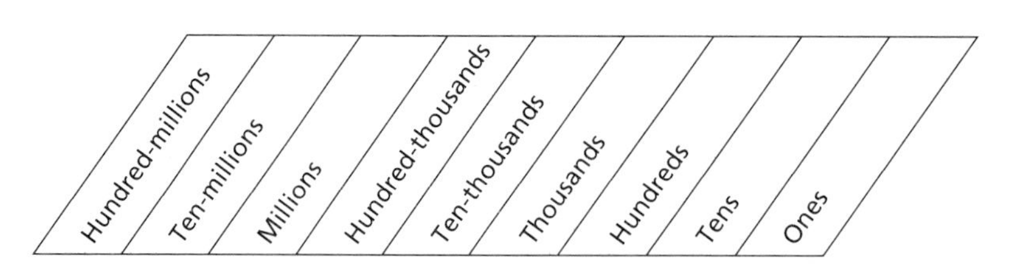

Example Write the name of the place of the underlined digit.

65,823	thousands
2,906	tens
4,790,098	millions

Exercise Write the name of the place for each underlined digit.

1) 23,456
2) 536
3) 5,126
4) 621
5) 150,341
6) 780,296
7) 3,103,615
8) 82,605
9) 26
10) 7,405
11) 41,811
12) 963
13) 31,005
14) 1,815
15) 1,007
16) 81,001
17) 567
18) 314,152
19) 72,855
20) 6,293,000

Review of Basic Skills 2

Rounding Whole Numbers

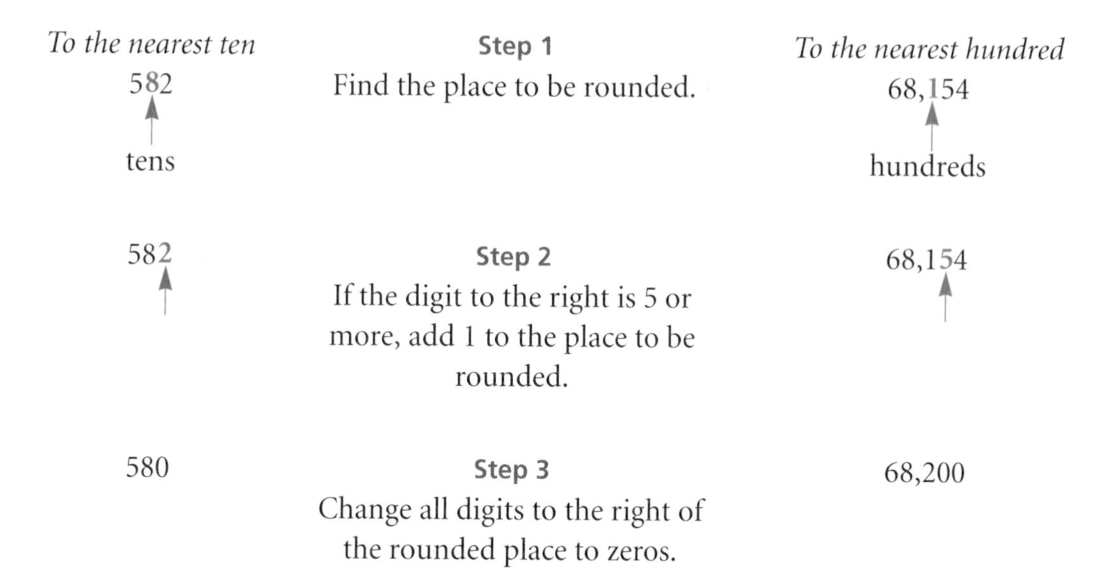

Exercise Round these numbers to the nearest:

		Ten	Hundred	Thousand
1)	26,311			
2)	40,592			
3)	7,098			
4)	415			
5)	89			
6)	49			
7)	2,900			
8)	3,200			
9)	4			
10)	129			

Review of Basic Skills 3

Adding Whole Numbers

Example $26 + 451 + 2 = ■$

Solution

$$\begin{array}{r} 26 \\ 451 \\ +\ \ 2 \\ \hline 479 \end{array} \quad \begin{array}{l} \left.\begin{array}{l} \\ \\ \\ \end{array}\right\} \text{Addends} \\ \leftarrow \text{Sum or total} \end{array}$$

Example $7 + 0 = ■$

Solution

$$\begin{array}{r} 7 \\ +0 \\ \hline 7 \end{array} \quad \begin{array}{l} \leftarrow \text{Addend} \\ \leftarrow \text{Addend} \\ \leftarrow \text{Sum or total} \end{array}$$

Exercise Write these addends in vertical form. Then add.

1) 235 + 62

2) 503 + 263

3) 211 + 623

4) 26 + 78 + 9

5) 395 + 75 + 37

6) 314 + 625 + 893

7) 512 + 726 + 89

8) 1,033 + 78 + 201

9) 1,515 + 301 + 201

10) 51 + 8,992 + 7

11) 72 + 6,203 + 45

12) 10,638 + 2,957

13) 6,203 + 89 + 1,458

14) 1,502 + 84 + 201

15) 302 + 895 + 102

16) 4,403 + 789 + 62

17) 5,067 + 29,835

18) 26 + 2,419 + 231

19) 45 + 671

20) 215 + 823

21) 305 + 876

22) 516 + 23 + 8

23) 3,007 + 926 + 85

24) 27 + 851 + 623

25) 351 + 603 + 1,151

26) 403 + 1,151 + 69

27) 62 + 89 + 5 + 301

28) 702 + 98 + 304

29) 1,346 + 62 + 891

30) 29,063 + 29 + 305

31) 62,301 + 89 + 901

32) 375 + 1,002 + 962

33) 1,302 + 63 + 115

34) 463 + 891 + 200

35) 135 + 60,039 + 12

36) 48 + 121 + 2,635

Subtracting Whole Numbers

Example Subtract 26 from 235. The number following "from" is written first.

Solution

$$\begin{array}{r} 235 \\ -\ 26 \\ \hline 209 \end{array} \quad \begin{array}{l} \text{Minuend} \\ \text{Subtrahend} \\ \text{Difference} \end{array}$$

Check

$$\begin{array}{r} 26 \\ +209 \\ \hline 235 \end{array}$$

Exercise Write these problems vertically. Then subtract.

1) 208 − 45
2) 351 − 290
3) 265 − 28
4) 208 − 177
5) 1,066 − 815
6) 1,210 − 986
7) 6,213 − 866
8) 7,019 − 669
9) 5,287 − 2,008
10) 1,010 − 935
11) 37,115 − 235
12) 5,351 − 709
13) 17,315 − 9,115
14) 20,061 − 4,805
15) 30,155 − 7,132
16) 23,103 − 9,163
17) 50,167 − 12,735
18) 37,451 − 16,203
19) 81,131 − 17,788
20) 16,683 − 6,891
21) 55,103 − 2,317
22) 88,471 − 73,115
23) 400 − 28
24) 614 − 326
25) 3,105 − 106
26) 4,992 − 885
27) 3,001 − 223
28) 8,191 − 310
29) 3,355 − 2,665
30) 3,274 − 2,275
31) 8,101 − 4,283
32) 9,000 − 862
33) 2,113 − 421
34) 48,300 − 9,301
35) 41,041 − 8,597
36) 14,724 − 7,026
37) 65,913 − 27,261
38) 10,991 − 2,815
39) 41,568 − 29,321
40) 20,972 − 3,811
41) 10,014 − 2,560
42) 57,221 − 10,811
43) 51,371 − 5,119
44) 14,014 − 7,958

Review of Basic Skills 5 and 6

Multiplying Whole Numbers (5)

Example $23 \times 6 = ■$

Solution

$$\begin{array}{r} 23 \\ \times \quad 6 \\ \hline 138 \end{array}$$

23 and 6: Factors
138: Product

Example $46 \times 35 = ■$

Solution

$$\begin{array}{r} 46 \\ \times \quad 35 \\ \hline 230 \\ +1\,38 \\ \hline 1{,}610 \end{array}$$

46 and 35: Factors
1,610: Product

Multiplying Whole Numbers With Zeros (6)

Example $267 \times 10 = ■$

Solution

$$\begin{array}{r} 267 \\ \times \quad 10 \\ \hline 2{,}670 \end{array}$$

10 ← One zero
2,670: One zero

Example $342 \times 100 = ■$

Solution

$$\begin{array}{r} 342 \\ \times \quad 100 \\ \hline 34{,}200 \end{array}$$

100 ← Two zeros
34,200: Two zeros

Exercise Write these problems in vertical form. Then multiply.

1) 23×6

2) 403×5

3) 313×4

4) 26×45

5) 72×35

6) 567×10

7) 109×50

8) 815×400

9) 701×202

10) 511×120

11) $2{,}215 \times 63$

12) $6{,}057 \times 40$

13) $5{,}063 \times 41$

14) $2{,}267 \times 19$

15) $2{,}830 \times 110$

16) $5{,}011 \times 300$

Review of Basic Skills 5 and 6

17) 7,706 × 250

18) 1,127 × 277

19) 90,681 × 22

20) 15,012 × 50

21) 21,305 × 100

22) 89,000 × 62

23) 4,805 × 1,001

24) 57,119 × 1,010

25) 77,805 × 601

26) 38 × 9

27) 206 × 8

28) 231 × 11

29) 52 × 60

30) 391 × 20

31) 435 × 39

32) 623 × 67

33) 516 × 200

34) 870 × 270

35) 603 × 250

36) 4,120 × 10

37) 1,403 × 27

38) 8,010 × 50

39) 3,115 × 28

40) 4,100 × 310

41) 8,214 × 200

42) 5,066 × 305

43) 6,405 × 115

44) 40,363 × 100

45) 71,106 × 602

46) 28,015 × 101

47) 10,376 × 203

48) 72,011 × 78

49) 90,301 × 201

50) 53,103 × 111

Review of Basic Skills 7–9

Dividing Whole Numbers With Zeros (7)

Example $576 \div 12 = \blacksquare$

Solution

$$\begin{array}{r} 48 \\ 12\overline{)576} \\ -48 \\ \hline 96 \\ -96 \\ \hline 0 \end{array}$$

Check

$$\begin{array}{r} 48 \\ \times\ 12 \\ \hline 96 \\ +48 \\ \hline 576 \end{array}$$

Dividing Whole Numbers With Fractional Remainders (8)

Example $3{,}191 \div 25 = \blacksquare$

Solution

$$\begin{array}{r} 127\frac{16}{25} \\ 25\overline{)3{,}191} \\ -25 \\ \hline 69 \\ -50 \\ \hline 191 \\ -175 \\ \hline 16 \end{array}$$

Write the remainder over the divisor

Check

$$\begin{array}{rl} 127 & \\ \times\ 25 & \\ \hline 635 & \\ +254 & \\ \hline 3{,}175 & \\ +\ 16 & \text{Remainder} \\ \hline 3{,}191 & \end{array}$$

Dividing Whole Numbers With Zeros in the Quotient (9)

Example $2{,}380 \div 14 = \blacksquare$

Solution

$$\begin{array}{r} 170 \\ 14\overline{)2{,}380} \\ -14 \\ \hline 98 \\ -98 \\ \hline 00 \end{array}$$

Check

$$\begin{array}{r} 170 \\ \times\ 14 \\ \hline 680 \\ +170 \\ \hline 2{,}380 \end{array}$$

Example $4{,}864 \div 16 = \blacksquare$

Solution

$$\begin{array}{r} 304 \\ 16\overline{)4{,}864} \\ -48 \\ \hline 064 \\ -64 \\ \hline 0 \end{array}$$

Check

$$\begin{array}{r} 304 \\ \times\ 16 \\ \hline 1{,}824 \\ +304 \\ \hline 4{,}864 \end{array}$$

Review of Basic Skills 7–9

Exercise A Copy these problems and divide.

1) $138 \div 6$

2) $882 \div 9$

3) $1,030 \div 5$

4) $1,806 \div 6$

5) $1,631 \div 7$

6) $3,060 \div 4$

7) $1,404 \div 52$

8) $4,980 \div 60$

9) $5,040 \div 70$

10) $5,700 \div 95$

11) $6,510 \div 105$

12) $9,108 \div 18$

13) $30,954 \div 77$

14) $15,257 \div 73$

15) $9,646 \div 91$

16) $19,520 \div 32$

17) $30,310 \div 70$

18) $32,040 \div 40$

19) $45,150 \div 15$

20) $56,221 \div 11$

21) $44,520 \div 12$

22) $65,160 \div 36$

23) $51,090 \div 13$

24) $80,080 \div 40$

25) $12,524 \div 31$

26) $371 \div 7$

27) $3,159 \div 9$

28) $1,744 \div 8$

29) $3,018 \div 6$

30) $2,564 \div 4$

31) $6,033 \div 3$

32) $1,539 \div 27$

33) $4,100 \div 82$

34) $8,820 \div 90$

35) $3,375 \div 25$

36) $3,450 \div 15$

37) $19,418 \div 38$

38) $31,626 \div 63$

39) $19,530 \div 62$

40) $10,160 \div 80$

41) $34,310 \div 47$

42) $52,920 \div 60$

43) $8,866 \div 22$

44) $138,253 \div 23$

45) $738,500 \div 35$

46) $50,300 \div 10$

47) $103,200 \div 24$

48) $82,212 \div 51$

49) $90,900 \div 30$

50) $57,414 \div 14$

Review of Basic Skills 7–9

Exercise B Copy these problems and divide. Write any remainders as fractions.

1) $335 \div 6$
2) $50 \div 8$
3) $711 \div 9$
4) $393 \div 6$
5) $7{,}151 \div 8$
6) $6{,}205 \div 15$
7) $60{,}600 \div 15$
8) $181{,}819 \div 18$
9) $30{,}091 \div 25$
10) $70{,}111 \div 80$
11) $41{,}015 \div 32$
12) $26{,}031 \div 26$
13) $13{,}315 \div 25$
14) $60{,}031 \div 81$
15) $53{,}010 \div 52$
16) $10{,}008 \div 50$
17) $27{,}023 \div 62$
18) $15{,}132 \div 25$
19) $90{,}615 \div 23$
20) $46{,}023 \div 23$
21) $23{,}310 \div 70$
22) $50{,}003 \div 85$
23) $22{,}022 \div 60$
24) $463{,}201 \div 71$
25) $57{,}231 \div 500$
26) $573 \div 6$
27) $908 \div 9$
28) $630 \div 9$
29) $721 \div 8$
30) $3{,}900 \div 9$
31) $8{,}003 \div 15$
32) $7{,}440 \div 22$
33) $32{,}331 \div 16$
34) $7{,}910 \div 19$
35) $51{,}631 \div 25$
36) $10{,}631 \div 81$
37) $35{,}103 \div 34$
38) $14{,}401 \div 72$
39) $42{,}002 \div 60$
40) $73{,}106 \div 73$
41) $53{,}010 \div 38$
42) $14{,}108 \div 80$
43) $62{,}031 \div 20$
44) $72{,}150 \div 80$
45) $81{,}035 \div 90$
46) $34{,}210 \div 81$
47) $78{,}311 \div 30$
48) $37{,}101 \div 51$
49) $72{,}101 \div 82$
50) $80{,}031 \div 198$

Review of Basic Skills 10

Finding Values of Numbers With Exponents

Example Find 3^4.

Solution $3^4 = 3 \times 3 \times 3 \times 3$ (4 times)
$= 81$

Example Find 2^3.

Solution $2^3 = 2 \times 2 \times 2$ (3 times)
$= 8$

Exercise Write the value of each expression.

1) 3^2
2) 5^3
3) 9^2
4) 19^2
5) 3^5
6) 8^2
7) 9^4
8) 18^2
9) 6^3
10) 2^6
11) 25^2
12) 7^2
13) 2^7
14) 26^2
15) 7^4
16) 30^2
17) 200^3
18) 70^2
19) 100^3
20) 80^3
21) 30^4
22) $1{,}000^2$
23) 46^2
24) 5^6
25) 10^4
26) 4^3
27) 4^2
28) 2^5
29) 7^3
30) 2^4
31) 11^2
32) 16^3
33) 5^4
34) 10^4
35) 15^2
36) 5^5
37) 8^4
38) 50^3
39) 5^3
40) 40^3
41) 77^2
42) 60^3
43) 92^2
44) 30^3
45) 80^2
46) 32^2
47) 16^2
48) 10^2
49) 8^3
50) 23^2
51) 5^2
52) 8^2
53) 9^3
54) 4^5
55) 6^2
56) 13^3
57) 12^2
58) 18^2
59) 28^2
60) 17^2
61) 24^2
62) 150^2
63) 300^4
64) 70^3
65) 22^2
66) 500^3
67) 15^3
68) 13^2
69) 42^2
70) 90^3
71) 10^3
72) 30^4
73) 63^2
74) 10^5
75) 3^3

Using the Order of Operations (Fundamental)

Rules

1. Evaluate expressions with exponents first.
2. Multiply and divide from left to right in order.
3. Add and subtract from left to right in order.

Example $2 + 3 \times 4 - 8 \div 4 = \blacksquare$

Solution

$2 + \underline{3 \times 4} - \underline{8 \div 4} =$

$2 + 12 - 2 = 12$

Example $2^3 + 3 \times 4 \div 2 - 48 \div 4^2 = \blacksquare$

$8 + \underline{3 \times 4 \div 2} - \underline{48 \div 16} =$

$\underline{12 \div 2} \quad \underline{3} =$

$8 + 6 - 3 = 11$

Exercise Use the rules for the order of operations. Find the answers.

1) $3 + 8 \times 2 \div 4$

2) $5 + 9 \times 4 \div 12 - 2$

3) $8 - 8 \div 4 + 3 \times 2$

4) $13 - 16 \times 3 \div 12 - 1$

5) $9 + 6 \times 3 - 8 \times 2 \div 4$

6) $1 + 16 \times 3 \div 12 - 4$

7) $14 + 32 \div 16 - 4 \times 2$

8) $32 \div 16 + 9 \div 3 \times 2$

9) $5 - 16 \div 4 + 1 + 3$

10) $35 - 25 \times 4 \div 20 + 5$

11) $2^3 + 8 \times 2^2 + 3$

12) $8 - 6^2 \div 12 + 2 \times 5$

13) $15 + 8^2 \div 4 - 6$

14) $26 + 13^2 \div 13 - 20$

15) $9^2 + 32 \div 8 \times 4 - 6$

16) $3 + 2^3 \div 2^2 - 4$

17) $5 + 8 \times 9 \div 6^2 - 4$

18) $25 + 11^2 + 8 \times 2 - 3$

19) $39 \div 13 + 12^2 \div 6 - 5$

20) $52 + 12 \div 2^2 - 82 \div 2 + 3^2$

21) $35 + 2^5 \div 2^4 \times 3^2 - 2^3$

22) $18 \div 3^2 + 6 \times 8 \div 4^2 - 5$

23) $4 \times 3 \times 5 \div 10 + 8 \times 2^3 \div 2^4$

24) $9 - 16 \times 3 \div 12 + 8 \div 2^2 - 2^2$

Finding an Average

Example Find the average for 98, 88, and 80.

Solution Add the numbers. Divide the sum by the number of addends.

$$\begin{array}{r} 98 \\ 88 \\ +80 \\ \hline 266 \end{array} \quad \text{3 addends} \qquad\qquad \begin{array}{r} 88\frac{2}{3} \\ 3\overline{)266} \\ -24 \\ \hline 26 \\ -24 \\ \hline 2 \end{array}$$

Answer The average is $88\frac{2}{3}$.

Exercise Compute the averages for each set of numbers.

1) 25, 63, 48, 52, 49, 38, 42, 67, 38

2) 98, 53, 42, 56, 72, 36, 72

3) 39, 40, 39, 62, 53, 86, 29, 34

4) 95, 83, 39, 42, 88, 77, 75, 42, 67

5) 88, 62, 42, 53, 96, 35, 35

6) 53, 60, 72, 43, 35, 39, 53

7) 52, 65, 83, 96, 35, 100, 92, 53

8) 91, 62, 39, 50, 42, 88, 53, 60, 83, 72

9) 36, 50, 42, 53, 46, 82, 80, 50, 52, 39

10) 81, 90, 92, 90, 83, 43, 46, 72, 53

11) 100, 103, 96, 105, 105, 97, 102, 120

12) 36, 42, 85, 92, 30, 33, 88, 29, 62, 50

13) 109, 156, 95, 108, 90, 83, 45, 80, 90, 98, 93, 96

14) 40, 42, 43, 40, 41, 42, 43, 48, 44, 42, 45, 42

15) 40, 38, 37, 35, 42, 43, 36, 49, 48, 53, 42, 39, 34

16) 21, 20, 23, 28, 25, 23, 20, 25, 24, 29, 28, 24, 22, 20

17) 52, 50, 59, 62, 63, 55, 54, 58, 60, 50, 52, 53, 57, 52, 51

18) 56, 50, 53, 65, 73, 72, 80, 95, 81, 87, 70, 82, 96, 68

19) 23, 12, 94, 71, 44, 39, 62, 57, 68, 25, 53, 22, 19, 80

Review of Basic Skills 13–14

Comparing Fractions (13)

Example Compare $\frac{3}{4}$ and $\frac{5}{8}$.

Solution

$$\overset{24}{\frac{3}{4}} \times \overset{20}{\frac{5}{8}}$$

Because $4 \times 5 = 20$ Because $3 \times 8 = 24$

24 is greater than 20; therefore, $\frac{3}{4}$ is greater than $\frac{5}{8}$.

Changing Fractions to Higher Terms (14)

Example Write $\frac{5}{6}$ as a fraction with 30 as the new denominator.

Solution

Step 1 $\frac{5}{6} = \frac{■}{30}$

Step 2 Divide 30 by 6. ⟶ $6\overline{)30}$ = 5

Step 3 Multiply $\frac{5}{6}$ by $\frac{5}{5}$. ⟶ $\frac{5 \times 5}{6 \times 5} = \frac{25}{30}$

Answer $\frac{5}{6} = \frac{25}{30}$

Exercise Express these fractions in higher terms.

1) $\frac{3}{4} = \frac{■}{48}$

2) $\frac{1}{3} = \frac{■}{21}$

3) $\frac{2}{3} = \frac{■}{15}$

4) $\frac{5}{6} = \frac{■}{18}$

5) $\frac{7}{8} = \frac{■}{56}$

6) $\frac{3}{5} = \frac{■}{20}$

7) $\frac{1}{7} = \frac{■}{49}$

8) $\frac{5}{12} = \frac{■}{24}$

9) $\frac{3}{7} = \frac{■}{21}$

10) $\frac{4}{12} = \frac{■}{36}$

11) $\frac{4}{9} = \frac{■}{45}$

12) $\frac{3}{3} = \frac{■}{18}$

13) $\frac{2}{11} = \frac{■}{121}$

14) $\frac{15}{16} = \frac{■}{48}$

15) $\frac{3}{10} = \frac{■}{30}$

16) $\frac{12}{14} = \frac{■}{70}$

17) $\frac{9}{12} = \frac{■}{144}$

18) $\frac{5}{15} = \frac{■}{45}$

19) $\frac{2}{8} = \frac{■}{96}$

20) $\frac{1}{6} = \frac{■}{72}$

21) $\frac{17}{24} = \frac{■}{120}$

Renaming Fractions to Simplest Terms

Example Rename $\frac{14}{16}$ to simplest terms.

Solution $\frac{14 \div 2}{16 \div 2} = \frac{7}{8}$

Choose a number that can be divided into the denominator and the numerator.

Answer $\frac{14}{16} = \frac{7}{8}$

Example Rename $\frac{24}{30}$ to simplest terms.

Solution $\frac{24 \div 3}{30 \div 3} = \frac{8}{10}$

The division process may occur more than once if the divisor is not large enough in the first step.

$\frac{8 \div 2}{10 \div 2} = \frac{4}{5}$

Answer $\frac{24}{30} = \frac{4}{5}$

Exercise Rename these fractions in simplest terms.

1) $\frac{24}{48}$

2) $\frac{10}{230}$

3) $\frac{45}{99}$

4) $\frac{5}{25}$

5) $\frac{13}{39}$

6) $\frac{56}{58}$

7) $\frac{63}{81}$

8) $\frac{6}{54}$

9) $\frac{16}{112}$

10) $\frac{39}{52}$

11) $\frac{12}{60}$

12) $\frac{16}{64}$

13) $\frac{18}{36}$

14) $\frac{22}{121}$

15) $\frac{53}{106}$

16) $\frac{18}{72}$

17) $\frac{5}{15}$

18) $\frac{55}{242}$

19) $\frac{10}{52}$

20) $\frac{48}{96}$

21) $\frac{28}{56}$

Review of Basic Skills 16 and 17

Renaming Improper Fractions as Mixed Numbers or Whole Numbers (16)

Example Rename $\frac{13}{5}$.

Solution Divide the numerator by the denominator.

$$\begin{array}{r} 2 \\ 5\overline{)13} \\ -10 \\ \hline 3 \end{array}$$ ← Remainder

Answer $\frac{13}{5} = 2\frac{3}{5}$ ← Write the remainder over the divisor.

Example Rename $\frac{42}{16}$.

Solution

$$\begin{array}{r} 2 \\ 16\overline{)42} \\ 32 \\ \hline 10 \end{array}$$

$2\frac{10}{16} = 2\frac{5}{8}$

Answer $\frac{42}{16} = 2\frac{5}{8}$

Writing Mixed Numbers in Simplest Terms (17)

Example Write $12\frac{4}{6}$ in simplest terms.

Solution $12\frac{4}{6} = 12 + \frac{4}{6} = 12 + \frac{2}{3} = 12\frac{2}{3}$

Answer $12\frac{4}{6} = 12\frac{2}{3}$

Review of Basic Skills 16 and 17

Exercise Rename these improper fractions as either mixed numbers or whole numbers.

1) $\frac{13}{5}$

2) $\frac{18}{3}$

3) $\frac{19}{6}$

4) $\frac{14}{3}$

5) $\frac{23}{4}$

6) $\frac{12}{2}$

7) $\frac{38}{5}$

8) $\frac{66}{11}$

9) $\frac{56}{11}$

10) $\frac{19}{5}$

11) $\frac{52}{32}$

12) $\frac{55}{8}$

13) $\frac{28}{6}$

14) $\frac{32}{4}$

15) $\frac{90}{3}$

16) $\frac{63}{8}$

17) $\frac{50}{6}$

18) $\frac{58}{7}$

19) $\frac{52}{10}$

20) $\frac{37}{3}$

21) $\frac{120}{10}$

22) $\frac{73}{8}$

23) $\frac{13}{2}$

24) $\frac{51}{4}$

25) $\frac{82}{9}$

26) $\frac{23}{5}$

27) $\frac{52}{8}$

28) $\frac{32}{15}$

Review of Basic Skills 18

Renaming Mixed Numbers as Improper Fractions

Example Write $2\frac{3}{4}$ as an improper fraction.

Solution **Step 1** Multiply the whole number by the denominator.

$2 \times 4 = 8$

Step 2 Add the numerator to the product from Step 1.

$3 + 8 = 11$

Step 3 Write the sum over the old denominator.

$\frac{11}{4}$

Answer $2\frac{3}{4} = \frac{11}{4}$

Exercise Rename these mixed numbers as improper fractions.

1) $3\frac{2}{5}$

2) $6\frac{2}{5}$

3) $5\frac{1}{6}$

4) $7\frac{2}{12}$

5) $2\frac{1}{6}$

6) $9\frac{1}{2}$

7) $4\frac{1}{9}$

8) $8\frac{2}{11}$

9) $5\frac{2}{3}$

10) $8\frac{1}{3}$

11) $6\frac{10}{13}$

12) $16\frac{2}{3}$

13) $7\frac{3}{8}$

14) $15\frac{2}{3}$

15) $13\frac{9}{14}$

16) $9\frac{2}{3}$

17) $5\frac{11}{10}$

18) $20\frac{2}{3}$

19) $16\frac{5}{21}$

20) $11\frac{1}{8}$

Multiplying Fractions

Example $\frac{5}{6} \times \frac{3}{4} = \blacksquare$

Solution $\frac{5 \times 3}{6 \times 4} = \frac{15}{24}$

$\frac{15}{24} = \frac{5}{8}$

Answer $\frac{5}{8}$

Example $7 \times \frac{4}{5} = \blacksquare$

Solution $\frac{7 \times 4}{1 \times 5} = \frac{28}{5}$

$\frac{28}{5} = 5\frac{3}{5}$

Answer $5\frac{3}{5}$

Exercise Multiply. Write your answers in simplest terms.

1) $\frac{1}{2} \times \frac{2}{3}$

2) $\frac{3}{5} \times \frac{5}{6}$

3) $\frac{7}{8} \times \frac{6}{13}$

4) $\frac{2}{9} \times \frac{3}{5}$

5) $\frac{6}{7} \times \frac{1}{2}$

6) $\frac{3}{11} \times \frac{2}{5}$

7) $\frac{2}{7} \times \frac{2}{9}$

8) $\frac{1}{6} \times \frac{1}{5}$

9) $\frac{5}{11} \times \frac{1}{4}$

10) $\frac{1}{6} \times \frac{2}{9}$

11) $\frac{5}{6} \times \frac{1}{4}$

12) $\frac{3}{11} \times \frac{2}{12}$

13) $\frac{4}{5} \times \frac{2}{9}$

14) $\frac{4}{7} \times \frac{1}{8}$

15) $\frac{3}{16} \times \frac{13}{21}$

16) $\frac{5}{21} \times \frac{7}{10}$

17) $\frac{5}{24} \times \frac{3}{13}$

18) $\frac{6}{28} \times \frac{7}{12}$

19) $\frac{2}{3} \times \frac{5}{6}$

20) $\frac{12}{21} \times \frac{7}{8}$

21) $\frac{13}{32} \times \frac{8}{26}$

22) $\frac{24}{25} \times \frac{5}{16}$

23) $\frac{1}{12} \times \frac{2}{7}$

24) $\frac{2}{17} \times \frac{3}{4}$

25) $\frac{10}{13} \times \frac{39}{100}$

26) $\frac{12}{18} \times \frac{9}{32}$

27) $\frac{2}{15} \times \frac{45}{50}$

28) $\frac{5}{11} \times \frac{55}{75}$

29) $\frac{4}{5} \times \frac{2}{13}$

30) $\frac{2}{11} \times \frac{3}{10}$

31) $\frac{3}{14} \times \frac{28}{30}$

32) $\frac{7}{13} \times \frac{39}{63}$

33) $\frac{24}{36} \times \frac{1}{3}$

Multiplying Mixed Numbers

Example $3\frac{2}{3} \times 1\frac{1}{2} = ■$

Solution $3\frac{2}{3} \times 1\frac{1}{2} = ■$ ← Change to improper fractions.

$$\frac{11}{\cancel{3}_1} \times \frac{\cancel{3}^1}{2} = \frac{11}{2}$$

$$\frac{11}{2} = 5\frac{1}{2}$$

Answer $5\frac{1}{2}$

Exercise Multiply these mixed numbers. Write your answers in simplest terms.

1) $2\frac{1}{2} \times \frac{1}{3}$

2) $\frac{1}{2} \times 1\frac{1}{5}$

3) $\frac{2}{7} \times 1\frac{1}{3}$

4) $\frac{1}{5} \times 1\frac{1}{7}$

5) $3\frac{1}{5} \times \frac{3}{4}$

6) $5\frac{2}{3} \times \frac{1}{5}$

7) $\frac{5}{7} \times 2\frac{3}{8}$

8) $1\frac{1}{2} \times \frac{15}{18}$

9) $4\frac{5}{7} \times \frac{7}{11}$

10) $2\frac{3}{5} \times 1\frac{1}{5}$

11) $2\frac{3}{7} \times 2\frac{1}{2}$

12) $5\frac{1}{7} \times 2\frac{1}{5}$

13) $5\frac{1}{6} \times 1\frac{1}{5}$

14) $1\frac{5}{6} \times 1\frac{1}{3}$

15) $1\frac{2}{7} \times 2\frac{1}{8}$

16) $6\frac{1}{2} \times 2\frac{3}{4}$

17) $2\frac{2}{5} \times 1\frac{3}{4}$

18) $4\frac{1}{2} \times 1\frac{1}{4}$

19) $3\frac{3}{7} \times 2\frac{1}{3}$

20) $5\frac{2}{9} \times 1\frac{1}{8}$

21) $5\frac{1}{4} \times 2\frac{1}{7}$

22) $6\frac{2}{5} \times 1\frac{1}{7}$

23) $13\frac{1}{3} \times 2\frac{1}{4}$

24) $1\frac{5}{9} \times 1\frac{3}{4}$

25) $3\frac{2}{5} \times 2\frac{2}{4}$

26) $5\frac{2}{5} \times 1\frac{1}{9}$

27) $5\frac{1}{3} \times 1\frac{1}{8}$

28) $5\frac{3}{9} \times 1\frac{1}{6}$

29) $1\frac{2}{8} \times 3\frac{1}{2}$

30) $3\frac{1}{2} \times 5\frac{1}{6}$

31) $2\frac{4}{5} \times 2\frac{1}{7}$

32) $4\frac{1}{5} \times 1\frac{5}{7}$

33) $3\frac{7}{8} \times 1\frac{1}{2}$

Review of Basic Skills 21

Dividing Fractions

Example $\frac{4}{7} \div \frac{1}{2} = \blacksquare$

Solution $\frac{4}{7} \div \frac{1}{2} = \blacksquare$ ← Invert the divisor. Then multiply.

$\frac{4}{7} \times \frac{2}{1} = \frac{8}{7}$

$\frac{8}{7} = 1\frac{1}{7}$

Answer $1\frac{1}{7}$

Exercise Divide. Write your answers in simplest terms.

1) $\frac{2}{5} \div \frac{2}{7}$

2) $\frac{5}{6} \div \frac{1}{3}$

3) $\frac{2}{7} \div \frac{1}{8}$

4) $\frac{4}{5} \div \frac{1}{6}$

5) $\frac{2}{7} \div \frac{5}{6}$

6) $\frac{3}{8} \div \frac{1}{2}$

7) $\frac{4}{5} \div \frac{5}{6}$

8) $\frac{8}{9} \div \frac{4}{5}$

9) $\frac{5}{6} \div \frac{2}{5}$

10) $\frac{5}{11} \div \frac{2}{22}$

11) $\frac{8}{11} \div \frac{5}{11}$

12) $\frac{5}{12} \div \frac{5}{6}$

13) $\frac{3}{8} \div \frac{5}{12}$

14) $\frac{2}{11} \div \frac{3}{22}$

15) $\frac{8}{13} \div \frac{24}{26}$

16) $\frac{3}{9} \div \frac{1}{5}$

17) $\frac{11}{12} \div \frac{24}{30}$

18) $\frac{5}{7} \div \frac{48}{49}$

19) $\frac{1}{2} \div \frac{5}{7}$

20) $\frac{5}{7} \div \frac{5}{14}$

21) $\frac{8}{9} \div \frac{3}{6}$

22) $\frac{3}{4} \div \frac{6}{7}$

23) $\frac{13}{14} \div \frac{3}{7}$

24) $\frac{8}{15} \div \frac{2}{5}$

25) $\frac{1}{2} \div \frac{1}{2}$

26) $\frac{2}{3} \div \frac{1}{7}$

27) $\frac{3}{7} \div \frac{15}{21}$

28) $\frac{5}{10} \div \frac{2}{6}$

29) $\frac{4}{7} \div \frac{5}{14}$

30) $\frac{2}{3} \div \frac{14}{21}$

31) $\frac{18}{20} \div \frac{15}{40}$

32) $\frac{22}{27} \div \frac{11}{18}$

33) $\frac{16}{30} \div \frac{8}{15}$

Review of Basic Skills 22

Dividing Mixed Numbers

Example $2\frac{3}{4} \div 3\frac{1}{3} = \blacksquare$

Solution $2\frac{3}{4} \div 3\frac{1}{3} = \blacksquare$ ← Rename mixed numbers as improper fractions.

$\frac{11}{4} \div \frac{10}{3} = \blacksquare$ ← Invert the divisor and multiply.

$\frac{11}{4} \times \frac{3}{10} = \frac{33}{40}$

Answer $\frac{33}{40}$

Exercise Divide. Write your answers in simplest terms.

1) $1\frac{1}{2} \div \frac{1}{2}$

2) $3\frac{2}{3} \div \frac{1}{9}$

3) $1\frac{1}{5} \div \frac{2}{5}$

4) $2\frac{1}{6} \div \frac{3}{12}$

5) $\frac{3}{12} \div 3\frac{1}{6}$

6) $\frac{13}{15} \div 1\frac{3}{5}$

7) $1\frac{2}{5} \div \frac{14}{15}$

8) $3\frac{1}{2} \div \frac{5}{6}$

9) $1\frac{1}{2} \div 1\frac{2}{5}$

10) $\frac{1}{2} \div 1\frac{1}{2}$

11) $1\frac{1}{12} \div 2\frac{1}{6}$

12) $2\frac{2}{3} \div 3\frac{5}{9}$

13) $2\frac{1}{2} \div 3\frac{1}{7}$

14) $1\frac{5}{7} \div \frac{6}{7}$

15) $2\frac{5}{8} \div \frac{21}{24}$

16) $3\frac{5}{7} \div \frac{13}{14}$

17) $5\frac{2}{5} \div \frac{3}{4}$

18) $4\frac{1}{3} \div \frac{26}{27}$

19) $5\frac{3}{7} \div \frac{1}{3}$

20) $3\frac{2}{9} \div \frac{1}{8}$

21) $5\frac{2}{5} \div \frac{9}{10}$

22) $8\frac{2}{3} \div \frac{1}{7}$

23) $6\frac{1}{7} \div \frac{7}{18}$

24) $5\frac{1}{5} \div 1\frac{1}{2}$

25) $2\frac{3}{4} \div 1\frac{1}{6}$

26) $1\frac{1}{7} \div 1\frac{1}{6}$

27) $1\frac{1}{8} \div 1\frac{1}{9}$

28) $13\frac{2}{3} \div \frac{1}{9}$

29) $3\frac{2}{3} \div \frac{22}{27}$

30) $3\frac{6}{7} \div 1\frac{1}{4}$

31) $5\frac{2}{7} \div 7\frac{2}{5}$

32) $2\frac{1}{6} \div 1\frac{1}{2}$

33) $1\frac{1}{12} \div 2\frac{1}{6}$

Adding Mixed Numbers With Like Denominators

Example $3\frac{2}{7} + 1\frac{3}{7} = \blacksquare$

Solution

$$\begin{array}{r} 3\frac{2}{7} \\ +1\frac{3}{7} \\ \hline 4\frac{5}{7} \end{array}$$

Step 1	Write in the vertical form.
Step 2	Add the numerators. $2 + 3 = 5$
Step 3	Keep the denominator.
Step 4	Add the whole numbers.

Answer $4\frac{5}{7}$

Exercise Add. Write your answers in simplest terms.

1) $\frac{2}{5} + \frac{2}{5}$

2) $\frac{5}{7} + \frac{1}{7}$

3) $\frac{8}{12} + \frac{3}{12}$

4) $\frac{5}{8} + \frac{1}{8}$

5) $\frac{2}{7} + \frac{5}{7}$

6) $\frac{8}{11} + \frac{4}{11}$

7) $1\frac{1}{6} + 2\frac{3}{6}$

8) $2\frac{5}{8} + \frac{1}{8}$

9) $5\frac{3}{10} + \frac{2}{10}$

10) $5\frac{1}{6} + \frac{1}{6}$

11) $8\frac{1}{12} + \frac{3}{12}$

12) $5\frac{1}{6} + \frac{3}{6}$

13) $8\frac{5}{11} + 1\frac{2}{11}$

14) $9\frac{1}{10} + 3\frac{3}{10}$

15) $8\frac{2}{5} + 3\frac{4}{5}$

16) $6\frac{2}{9} + \frac{5}{9}$

17) $8\frac{2}{12} + 6$

18) $11\frac{12}{21} + 2\frac{3}{21}$

19) $5 + 2\frac{1}{7}$

20) $7\frac{1}{7} + 13\frac{1}{7}$

21) $13\frac{12}{21} + 1\frac{3}{21}$

22) $8\frac{6}{13} + \frac{6}{13}$

Review of Basic Skills 24 and 25

Adding Fractions With Unlike Denominators (24)

Example $\frac{7}{15} + \frac{2}{5} = ■$

Solution

$$\frac{7}{15} = \boxed{\frac{7 \times 1}{15 \times 1}} = \frac{7}{15}$$

$$+\frac{2}{5} = \boxed{\frac{2 \times 3}{5 \times 3}} = +\frac{6}{15}$$

$$\frac{13}{15}$$

Rename the fractions with like denominators.

Add the numerators.

Answer $\frac{13}{15}$

Adding Mixed Numbers With Unlike Denominators (25)

Example $5\frac{5}{8} + 2\frac{7}{12} = ■$

Solution

$$5\frac{5}{8} \qquad \frac{5}{8} = \frac{5 \times 3}{8 \times 3} = \frac{15}{24} \qquad 5\frac{5}{8} = 5\frac{15}{24}$$

$$+2\frac{7}{12} \qquad \frac{7}{12} = \frac{7 \times 2}{12 \times 2} = \frac{14}{24} \qquad +2\frac{7}{12} = 2\frac{14}{24}$$

$$7\frac{29}{24} = 8\frac{5}{24}$$

Rename the fractional portion with like denominators.

Rename $7\frac{29}{24}$.

$$7 + \frac{29}{24} = 7 + 1\frac{5}{24} = 8\frac{5}{24}$$

Answer $8\frac{5}{24}$

Review of Basic Skills 24 and 25

Exercise Find common denominators and add. Write your answers in simplest terms.

1) $\frac{3}{7} + \frac{1}{3}$

2) $\frac{5}{6} + \frac{1}{3}$

3) $\frac{8}{12} + \frac{1}{8}$

4) $\frac{4}{17} + \frac{3}{34}$

5) $\frac{6}{11} + \frac{3}{4}$

6) $\frac{8}{15} + \frac{1}{6}$

7) $\frac{2}{15} + \frac{3}{45}$

8) $\frac{5}{8} + \frac{5}{6}$

9) $\frac{7}{9} + \frac{5}{27}$

10) $2\frac{1}{6} + \frac{2}{9}$

11) $12\frac{3}{10} + \frac{1}{15}$

12) $5\frac{6}{72} + \frac{1}{8}$

13) $8\frac{5}{16} + 2\frac{1}{8}$

14) $15\frac{2}{17} + 1\frac{1}{3}$

15) $26\frac{5}{7} + 2\frac{4}{21}$

16) $10\frac{6}{11} + 2\frac{5}{121}$

17) $8\frac{3}{36} + 2\frac{1}{12}$

18) $9\frac{5}{18} + 2\frac{5}{54}$

19) $5\frac{1}{2} + 2\frac{1}{17}$

20) $7\frac{3}{36} + 2\frac{1}{12}$

21) $3\frac{5}{18} + 1\frac{5}{54}$

22) $10\frac{1}{2} + 12\frac{1}{17}$

Subtracting Mixed Numbers With Like Denominators

Example

$$\begin{array}{r} 14\frac{5}{11} \\ -6\frac{2}{11} \\ \hline 8\frac{3}{11} \end{array}$$

Step 1 Subtract 2 from 5.
5 − 2 = 3

Step 2 Keep the denominator.

Step 3 Subtract the whole number portions.
14 − 6 = 8

Answer $8\frac{3}{11}$

Exercise Subtract. Write your answers in simplest terms.

1) $\frac{5}{8} - \frac{2}{8}$

2) $\frac{6}{13} - \frac{2}{13}$

3) $\frac{4}{15} - \frac{1}{15}$

4) $\frac{12}{17} - \frac{2}{17}$

5) $\frac{8}{9} - \frac{5}{9}$

6) $\frac{6}{7} - \frac{3}{7}$

7) $\frac{8}{19} - \frac{2}{19}$

8) $2\frac{3}{5} - \frac{2}{5}$

9) $8\frac{7}{8} - \frac{3}{8}$

10) $5\frac{6}{10} - 4\frac{1}{10}$

11) $15\frac{12}{13} - 4\frac{1}{13}$

12) $7\frac{7}{10} - 5\frac{2}{10}$

13) $18\frac{15}{16} - 5\frac{7}{16}$

14) $12\frac{5}{8} - 2\frac{2}{8}$

15) $17\frac{3}{4} - 5\frac{2}{4}$

16) $31\frac{5}{18} - 2$

17) $39\frac{16}{21} - 5\frac{6}{21}$

18) $14\frac{5}{6} - 2\frac{2}{6}$

19) $22\frac{3}{10} - 5\frac{3}{10}$

20) $9\frac{35}{40} - 6\frac{10}{40}$

21) $3\frac{1}{7} - \frac{1}{7}$

22) $16\frac{3}{8} - 12\frac{1}{8}$

Subtracting With Unlike Denominators

Example

$$18\frac{2}{3} \qquad -5\frac{1}{7}$$

$$\frac{2}{3} = \frac{2 \times 7}{3 \times 7} = \frac{14}{21}$$
$$\frac{1}{7} = \frac{1 \times 3}{7 \times 3} = \frac{3}{21}$$

Rename the fractional portions with like denominators.

$$18\frac{2}{3} = 18\frac{14}{21}$$
$$-5\frac{1}{7} = 5\frac{3}{21}$$
$$13\frac{11}{21}$$

Subtract the numerators and the whole numbers.

Answer $13\frac{11}{21}$

Exercise Find common denominators and subtract. Write your answers in simplest terms.

1) $13\frac{4}{5} - 5\frac{2}{3}$

2) $9\frac{7}{8} - 3\frac{1}{3}$

3) $5\frac{5}{6} - 2\frac{1}{3}$

4) $18\frac{4}{8} - 5\frac{2}{24}$

5) $15\frac{10}{24} - 5\frac{1}{6}$

6) $3\frac{5}{8} - 1\frac{2}{6}$

7) $10\frac{13}{14} - 3\frac{1}{2}$

8) $36\frac{2}{5} - 5\frac{1}{6}$

9) $11\frac{8}{9} - 5\frac{2}{8}$

10) $16\frac{9}{13} - 2\frac{2}{3}$

11) $8\frac{15}{17} - 2\frac{2}{3}$

12) $28\frac{10}{32} - 5\frac{1}{8}$

13) $18\frac{2}{7} - 16\frac{1}{28}$

14) $31\frac{5}{12} - 4\frac{3}{48}$

15) $16\frac{7}{13} - 5\frac{2}{39}$

16) $32\frac{5}{12} - 8\frac{2}{24}$

17) $28\frac{1}{6} - 3\frac{1}{9}$

18) $3\frac{1}{3} - 1\frac{1}{7}$

19) $56\frac{3}{11} - 5\frac{1}{9}$

20) $15\frac{32}{33} - 8$

21) $8\frac{15}{16} - 2\frac{3}{24}$

22) $23\frac{8}{15} - 6\frac{9}{20}$

Subtracting With Renaming

Example

$$\begin{array}{r} 12 \\ -\ 3\frac{1}{7} \\ \hline \end{array}$$

Solution

Step 1 Rename.

$$12 = 11 + 1$$

$$12 = 11 + \frac{7}{7}$$

$$12 = 11\frac{7}{7}$$

Step 2 Subtract.

$$\begin{array}{rcr} 12 & = & 11\frac{7}{7} \\ -\ 3\frac{1}{7} & = & 3\frac{1}{7} \\ \hline & & 8\frac{6}{7} \end{array}$$

Answer $8\frac{6}{7}$

Example

$$\begin{array}{r} 21\frac{1}{5} \\ -\ 4\frac{3}{5} \\ \hline \end{array}$$

Solution

Step 1 Rename.

$$\begin{aligned} 21\frac{1}{5} &= 21 + \frac{1}{5} \\ &= 20 + 1 + \frac{1}{5} \\ &= 20 + \frac{5}{5} + \frac{1}{5} \\ &= 20\frac{6}{5} \end{aligned}$$

Step 2 Subtract.

$$\begin{array}{rcr} 21\frac{1}{5} & = & 20\frac{6}{5} \\ -\ 4\frac{3}{5} & = & 4\frac{3}{5} \\ \hline & & 16\frac{3}{5} \end{array}$$

Answer $16\frac{3}{5}$

Review of Basic Skills 28

Exercise Find common denominators and subtract. Write your answers in simplest terms.

1) $13\frac{2}{5} - 5\frac{6}{7}$

2) $18\frac{1}{5} - 2\frac{3}{5}$

3) $14\frac{3}{10} - 2\frac{1}{2}$

4) $26\frac{5}{7} - 5\frac{13}{14}$

5) $10\frac{5}{12} - 6\frac{3}{4}$

6) $24\frac{1}{11} - 5\frac{6}{22}$

7) $8\frac{2}{9} - 3\frac{4}{5}$

8) $6\frac{1}{12} - 3\frac{1}{2}$

9) $13\frac{1}{7} - 6\frac{3}{8}$

10) $14 - 2\frac{5}{11}$

11) $28\frac{2}{13} - 6\frac{7}{8}$

12) $12 - 8\frac{3}{7}$

13) $25\frac{5}{6} - 1\frac{9}{10}$

14) $9\frac{2}{15} - 4\frac{4}{5}$

15) $42\frac{1}{5} - 3\frac{3}{8}$

16) $53\frac{6}{9} - 4\frac{17}{18}$

17) $13\frac{5}{11} - 1\frac{21}{22}$

18) $30 - 6\frac{15}{19}$

19) $18\frac{1}{9} - 3\frac{2}{3}$

20) $33\frac{12}{40} - 8\frac{9}{10}$

21) $5\frac{5}{13} - 2\frac{30}{39}$

22) $16\frac{7}{10} - 4\frac{49}{50}$

23) $7\frac{1}{18} - 2\frac{2}{3}$

24) $13\frac{1}{11} - 3\frac{4}{22}$

25) $36 - 8\frac{3}{7}$

26) $13\frac{1}{4} - 5\frac{3}{5}$

27) $27\frac{5}{13} - 6\frac{25}{26}$

28) $14\frac{1}{6} - 3\frac{5}{8}$

29) $18\frac{2}{9} - 6\frac{3}{4}$

30) $6\frac{27}{30} - 5\frac{13}{15}$

31) $7\frac{8}{11} - 1\frac{21}{34}$

32) $6\frac{1}{5} - 4\frac{7}{8}$

33) $4\frac{1}{2} - 2\frac{7}{12}$

34) $16\frac{5}{9} - 3\frac{17}{18}$

35) $14\frac{3}{17} - 2\frac{5}{34}$

36) $2 - 1\frac{5}{11}$

37) $45\frac{4}{9} - 5\frac{4}{5}$

38) $32\frac{5}{16} - 5\frac{15}{32}$

39) $8\frac{3}{14} - 2\frac{6}{7}$

40) $29\frac{1}{10} - 3\frac{10}{15}$

41) $13\frac{5}{16} - 8\frac{23}{24}$

42) $4\frac{2}{7} - 2\frac{4}{5}$

43) $13\frac{15}{35} - 1\frac{6}{7}$

44) $10\frac{2}{3} - 8\frac{8}{9}$

45) $15\frac{11}{20} - 4\frac{4}{5}$

Review of Basic Skills 29 and 30

Identifying Place Value With Decimals (29)

Example Write the place value of the underlined digits.

1) 23.0$\underline{6}$71 Hundredths

2) 105.106$\underline{2}$ Ten-Thousandths

Ten Thousands	Thousands	Hundreds	Tens	Ones		Tenths	Hundredths	Thousandths	Ten-Thousandths
			2	3	.	0	6	7	1
		1	0	5	.	1	0	6	2

Comparing Decimals (30)

Example Compare 2.38 and 2.4. Use the symbols $<$ or $>$.

Solution Insert zeros to give each decimal the same number of places.

1) 2.38 and 2.4

2) 2.38 and 2.40 (After inserting a zero.)

Since 38 is less than 40, then $2.38 < 2.40$.

Example Compare 19.2 and 8.8943.

Solution Since the whole number 19 is greater than 8, then $19.2 > 8.8943$.

Exercise Write the place name for each underlined digit.

1) 35.$\underline{0}$6

2) .52$\underline{6}$03

3) 5.681$\underline{1}$

4) 1.06$\underline{1}$1

5) .5811$\underline{1}$

6) .40101$\underline{5}$

7) .00$\underline{2}$731

8) $\underline{2}$76.03

9) 2.0$\underline{8}$35

10) .2850$\underline{1}$

11) 12.3005$\underline{2}$

12) 52.083$\underline{1}$

13) .306$\underline{1}$11

14) .56$\underline{0}$891

15) 1.0065$\underline{1}$

16) 60.0$\underline{0}$79

17) 14.000$\underline{8}$1

18) 156.0$\underline{1}$23

19) 133.$\underline{0}$1

20) 15.0$\underline{1}$911

21) 1.9$\underline{9}$115

22) 8.567$\underline{2}$3

23) 12.03587$\underline{6}$

24) $\underline{8}$,315.67

Rounding Decimals

Example Round 2.7017 to the nearest thousandth.

Solution 2.7017 ◄— Number (7) to the right of the thousandth place is 5 or more, so add 1 to the thousandths place and drop all digits to the right.

Answer 2.7017 ≈ 2.702 (≈ means "about equal to.")

Example Round 8.1649 to the nearest hundredth.

Solution 8.1649 ◄— Number (4) to the right of the hundredth place is less than 5, so drop the 4 and 9.

Answer 8.1649 ≈ 8.16

Exercise Round each decimal to the places named.

		Tenths	Hundredths	Thousandths
1)	2.063	______	______	______
2)	.0891	______	______	______
3)	1.0354	______	______	______
4)	.15454	______	______	______
5)	32.70391	______	______	______
6)	7.63	______	______	______
7)	19.808964	______	______	______
8)	34.00354	______	______	______
9)	2.061155	______	______	______
10)	139.4181891	______	______	______

Adding Decimals

Example 23 + .62 +1.9 = ■

Solution

```
   23.                                 23.00 ← Inserting zeros
  .62 ← Line up all the                  .62   may help.
+ 1.9   decimal points.             +  1.90
25.52                                 25.52
```

Answer 25.52

Exercise Write these problems in vertical form. Then add.

1) 2.3 + 6 + 8.41
2) .413 + 9.6 + .2
3) 17 + .205 + 1.6
4) 2 + .63 + .5 + 1.1
5) 3.5 + 8.21 + .006
6) 8 + .15 + 1.61 + 2
7) 81.7 + 10.73 + 1.673
8) .02 + .603 + 8 + .11
9) 13.06 + 1.5 + 9 + .41
10) 2.71 + .031 + 8 + 9.9
11) 39.4 + 3 + 8.27 + .1
12) 5 + 8.4 + .07 + 6
13) 42 + .126 + .1 + .23
14) 6.28 + .28 + 5.4
15) 7.6 + 1 + .212
16) .561 + 4.7 + 215
17) 81.4 + 6.7 + 8.41
18) 50.51 + 2.6 + 9.15
19) 42.6 + .57 + 23.5
20) 39.6 + .003 + 1.81
21) 95.1 + 1.63 + 101.1
22) 8 + 1.53 + .007
23) .203 + .72 + .025
24) 1.56 + 1.231 + .07
25) 13 + .92 + 6.7
26) 83 + 9.6 + 1.305
27) 5.03 + .607 + .19
28) 18.95 + 1.4 + .071
29) 39.9 + 14.62 + 2.3
30) 2.3 + 1.78 + .663
31) 8.702 + 3.7 + .63
32) 3.0101 + .62 + 4
33) 2.7 + .063 + 1.77
34) 12.8 + .14 + .03 + 3
35) 1.9 + 5.621 + .03
36) 4.7 + .726 + 89.1
37) 1.7 + 2.31 + .631
38) 6.7 + .815 + 2
39) .37 + 2.9 + 8
40) 6.09 + .261 + 9.2
41) 23 + 1.003 + 5.4
42) 5.21 + .53 + 15.6
43) 63 + 1.92 + 88.8
44) .38 + 7.02 + .115
45) 5 + .27 + 1.919
46) 1 + .006 + .0071 + 1.8
47) 11.001 + 1.1 + 6.27
48) 3.9 + 1.06 + .081

Subtracting Decimals

Example 12 − 1.68 = ■

Solution

```
  12.00  ◄── Line up the decimal points and insert zeros.
−  1.68
  10.32
```

Answer 10.32

Exercise Write these problems in vertical form. Then subtract.

1) 6.59 − .48
2) 36 − 2.3
3) 19.83 − 2.3
4) 33.89 − .32
5) 5.2 − .156
6) 31.4 − 8
7) 38.5 − 1.67
8) 7.6 − .67
9) .091 − .0197
10) 1.1 − .99
11) 7.7 − 2.63
12) 36.5 − 1.83
13) 6.7 − 2.34
14) 1.6 − 1.08
15) .89 − .098
16) 2.31 − .9
17) .011 − .00201
18) .3 − .234
19) 1.03 − .89
20) 75 − .108
21) 8.7 − 2.31
22) 1 − .9
23) 8.3 − .99
24) 45.1 − .06
25) .101 − .0982
26) 53.72 − 1.8
27) 9.01 − .6
28) 2.171 − .18
29) 5.6 − .42
30) 2.1 − .8
31) 9 − .62
32) 12 − 4.35
33) 1 − .08
34) .1 − .0356
35) .35 − .19
36) 5.51 − .6
37) 19.5 − .34
38) 2.81 − .931
39) 11.23 − 9.9
40) 31.3 − .61
41) 4.35 − .6
42) .68 − .086
43) .1 − .06
44) 1.63 − .89
45) 7.5 − 6
46) 3 − .4
47) 5.52 − .66
48) 6 − .9
49) .32 − .0832
50) 1 − .662

Multiplying Decimals

Example $.26 \times 1.3 = \blacksquare$

Solution

$$\begin{array}{r} .26 \\ \times\ 1.3 \\ \hline 78 \\ +26 \\ \hline .338 \end{array}$$

.26 ← 2 places plus
× 1.3 ← 1 place equals
.338 ← 3 places

Example $.321 \times .002 = \blacksquare$

Solution

$$\begin{array}{r} .321 \\ \times\ \ .002 \\ \hline .000642 \end{array}$$

.321 ← 3 places plus
× .002 ← 3 places equals
.000642 ← 6 places

Exercise Write these problems in vertical form. Then multiply.

1) $.2 \times .3$
2) $.7 \times 1.2$
3) $1.9 \times .3$
4) 2.6×8
5) $.26 \times .2$
6) $.62 \times .3$
7) $.81 \times 1.2$
8) $.42 \times 6.3$
9) $.92 \times .21$
10) $.65 \times .07$
11) 1.23×1.2
12) $.128 \times .52$
13) $5.8 \times .006$
14) $.081 \times .02$
15) $.96 \times .73$
16) $8.03 \times .67$
17) $.126 \times .73$
18) $25.3 \times .62$
19) $.5 \times 6$
20) $1.3 \times .8$
21) $2.3 \times .5$
22) $4.3 \times .8$
23) $3.5 \times .7$
24) $.85 \times 3$
25) $.26 \times 1.5$
26) $1.8 \times .18$
27) $4.8 \times .06$
28) $.31 \times .09$
29) $3.62 \times .05$
30) $.402 \times .11$
31) $.71 \times .62$
32) $1.62 \times .71$
33) $52.6 \times .36$
34) $4.2 \times .008$
35) $703 \times .02$
36) $.91 \times .083$

Scientific Notation

Example Express 2,800 in scientific notation.

Solution $2{,}800 = 2.800 \times 10^3$ ⟵ 3 places

or

2.8×10^3

Example Express 0.00039 in scientific notation.

Solution $0.00039 = 3.9 \times 10^{-4}$ ⟵ 4 places

(Use the negative sign ($^{-4}$) when the decimal point is moved to the right.)

Exercise Write these numbers in scientific notation.

1) 3,600
2) 35,100
3) 46,000
4) 75,100
5) 6,530
6) 391,000
7) 1,725,000
8) 5,301,000
9) 87,100,000
10) 267,000,000
11) 100,000
12) 1,700,000,000
13) 34,000,000
14) 306.2
15) 12.721
16) .0000623
17) .00002
18) .1602
19) 623.05
20) .000000005
21) .00000101
22) .00663
23) 510
24) 8,702
25) 92,300
26) 18,000
27) 980,000
28) 5,600,000
29) 7,810,000
30) 1,000,000
31) 45,000,000
32) 9,720,000
33) 5,300,000,000
34) 961,000,000
35) 171,800,000
36) 48.39
37) 150.82
38) .0000031
39) .000175
40) .003
41) .00231
42) .000000453
43) .000119
44) .0024

Review of Basic Skills 36–39

Dividing Decimals by Whole Numbers (36)

Example $.168 \div 14 = \blacksquare$

Solution

$$\begin{array}{r} .012 \\ 14\overline{\smash{)}.168} \\ -14 \\ \hline 28 \\ -28 \\ \hline 0 \end{array}$$

Place the decimal point in the quotient directly above the one in the dividend.

Example $68.6 \div 28 = \blacksquare$

Solution

$$\begin{array}{r} 2.45 \\ 28\overline{\smash{)}68.60} \\ -56 \\ \hline 12\ 6 \\ -11\ 2 \\ \hline 1\ 40 \\ -1\ 40 \\ \hline 0 \end{array}$$

Adding a zero may terminate the answer.

Dividing Decimals by Decimals (37)

Example $8.04 \div .6 = \blacksquare$

Solution

$$\begin{array}{r} 13.4 \\ .6\overline{\smash{)}8.0\ 4} \\ -6 \\ \hline 2\ 0 \\ -1\ 8 \\ \hline 2\ 4 \\ -2\ 4 \\ \hline 0 \end{array}$$

Step 1 Move the decimal point in the divisor to the right.

Step 2 Move the decimal point in the dividend the same number of places to the right.

Step 3 Divide and bring the decimal point straight up into the quotient.

Renaming Decimals as Fractions (38)

Example Rename .13 as a fraction.

Solution $.13 = \frac{13}{100}$

Example $.026 = \blacksquare$

Solution $.026 = \frac{26}{1{,}000}$ or $\frac{13}{500}$

Renaming Fractions as Decimals (39)

Example Rename $\frac{13}{25}$ as a decimal.

Solution $\frac{13}{25} = \frac{13 \times 4}{25 \times 4} = \frac{52}{100}$

$= .52$ OR

$$
\begin{array}{r}
.52 \\
25\overline{)13.00} \\
-12\,5 \\
\hline
50 \\
-50 \\
\hline
0
\end{array}
$$

Choose a multiplier that will give you a denominator that is a power of 10. (10, 100, 1,000, 10,000...)

Dividing the numerator by the denominator will also give the decimal equivalent.

Exercise Copy these problems and divide. Rename decimals as fractions.

1) $4.7 \div 2$
2) $.78 \div 3$
3) $1.448 \div .8$
4) $2.88 \div .9$
5) $10.2 \div 1.2$
6) $11.55 \div 2.1$
7) $4.545 \div .9$
8) $2.807 \div .7$
9) $.351 \div .09$
10) $4.004 \div .22$
11) $.777 \div .15$
12) $13.7046 \div .91$
13) $.0615 \div 1.5$
14) $.00902 \div .41$
15) $.01952 \div 3.2$
16) $.00206 \div .002$
17) $32.92 \div .4$
18) $.12741 \div .31$
19) $.08833 \div .11$
20) $.0084 \div .007$
21) $6.2432 \div 1.6$
22) $36.8 \div 8$
23) $3.51 \div 9$
24) $7.23 \div 3$
25) $2.412 \div .6$
26) $8.32 \div 3.2$
27) $10.44 \div 2.9$
28) $.159 \div .15$
29) $.266 \div .07$
30) $2.173 \div 4.1$

Review of Basic Skills 40–45

Solving Proportions (40)

Example $\frac{25}{n} = \frac{5}{6}$

Solution $\frac{{}^{5}\!\!\!\not{25}}{n} = \frac{5}{6}$

$5 \times n = 25 \times 6$

$5 \times n = 150$

$n = 150 \div 5$

$n = 30$

Changing Percents to Decimals (41)

Example Write 32% as a decimal.

Solution 32% = .32

Move the decimal point 2 places to the left and remove the % sign.

Example Write 6.3% as a decimal.

Solution 6.3% = .063

Changing Percents to Fractions (42)

Example Write 45% as a fraction.

Solution 45% = .45

$45\% = \frac{45}{100}$

$45\% = \frac{9}{20}$

Renaming Decimals as Percents (43)

Example Write .231 as a percent.

Solution .231 = 23.1%

Move the decimal point 2 places to the right.

Renaming Fractions as Percents (44)

Example Write $\frac{7}{8}$ as a percent.

Solution First express $\frac{7}{8}$ as a decimal.

$$\begin{array}{r} .875 \\ 8\overline{)7.000} \\ -6\,4 \\ \hline 60 \\ -56 \\ \hline 40 \\ -40 \\ \hline 0 \end{array}$$

$$\frac{7}{8} = .875$$
$$= 87.5\% \text{ or } 87\tfrac{1}{2}\%$$

Answer 87.5%

Finding the Percentage (45)

Example 23% of 35 is what number?

Solution $.23 \times 35 = n$

$8.05 = n$

Exercise A Find the percentage.

1) 20% of 52 is ___
2) 35% of 60 is ___
3) 70% of 50 is ___
4) 10% of 82 is ___
5) 2% of 39 is ___
6) 5% of 7 is ___
7) 14% of 2.8 is ___
8) 39% of 6 is ___
9) 3% of 4.9 is ___
10) 6% of .42 is ___
11) 18% of 5.6 is ___
12) 56% of 23.5 is ___
13) 7% of .82 is ___
14) 32% of .38 is ___
15) 25% of 75 is ___
16) 62% of 35 is ___
17) 9% of 150 is ___
18) 15% of 20 is ___
19) 26% of 40 is ___
20) 3% of 35 is ___
21) 23% of 5 is ___
22) 19% of 8 is ___
23) 8% of 7.02 is ___
24) 11% of 3.6 is ___
25) 13% of 2.5 is ___
26) 70% of .38 is ___
27) 53% of .72 is ___
28) 6.2% of 32 is ___

Review of Basic Skills 40–45

Exercise B Find the rate.

1) ___% of 72 is 1.44
2) ___% of 350 is 14
3) ___% of 380 is 34.2
4) ___% of 2.8 is .42
5) ___% of 4.5 is .18
6) ___% of 5.1 is 1.632
7) ___% of .26 is .1248
8) ___% of 1.5 is .48
9) ___% of .03 is .0021
10) ___% of 1.8 is .09
11) ___% of 30 is .87
12) ___% of 80 is 4.96
13) ___% of 35 is 2.065
14) ___% of 80 is 7.36
15) ___% of 90 is 5.4
16) ___% of 10 is .8
17) ___% of 320 is 16
18) ___% of 6.3 is 1.26
19) ___% of 6.1 is .61
20) ___% of 5.3 is 2.067
21) ___% of .41 is .2214
22) ___% of 4.5 is 1.71
23) ___% of .9 is .594
24) ___% of .3 is .0243
25) ___% of 50 is 2.1
26) ___% of 53 is 4.823
27) ___% of 60 is 1.68
28) ___% of 90 is 6.48

Exercise C Find the base.

1) 6% of ___ is .03
2) 7% of ___ is .021
3) 8% of ___ is .152
4) 15% of ___ is 145.5
5) 23% of ___ is 8.05
6) 4% of ___ is 2.48
7) 3.5% of ___ is 53.2
8) 7% of ___ is .042
9) 15% of ___ is .345
10) 2.3% of ___ is 2.185
11) .14% of ___ is .0462
12) .91% of ___ is .5733
13) .26% of ___ is .0208
14) .9% of ___ is .0216
15) 28% of ___ is 82.88
16) 235% of ___ is 18.8
17) 110% of ___ is 42.9
18) .07% of ___ is .0035
19) 9% of ___ is .81
20) 4% of ___ is .52
21) 6% of ___ is 1.68
22) 22% of ___ is 75.02
23) 4% of ___ is 11.2
24) 9% of ___ is 90
25) 5% of ___ is .045
26) 9% of ___ is 0.153
27) 18% of ___ is .0234
28) 4.2% of ___ is 2.646
29) 5.9% of ___ is 11.8
30) .11% of ___ is .033
31) 20.3% of ___ is 1.827
32) .5% of ___ is .0025
33) 41% of ___ is 37.843
34) 140% of ___ is 74.2
35) 99% of ___ is 97.02
36) .06% of ___ is .0078

Exercise D Find the missing numbers.

1) 2% of ___ is .16.

2) 18% of 25 is ___.

3) ___% of 150 is 43.5.

4) 7% of ___ is 1.96.

5) 53% of 69 is ___.

6) ___% of 36 is 3.6.

7) 8% of ___ is 4.48.

8) 17% of 39 is ___.

9) ___% of 32 is 8.

10) 26% of ___ is .676.

11) 52% of 35 is ___.

12) ___% of 8.5 is 1.36.

13) 75% of ___ is 19.65.

14) 30% of 35.4 is ___.

15) ___% of 15.2 is 13.832.

16) 2.8% of 60 is ___.

17) 2.9% of 60 is ___.

18) ___% of 7.7 is .77.

19) 95% of ___ is 9.5.

20) 11% of 19 is ___.

21) ___% of 77.1 is 21.588.

22) 15% of ___ is 5.4.

23) .07% of 276 is ___.

24) ___% of 378 is .756.

25) .08% of ___ is .0312.

26) 6% of 2.8 is ___.

27) 32% of ___ is 16.96.

28) ___% of 16 is .8.

29) 43% of ___ is 13.76.

30) 9% of 156 is ___.

31) 92% of ___ is 184.

32) ___% of 100 is 3.9.

33) 19% of 56 is ___.

34) 75% of ___ is 28.5.

35) ___% of 81 is 7.29.

36) 80% of 30 is ___.

37) 35% of ___ is 3.185.

38) ___% of 30 is 5.4.

39) 28% of 6.5 is ___.

40) 20% of ___ 6.44.

41) ___% of 60 is 3.18.

42) 4.3% of 50 is ___.

43) 13% of ___ is .507.

44) ___% of 31 is 1.736.

45) 62% of 24 is ___.

46) 3.4% of ___ is 2.754

47) ___% of 37 is 13.69.

48) 29% of 300 is ___.

49) .25% of ___ is .0375

50) ___% of 4.2 is .21.

Calculator Handbook

There are many kinds of electronic calculators. Each calculator is a little different from others. Some have more keys than others. The keys may be placed differently. You may have to press the keys in a certain order. Most calculators, however, are very similar.

Here is a calculator that has the basic functions you find on most calculators.

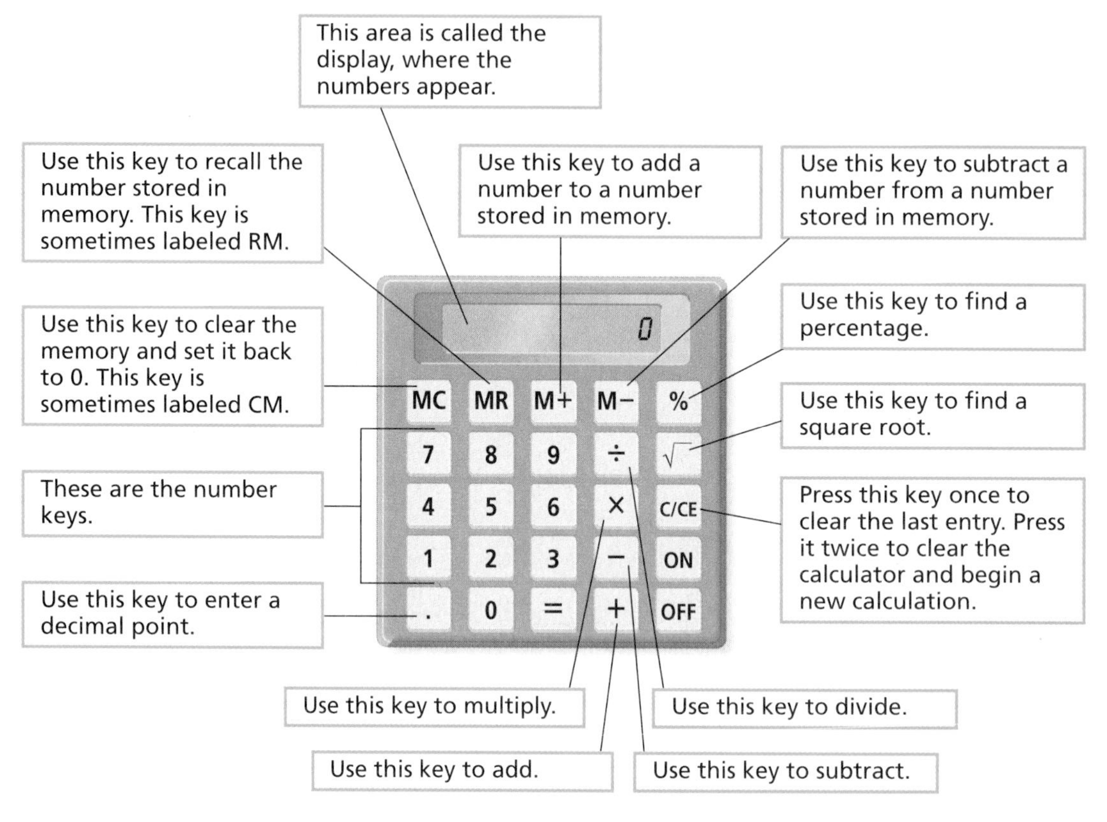

You can use a calculator to help you do arithmetic quickly and accurately. In many cases, you key the calculation the same way you would write it on paper.

Press 23 [+] 61 [=]
The display will read 84.
$23 + 61 = 84$

Press 12 [×] 12 [=]
The display will read 144.
$12 \times 12 = 144$

Press 98 [−] 18 [=]
The display will read 80.
$98 - 18 = 80$

Press 63 [÷] 9 [=]
The display will read 7.
$63 \div 9 = 7$

It's a good idea to look at the display after you key in each number. It helps to check that you haven't pressed a wrong key by mistake.

The [√] key will give you the square root of a number.

Example What is the square root of 81?
Press 81 [√]
The display will read 9.

The [%] key will help you find a percentage. The [%] key works differently on different kinds of calculators. You may need to press [=] after [%] on some calculators. The examples show how the key works on most calculators.

Examples What is 25 percent of 44?
Press 44 [×] 25 [%]
The display will read 11.

What is 10 percent more than 50?
Press 50 [+] 10 [%]
The display will read 55.

What is 20 percent less than 65?
Press 65 [−] 20 [%]
The display will read 52.

If you are going to use the same number, or constant, in a series of calculations, you can store it in memory. Remember to clear the memory by pressing [MC] before you begin.

Examples What is 18 times 4? 18 times 12? 18 times 31?

Press 18 [M+] [C/CE]
The display reads 0. The number 18 is stored in memory.

Press [MR] [×] 4 [=] The display reads 72.

Press [MR] [×] 12 [=] The display reads 216.

Press [MR] [×] 31 [=] The display reads 558.

You can add to or subtract from the number in memory by using the [M+] and [M−] keys. Remember to clear the memory by pressing [MC] before you begin.

Press	Display	Number in Memory
22	22	0
[M+]	22	22
6	6	22
[M+]	6	28
20	20	28
[M−]	20	8

Glossary

A

Advance—to move forward (p. 54)
Area—amount of space inside a shape (p. 18)
Assist—in baseball, a fielder's defensive play that helps a teammate to make a putout (p. 181)
Average—the number obtained by dividing the sum of two or more quantities by the number of quantities (p. 42)

B

Balance—money you have in a bank; money you owe (p. 209)
Base—amount that a percent is taken of (p. 197)
Baserunning average—ratio of stolen bases to attempted steals (p. 179)
Batting average—a measure of how well a batter hits; a ratio of hits to at bats (p. 174)
Beneficiary—a person who receives the face value of an insurance policy (p. 238)
Budget—a plan for managing money (p. 195)

C

Calculate—to get an answer by adding, subtracting, multiplying, or dividing (p. 40)
Calorie—measure for energy that food provides; the amount of heat needed to raise the temperature of one gram of water one degree Celsius (p. 2)
Celsius—a temperature scale with 0 degrees as the freezing point and 100 degrees as the boiling point of water (p. 275)
Circle graph—pictorial way to show comparisons by using the segments of a circle (p. 199)
Clockwise—in the direction in which the hands of a clock rotate (p. 55)
Compare—to examine two numbers to determine which is larger (p. 77)
Compound interest—interest computed on principal plus interest (p. 209)
Compute—to calculate or figure out (p. 40)
Construction class—type of house (p. 227)
Consume—to use; to eat or drink up (p. 2)
Conversion factor—a number by which you multiply a measurement to obtain an equivalent measurement (p. 152)
Convert—to change to something of equal value (p. 68)
Coverage—insurance protection (p. 222)
Credit—a way to buy now and pay later (p. 214)
Cubic—the volume of a cube whose length, width, and depth each measure the same (p. 254)
Currency—money (p. 152)

D

Decimal—a whole number followed by a dot and places to the right. The numbers to the dot's right equal less than one. (p. 110)
Decimal places—positions to the right of the decimal point (p. 110)
Degree—1⁄360th of a circle (p. 199)
Dice sum—the total points shown on two or more dice (p. 52)
Die—(*plural:* **dice**) small cube of bone, plastic, etc., marked on each side with from one to six spots and used usually in pairs (p. 51)
Discount—the amount taken off the usual price (p. 193)
Double roll—an amount of wallpaper that covers twice the wall area of a single roll (p. 24)
Double time—payment of two times the hourly rate (p. 126)
Draw—to get or pick at random (p. 59)

E

Earned run average (ERA)—the measure of how many runs a pitcher allows in a game; ERA = 9 × Earned Runs ÷ Innings Pitched (p. 182)
Elapse—to slip by; to pass (p. 160)
Elapsed time—the difference between the starting time and the ending time (p. 160)
Endowment insurance—insurance where premiums are paid for a period and then the face value is paid to the insured (p. 238)
Equivalent—a thing that is equal to another in a particular way (p. 68)
Error—a bad baseball play that allows a runner who should have been out to be safe or remain at bat, or that permits a runner to advance (p. 181)

Estimate—to give a reasonable or approximate number; to make a general but careful guess of the number, size, or value of something (p. 11)

Expect—to look forward to (p. 57)

Experiment—trials or tests; a procedure used to test a theory (p. 57)

F

Fabric guide—a chart showing the amount of material needed to make garments of different sizes (p. 82)

Face value—the worth printed or written on a bill, bond, etc. (p. 232)

Factors—numbers that when multiplied together form a product; numbers being multiplied (p. 70)

Fahrenheit—a temperature scale with 32 degrees as the freezing point and 212 degrees as the boiling point of water (p. 275)

Fat calories—calories that come from the fat in food (p. 5)

Fielding percentage—ratio of assists and putouts to total chances (p. 181)

Finance charge—cost of borrowing money; the rate of payment, expressed as a percentage per unit of time (p. 214)

Fixtures—toilet, sink, bathtub, or shower (p. 226)

Formula—a rule or method of doing something (p. 51)

Frame—in bowling, any of the divisions of a game in which all ten pins are set up anew (p. 30)

G

Games back—the sum of the difference of wins and losses between a team and the first place team divided by two (p. 187)

Geometric—formed of straight lines, triangles, circles, etc., as a pattern (p. 84)

Graph—a pictorial way to display information (p. 10)

Gross pay—pay before deductions (p. 120)

H

Height—the distance from the bottom to the top (p. 18)

I

Improper fraction—a fraction whose numerator is equal to or greater than the denominator (p. 70)

Income—money that is earned (p. 195)

Increase—to make larger (p. 10)

Insurance—coverage by a contract in which one party guarantees another against loss (p. 222)

Interest—amount paid for the use of money (p. 206)

Interest rate—percent paid or charged for the use of money (p. 206)

Invert—to change to the direct opposite (p. 103)

K

Kilowatt—unit of electrical power (p. 262)

L

Lend—to make a loan (p. 211)

Length—the distance from end to end (p. 18)

Liability—insurance that protects the owner against claims resulting from an accident that is his or her fault (p. 234)

Limited-payment life insurance—insurance where the policyholder is insured until death (p. 238)

Line segment—a part of a line (p. 248)

Loan—money given to a borrower that is to be returned later with interest (p. 206)

Location multiplier—a chart that helps determine a home's replacement cost based on its ZIP code location (p. 230)

M

Macramé—a coarse fringe or lace of thread or cord knotted into designs (p. 84)

Major medical insurance—insurance to cover larger medical expenses (p. 224)

Meter—an instrument for measuring and recording how much gas, electricity, water, etc., passes through it (p. 265)

Metered parking space—a parking space where you must put money in a parking meter (p. 165)

O

Odometer—an instrument for measuring the distance traveled by a vehicle (p. 140)

Ordinary life insurance—insurance where payments are made as long as the insured is alive (p. 238)

Overtime—time beyond the estimated limit (p. 126)

P

Peak hours—the time when usage is greatest (p. 270)

Per—for each; for every (p. 120)

Percent—number per hundred (p. 179)

Percentage—a given part or amount in every hundred; the part in a percent (p. 192)

Perimeter—the distance around all the sides of a polygon (p. 246)

Possibilities—outcomes that can occur (p. 52)

Possible outcomes—results that can happen (p. 50)

Predict—to state what will happen (p. 58)

Premium—amount paid for insurance (p. 222)

Premium chart—list of amounts to be paid for insurance (p. 222)

Principal—amount of a loan or a deposit (p. 206)

Probability—the number of successful outcomes divided by the total number of possible outcomes; how likely an event is to happen (p. 51)

Probability tree—a diagram showing all possible outcomes (p. 50)

Proper fraction—a fraction whose numerator is less than the denominator (p. 71)

Protractor—an instrument in the form of a half-circle marked with degrees, for plotting and measuring angles (p. 199)

Putout—baseball play in which the batter or runner is retired (p. 179)

Q

Quarterly—happening at regular intervals four times a year (p. 209)

R

Radius—a straight line from the center to the outside of a circle (p. 199)

Rate—percent (p. 192) (p. 206)

Rate factor—an amount by which the basic premium is multiplied (p. 236)

Recipe—directions for making something (p. 68)

Rectangular prism—a solid figure with bases or ends that are parallel and sides that are rectangles (p. 254)

Regroup—to group again; to reorganize (p. 86)

Rename—to express in another form equal to the original (for example, 1 hour = 60 minutes) (p. 71)

Repeat—to do or make again (p. 90)

Replacement cost—the cost to replace insured property (p. 230)

Round up—to round to the next highest number (p. 24)

Rummy—card games in which the object is to match cards into sets of the same denomination or sequences of the same suit (p. 60)

S

Sacrifice outs—outs made to advance base runners (p. 174)

Salary—a fixed amount of money regularly paid to a worker for work done (p. 132)

Sale price—reduced price of an item (p. 193)

Sales tax—a tax on sales or services, added to the price a customer pays (p. 192)

Scale—ratio of the real size of an object or area to the map size (p. 249)

Scale drawing—a picture that shows relative sizes of real objects (p. 249)

Semimonthly—twice per month (p. 224)

Simple interest—interest computed on principal only (p. 206)

Slugging percentage—ratio of total bases to at bats (p. 175)

Spare—knocking down all the bowling pins with the second roll of a frame (p. 33)

Speedometer—an instrument that measures how fast a car is traveling (p. 140)

Standard—a rule or model for measuring (p. 22)

Statistics—facts collected and arranged to show information (p. 174)

Strike—knocking down all ten bowling pins with the first roll of a frame (p. 35)

Suit—any of the four sets of thirteen playing cards (p. 59)

Symbol—a character that stands for something else (p. 77)

T

Term insurance—insurance where payments and insurance last for a fixed amount of time (p. 238)

Time—duration of a loan or deposit (p. 206)

Time and one-half—payment of 1.5 times the hourly rate for work (p. 126)

U

Unit—any fixed amount, quantity, etc., used as a standard (p. 18)

Unit count—a way to determine a house's size for insurance purposes (p. 225)

V

Vary—to change (p. 10)

Volume—the amount of space occupied in three dimensions (p. 254)

W

Watt—unit of electrical power (p. 262)

Width—the distance from side to side (p. 23)

Won-lost percentage—ratio of wins to games played (p. 184)

Index

F

G

H

N

O

P

Q

R

S